LAND COVER CHANGE:
SCOTLAND FROM THE 1940S TO THE 1980S

THE NATURAL HERITAGE OF SCOTLAND

This series of books deals with the variety of topics that encompass the natural heritage of Scotland. Some titles will be specially written for the series, whilst others will be based on Scottish Natural Heritage (SNH) conferences. Each year since it was founded in 1992, SNH has organised or jointly organised a conference that has focused attention on a particular aspect of Scotland's natural heritage. The papers read at the conferences, or the specially written manuscripts, all go through a rigorous process of refereeing and editing before being submitted for publication. The titles already published in this series are:

1. *The Islands of Scotland: a Living Marine Heritage*
   Edited by J. M. Baxter and M. B. Usher (1994), x + 286pp.

2. *Heaths and Moorland: Cultural Landscapes*
   Edited by D. B. A. Thompson, A. J. Hester and M. B. Usher (1995),
   xvi + 400pp.

3. *Soils, Sustainability and the Natural Heritage*
   Edited by A. G. Taylor, J. E. Gordon and M. B. Usher (1996), xvii + 316pp.

4. *Freshwater Quality: Defining the Indefinable?*
   Edited by P. J. Boon and D. L. Howell (1997), xx + 552pp.

5. *Biodiversity in Scotland: Status, Trends and Initiatives*
   Edited by L. V. Fleming, A. C. Newton, J. A. Vickery and M. B. Usher
   (1997), xviii + 310pp.

This is the sixth book in the series.

Forthcoming in this series

Scotland's Living Coastline
Edited by J. M. Baxter, K. Duncan and S. M. Atkins.

Also available

Conserving Bogs: The Management Handbook
by S. Brooks and R. Stoneman (1997), xiv + 286 pp.

LAND COVER CHANGE: SCOTLAND FROM THE 1940S TO THE 1980S

Edward C. Mackey, Michael C. Shewry
and Gavin J. Tudor

SCOTTISH
NATURAL
HERITAGE

EDINBURGH: THE STATIONERY OFFICE

First published 1998

ISBN 0 11 495882 3

British Library Cataloguing in Publication Data
A catalogue record for this book is available from the British Library.

Published by The Stationery Office and available from:

The Publications Centre
(mail, telephone and fax orders only)
PO Box 276, London SW8 5DT
General enquiries 0171 873 0011
Telephone orders 0171 873 9090
Fax orders 0171 873 8200

The Stationery Office Bookshops
123 Kingsway, London WC2B 6PQ
0171 242 6393 Fax 0171 242 6394
68–69 Bull Street, Birmingham B4 6AD
0121 236 9696   Fax 0121 236 9699
33 Wine Street, Bristol BS1 2BQ
0117 9264306 Fax 0117 9294515
9–21 Princess Street, Manchester M60 8AS
0161 834 7201 Fax 0161 833 0634
16 Arthur Street, Belfast BT1 4GD
01232 238451 Fax 01232 235401
The Stationery Office Oriel Bookshop
The Friary, Cardiff CF1 4AA
01222 395548 Fax 01222 384347
71 Lothian Road, Edinburgh EH3 9AZ
0131 228 4181   Fax 0131 622 7017

The Stationery Office's Accredited Agents
(see Yellow Pages)

and through good booksellers

CONTENTS

Foreword   ix

Preface   xi

Introduction   xv

PART ONE: THE METHOD   1

  1   Why NCMS?   3

  2   The Measurement of Change   5

  3   The Presentation of Results   19

PART TWO: OVERVIEW OF KEY FINDINGS   23

  4   Land Cover Change in Scotland   25

PART THREE: THEMATIC ANALYSIS OF LAND COVER GROUPS   39

  5   Grassland   41

  6   Mire   58

  7   Heather Moorland   70

  8   Arable   78

  9   Woodland   85

 10   Fresh Water Environments   110

 11   Built and Bare Ground   124

 12   Bracken and Scrub   141

 13   Hedgerows and Trees   151

PART FOUR: GEOGRAPHICAL ANALYSIS OF REGIONAL VARIATION   155

 14   Borders   159

 15   Central   165

 16   Dumfries & Galloway   171

 17   Fife   177

 18   Grampian   183

 19   Highland   189

20 Lothian   195

21 Strathclyde   201

22 Tayside   207

23 Orkney Islands   213

24 Shetland Islands   219

25 Western Isles   225

PART FIVE: SECTORAL ANALYSIS AND CONCLUDING POINTS 231

26 Discussion   233

   Epilogue   245

Index   253

LIST OF PLATES

(between pages 150 and 151)

Plate 1   The NCMS method (Photos: E. Hume, Planning & Mapping Ltd and P. Shaw).

Plate 2   Farmland (Photos: L. Gill).

Plate 3   Mire and moorland (Photos: L. Gill and J. Macpherson).

Plate 4   Woodland (Photos: L. Gill).

Plate 5   Built land (Photos: L. Gill).

Plate 6   Fresh waters/bracken and scrub (Photos: L. Gill and F. MacPherson).

Plate 7   Linear features (Photos: L. Gill and S. Moore).

Plate 8   Environmental education.

Cover photography

(Background) Birch wood at Craigellachie near Aviemore (Photo: L. Gill).

(Foreground) Blackface sheep at Cairnsmore of Fleet (Photo: L. Gill).

FOREWORD

When Scottish Natural Heritage (SNH) was formed in 1992, it inherited from its predecessor bodies – the Nature Conservancy Council for Scotland and the Countryside Commission for Scotland – a major research project called the National Countryside Monitoring Scheme (NCMS). This was an ambitious project which set out not only to identify the post-war changes in Scotland's land cover but also to quantify them. The preliminary volume, covering the 1940s to 1970s, was published in 1994. The extension of research to the 1980s has now been completed, and it is with great pleasure that we are now publishing the results.

Some of the changes to Scotland's land surface are what we might have predicted. There has been a substantial programme of afforestation, which is borne out by a 929% increase in young plantations and a 462% increase in more mature coniferous plantations. We have heard much about the loss of heather, and now this can be quantified as a 23% decrease in heather moorlands and a 21% decrease in mires. The results of the NCMS also contain some surprises: it was not previously known that Scotland had lost over 50% of its hedgerow length since the 1940s, or that there had been such a marked degree of land use specialisation in lowland farming settings.

The results of a major study such as the NCMS are inevitably complicated. If they are to be widely understood and used, it is important that the results are viewed in several ways. In this book the data are explored thematically and geographically. The themes relate to the major land uses of agriculture, forestry, urban development and fresh water. Geographically there are considerable differences, and so Scotland has been looked at both locally and as a whole in order both to explain what has happened and to understand the driving forces behind the changes. In addition, SNH is developing other means of dissemination – teaching packs for schools, electronic data, and demonstration material.

Scotland has a natural heritage which is cherished and enjoyed both by the people of Scotland and by its many visitors. The NCMS reminds us that we inhabit, in large part, a managed landscape which is ever-changing. It requires a great deal of care and consideration if it is to be passed on to future generations in a healthy and productive state for both its wildlife and its people.

This book fills an important gap in our knowledge about the current state of Scotland's land cover. I am sure that it will be of interest and value to all scholars, practitioners, policy-makers and environmentalists who have regard for Scotland's natural heritage.

Magnus Magnusson KBE
Chairman, Scottish Natural Heritage

PREFACE

The National Countryside Monitoring Scheme (NCMS) would have been remarkable indeed had it escaped the many pitfalls which are to be encountered when attempting to characterise changes in the diversity of Scotland's land cover. Such diversity extends from readily identifiable features of the built environment, through a managed countryside of farming, forestry and sporting estate, and into less clearly differentiated habitats of rough grassland, moor and bog which characterise much of the unenclosed uplands. This volume documents the results of innovative work, in which numerous difficulties have been tackled and overcome. It has called at times for dogged determination when there was little to show outwardly. Ever-challenging, in hindsight daunting, it has been rewarded ultimately with tangible success.

As a time series, the NCMS is a defining study. Crucially, it now fills a gap in the literature with detailed results for Scotland. The study investigated land cover change from around 1947, as socio-economic reconstruction was getting underway in the immediate aftermath of the Second World War, to around 1973 when the UK joined the European Economic Community, and then to 1988 as environmental awareness throughout Britain and Europe was gaining ascendancy. Air photography provided a record of land cover for those milestones, during an extraordinarily dynamic period of countryside change. Awareness of our historical inheritance can help to explain the state of Scotland's land cover in the 1940s and so set the NCMS findings into context.

In view of the dramatic changes which have taken place in the second half of the twentieth century, the late 1940s serves as an excellent baseline for monitoring land cover change in Scotland. This is necessarily a retrospective view. What of the future? The NCMS is dependent on Scotland-wide air photography or comparable remotely sensed imagery. Any future air photo coverage, for instance if the Land Cover of Scotland census was to be repeated, could provide an opportunity to extend the NCMS time series and bring it more up to date. The millennium would be an auspicious milestone, offering the prospect of a series extending over 50 years. Environmental measures of the 1990s may become discernible in the countryside, with qualitative changes in agricultural and forestry development against a backdrop of relentless urban growth.

A strength of the NCMS method is that it is repeatable. In the meantime the dataset is being made available for on-going analysis and use. Results are already being applied to environmental audit by Scottish Natural Heritage (SNH), local authorities and others to provide a context for environmental investigations at different geographical scales. A more detailed account of the method is being documented for scholarship and enquiry. The potential of electronic media for interactive use is being explored. In partnership with the Scottish Association of Geography Teachers, curriculum support materials are being made available to schools throughout Scotland under SNH's environmental education programme. Collaboration with the Royal Museums of Scotland means that one day it may be possible to experience NCMS outputs there too.

This is the most satisfying part of a long project, and a tribute to the many individuals who have been involved. Many organisations and individuals have assisted in bringing this phase of the NCMS to completion. Notable among these were the following:

1   The Nature Conservancy Council, which initiated the study in 1983 and supported it until 1991 (when it became the Nature Conservancy Council for Scotland). When the focus of the study moved to Scotland, the Countryside Commission for Scotland provided joint funding from 1986 until 1991.

2   Scottish Natural Heritage, which inherited the project and supported it from 1992 to 1998. For their unfailing interest and encouragement, particular thanks are due to Professor Roger Crofts for his support in the role of Chief Executive, and to Professor Michael B Usher for his mentoring role as Chief Scientist.

3   Dr Art Lance, who was instrumental in setting up the project and Dr Jonathan Budd, who originally managed the project.

4   The staff of the Unit of Statistics of the Agricultural and Food Research Council at the University of Edinburgh, who assisted in establishing the project methodology. George Jolly designed the sampling and statistical procedures; Jean Wood and Dr Chris Kershaw assisted in the development of statistical software.

5   Elizabeth Hume and Graham Mortimer carried out satellite image processing. David Yule contributed photogrammetric and computing skills. Hilary Anderson assisted in the training of project staff and the development of the air photo-interpretation method.

6   Members of the NCMS team past and present, who were Hilary Anderson, Janet Bateson, Jonathan Budd, Fiona Cocks, Hugh Devitt, Graham Gauld, Anthony Giblin, Phil Holden, John Holt, Elizabeth Hume, Perry Iles, Sarah Jewitt, Christina Karlonas, Annie Lewis, Simon Lewis, Karin Loch, Mairead McMullan, Anne Messer, Graham Mortimer, Muriel Randall, Dawn Scott, Paul Smyth, David Stewart, Jackie Stewart, Karen Sutherland, Ruth Thomas, David Yule and Simon Zisman.

7   The NCMS Review Group in 1992, chaired by Professor Jeff Maxwell of the Macaulay Land Use Research Institute. The Review Group members were Colin Barr, Institute of Terrestrial Ecology, Merlewood; Professor

Steve Buckland, University of St Andrews; Professor Donald Davidson, Department of Environmental Science, University of Stirling; and Don Futty (Secretary), Macaulay Land Use Research Institute.

8   Fiona Underwood of Scottish Natural Heritage, who contributed statistical advice from 1993 to 1995, Stuart Gardner, who developed the use of NCMS in ArcInfo and ArcView GIS environments, Julian Holbrook for managerial support and advice, and Graham Gibson for invaluable administrative support.

9   Advisory staff of Scottish Natural Heritage, for specialist feedback during the documentation of the study.

10   The eight external reviewers, for devoting their time, skill and knowledge towards the completion of this study. Comment and suggestions were invariably thoughtful and constructive, and invaluable in the honing of the final text.

Edward C. Mackey
Head of Environmental Audit Unit
Michael C. Shewry
Environmental Statistician
Gavin J. Tudor
NCMS Project Manager 1986–1997
Scottish Natural Heritage

Introduction: Land Cover, Land Use and their Dynamics

Michael B. Usher

Chief Scientist, Scottish Natural Heritage

The National Countryside Monitoring Scheme

The last 50 years have seen huge changes in the use of land. Immediately follow-ing the Second World War, there were pressures to produce more food and more timber. Both pressures came from the desire to be self-sufficient and hence to rely less on imported goods. There have also been huge political changes, necessitat-ing changes in policies for the support of rural industries. There have been tremendous technological changes, reflected in the mechanisation of agriculture and forestry as well as in the breeding of higher-yielding crops. And there have been changes in concept, especially relating to the focus on sustainability in both scientific and political circles. Have we ever witnessed such a half century of changes before?

Reflecting these changes has been the land cover. As people respond to policy shifts, the way that they use the land changes. Land cover is thus a reflection of both the environment and the local ecology, as well as of the socio-economic sta-tus of the local community of people. This is true of anywhere in the world, except perhaps for the hot dry deserts and the cold ice-covered land of Antarctica.

It is against this background that the National Countryside Monitoring Scheme (NCMS), a case study of change in Scotland, was initiated. In the southeast there are areas of intensive arable activity; in the southwest well-established pastoral activities; and in the north extensive areas of semi-natural habitats subject to extensive grazing and forestry. Scotland therefore represents a microcosm of human activities, a wide range of habitat types, and a great range of altitudes from sea level to plateaux above 1,000 m.

This book describes this case study of Scotland, recognising that the methods used have much wider applicability. The results, although relating to Scotland, also reflect the period of post-war reconstruction and the subsequent consolidation. The methods and results therefore have direct relevance to other parts of the world where land is being used. However, before describing the methods and results, it is important to understand land cover and its dynamics.

What is land cover?

Land cover has been defined in various ways, but as Skole[1] said, 'when we think about what covers the Earth's land surface, we think first of vegetation'. Such a reflection clearly relates to an anthropocentric view of the world, but it has a long lineage; for example, Sir Arthur Tansley's 1949 book had as its primary title *Britain's Green Mantle*.[2] In a country such as the United Kingdom, with a temperate and moist climate, it is inevitable that the 'green veneer' of the land will feature prominently. However, if the territory contained a large amount of desert, or ice, or water, the view of land cover might not be so plant-orientated. Indeed, three categories of land cover can be considered, namely:

- vegetation composed of the species that occur naturally in that geographical area;

- predominantly or totally unvegetated natural features, such as desert, water, ice, shingle or rock; and

- landscapes created by human activities, such as the predominantly unvegetated urban area, roads and airstrips, or vegetated areas such as farmland and plantation forests.

It is clear that the majority of land in the UK falls into the third category; Brown[3] indicated that about 75% of the land was agricultural, just over 10% was urban and at least a further 10% was covered in forest and woodland (of which two-thirds are coniferous plantation). Thus, some 92% of the land surface of the UK is in the third category, with the remaining 8% being split between the natural or semi-natural vegetation and the more or less unvegetated features.

Implicit in any analysis of land cover is a classification. The classification used above separates three types – natural and semi-natural vegetated cover, natural unvegetated cover, and human-induced cover, be it vegetated or unvegetated. Such a classification is brief, and most studies would need to recognise far more cover types than these three. For example, in Great Britain the first of these three categories might be sub-divided into the approximately 220 communities of the National Vegetation Classification,[4] and many of these communities can be further divided into sub-communities. Such a classification of land cover has the advantage that it is widely used in Great Britain, but it also has a number of disadvantages. These include the fact that it is too detailed for the majority of applications, that it requires detailed work on the site, that the communities and sub-communities cannot be identified remotely (i.e. from aerial photography or from satellite imagery), and that it is not international. The first two points are particularly important, though the latter point can be addressed because the system of classification of natural and semi-natural vegetation can be extended more widely, as for example by the CORINE system.[5]

Given the difficulty of using such classifications, it has become customary for land cover studies to devise their own classifications. These tend to be *ad hoc*, relying on the recognition of the land cover types that are likely to be of interest.

If the focus of the study is on landscape character, then the classification that is adopted will tend to favour this one feature. It will also reflect the geology and soils of the area, the type of vegetation that these soils support, and the human influence on the landscape through both the artefacts that are built and the way that the land is used. An example of this approach is the Countryside Commission's development of a *New Map of England*; in the southwest (the counties of Avon, Cornwall, Devon and Somerset) a total of 38 landscape types are recognised, together with an additional type for major urban areas.[6] The important point to note is that this collection of 39 types covers the whole of the study area, and no two types overlap. Thus any parcel of land, of whatever size, can be assigned to one, and only one, of the landscape types.

Pragmatic approaches to land cover classification are the norm. For the UK's Biodiversity Action Plan a series of about 40 broad habitat types has been adopted.[7] For the Land Cover of Scotland (LCS88) study a series of nine 'open countryside' types was used, together with seven 'woodland' types, five 'wet ground' types and two 'developed' types, giving a total of 23 land cover types, to which were added two further categories – land that could not be classified because it was obscured or the photography was missing, and land that was a mosaic of other types.[8] The LCS88 is therefore hierarchical. The Countryside Surveys of Great Britain[9] have derived from field surveys a set of 59 'dominant land cover types', which were then grouped hierarchically into 11 'major land cover types'. For example, the major cover type referred to as 'built up' consisted of two 'key cover types' – 'communications' and 'built up'. The former consisted of two 'dominant cover types' – 'railway' and 'road' – and the latter of three 'dominant cover types' – 'agricultural buildings', 'residential buildings', and 'other buildings'. Hierarchical classifications have a value for reporting, either with considerable detail or at a more aggregated level so that more generic patterns can be seen.

This brief review of land cover indicates four general points which are implicit in research on land cover and changes in land cover.

First, any parcel of land, which in some way, however small, will be different from all other parcels of land,[10] must unambiguously belong to only one of the land cover types selected. Thus, the suite of land cover types cover 100% of the study area. There may be various ploys to achieve this condition, for example by defining additional land cover types for mosaics of two or more of the types, or for parcels of land that cannot be assigned to any other land cover type to be classified as 'other' independent of whether or not they are similar.

Second, though not absolutely necessary, the classification should be hierarchical. Reporting on the results may need to be done at several different levels of detail, and this is facilitated by the existence of a definite hierarchical structure. Thus, in the Countryside Survey 1990,[11] reporting could be on the basis of the actual crops being grown in tilled fields (wheat, oil-seed rape, potatoes, horticultural crops, etc.) or just on the basis of land being tilled that season (and that is a combination of 17 separate crop types).

Third, the majority of classifications have to be derived pragmatically, as indeed has the one outlined in subsequent chapters of this book. The National Vegetation Classification[12] achieves an objectivity in the basis of the classification proposed. However, in the majority of studies the users define their own land cover types for their own purposes, and hence there are considerable difficulties in comparing different studies. Wyatt *et al.*[13] described the results of research into the relationships between different classifications of land cover and land use. Their report comprised qualitative and quantitative comparisons between 17 nationally and internationally important surveys, including the NCMS, which have been used in the UK. The difficulties of deriving an appropriate classification were considered by Weixelman *et al.*,[14] who advocated the use of multivariate statistics for the definition of types and the comparison of components. Such statistics were used in the creation of the National Vegetation Classification, but they have not yet been widely used in comparative studies.

Fourth, there remains a problem with linear features. All of the other land cover types can be recorded on the basis of their area, and indeed this is convenient when working with aerial photographs, satellite images and maps. Features such as hedgerows, an important landscape component, are shown as lines. From ground survey, the width of a hedgerow can be measured, and an area estimate gained. However, unless a standard width is assigned, the use of mapped data implies the existence of such linear features but gives them no area. As in the National Countryside Monitoring Scheme (NCMS), it is useful to separate out linear features and to record them by length rather than by area as separate categories in the classification. This has the advantages of simplicity and of being closer to the way that such linear features are perceived, but it has the disadvantage of assigning to them a zero area.

There is no perfect classification of land cover types. In choosing a classification there has to be a balance between *objectivity* in the types selected, *usefulness* and fitness for purpose in the results obtained, and *comparability* between the present study and previous or other studies of the same land area. All three of these factors are linked with the use that is made of the land, which will be explored in the following section.

Land cover and land use

Definition and classification

Skole defined land use as 'the human employment of a land-cover type, the means by which human activity appropriates the results of net primary production as determined by a complex set of socio-economic factors'.[15] Land cover is therefore purely a description, albeit in anthropocentric terms, of what covers the land at some instant in time; land use, on the other hand, specifically relates to the human use of the land, and there may be many reasons why a particular parcel of land is either used or not used. The NCMS is essentially concerned with land cover, those features of the land that can be directly observed from the ground, from the air, or from space. In contrast, land use is not generally directly observable, but knowledge of it can be gained from an understanding of both the land cover and the socio-economic factors of the local human population.

Even though there is a conceptual difference between the terms 'land cover' and 'land use', they are often used interchangeably. Thus, Brown[16] included a chapter of statistics on land use and land cover in the UK and its constituent parts. When the two concepts are mixed together, it becomes apparent that any parcel of land can have only one land cover type, but several land use types. Thus, although nearly 20% of the U.K is covered by National Parks (England and Wales only), Areas of Outstanding Natural Beauty (England, Northern Ireland and Wales) and National Scenic Areas (Scotland only), the land in these areas will be used for agriculture, forestry, nature conservation, recreation, etc. Whilst the sum of the land cover must of necessity be 100% of the area being studied, the sum of the land use (including land not being used) is likely to be considerably more than 100% because of multiple usage. As is highlighted by Campbell,[17] land use incorporates an economic function, and hence its study involves both the social and natural sciences.

Some classifications attempt to hybridise the concepts of land use and land cover. For example, the early attempt by Bunce and Last[18] to characterise the habitats of Scotland used actual data such as the solid geology, drift geology and topography of a parcel of land, inferred data such as the mean daily minimum January temperature and the mean daily duration of bright sunshine interpolated from climate maps, and human artefact data on roads and buildings taken from Ordnance Survey maps. In this way they derived a series of 32 land classes for Great Britain, some of which are confined to Scotland and five others of which only occur in the southern half of England and in Wales. The hybrid system is valuable in providing a stratification of Scotland and is clearly strongly correlated with both land cover and land use, but it cannot be used as a substitute for either land use or land cover.

Biodiversity conservation

Of increasing importance is one aspect of land use, the conservation of biodiversity. Not only are the land cover types themselves important, but within them a number of species live and reproduce, and within the species there is the genetic variation that has been used traditionally in plant and animal breeding and more recently in genetic engineering. Land use influences the balance of species, creating habitats that are favourable for some species and unfavourable for other species. Land use therefore has the potential to change the biodiversity of an area. Under more intensive forms of land use there is generally a decrease in the number of species, replacing those that are longer-lived and more specialised by those that are shorter-lived and more generalist. On the most intensively used land, the vascular plant species assemblage in general consists of 'weeds' – species that are annual, ruderal in character and opportunistic in where they occur. A realisation of such changes in the species complement has led to a social phenomenon, the demand for 'green or ecological networks'. Such networks 'are increasingly integrated into the strategies, policies, and practical projects for nature conservation across the Euroregion. Although not a new concept, green networks are attracting a lot of interest and seem to capture people's imagination. Recent research emphasises the need not only to protect habitats, but to develop, maintain and, where necessary, restore the linkages between them to protect their long-term viability.'[19]

This quotation is important because it emphasises strategies, policies and practical projects. An analysis of land cover, and how it changes, can inform the development of such strategies, policies and projects. However, it is the interaction of the natural and social sciences that is going to be important in the future.

Factors causing land cover change

Without the influences of human society, there would be two short- to medium-term processes leading to land cover change – ecological succession and the effect of catastrophic events – and the long-term process of climate change. In their use of the land, human societies are also forcing other changes, be they direct, such as the clearance of forest for agriculture or the exploitation of peat bogs, or indirect, such as the human effects on climate.[20] There is, therefore, a multiplicity of factors that lead to a change in land cover, and many of these factors are interrelated.

Ecological context

Ecological succession has been described for many types of habitat, but Connell and Slatyer[21] formulated three theoretical pathways relating to the dynamics of the species and communities. Suffice it to say that any parcel of land, left without human input, will undergo an ecological succession. If the land is bare, it will be colonised by a variety of organisms, and over time one suite of species will be replaced by other suites of species so that the characteristics of the land change.[22] In the temperate regions of the Earth, the tendency is towards woodland, though this will be modified by local climatic and edaphic conditions. The speed of change during an ecological succession may appear to be faster earlier on, when the structure of the vegetation is changing, and may appear to be slower after a few hundred years, when there is a community of trees and shrubs, but one of the points of discussion amongst ecologists is whether a 'climax' is ever reached after which there is no further change. With an ever-changing climate, it is perhaps true that there is no such stable state with a non-changing climax vegetation.

Successions are always being restarted as a result of catastrophic events. These are events that occur infrequently and unpredictably, and return the parcel of land on which they occur to a previous stage in the ecological succession. Examples of catastrophes include the effects of fire following a lightning strike, massive damage caused to woodlands (or indeed coral reefs) during severe gales, cliff falls either on the coast or in the mountains, or a 'bog burst'. It may be that the catastrophic event leads to the start of a primary succession, or that some organisms remain and the site commences a secondary succession; in either case, the result is a changing land cover type over time. Some of the ecological drivers for these processes were reviewed by Usher.[23] Land cover in Scotland has also changed markedly over the last 10,000 years or so since the end of the last glaciation, first with warming of the climate, then with a period of cooling, and then with warming again, and also with non-synchronous changes in the amount of precipitation.[24–27] The environment is ever-changing, and land cover, a summation of the effects of climate, geology and species, will also be changing, buffered from extreme swings due to the longevity of most plants, but nevertheless changing naturally in the medium-to-long term.

Socio-economic context

On top of this dynamic, ever-changing system, one must add the effects of human society, often creating change in the short term. The social, economic and political context[28] is important in understanding how changes may occur in one direction this year, or decade, and in a different direction next year, or decade. Agriculture is often implicated as the major cause of change,[29] and indeed an analysis in many parts of Europe[30] would tend to support this contention. The impacts of agriculture can be local (i.e. the effects in the field itself)[31] but can also be more widespread. For example, emissions of pollutants to water and air can have significant effects at great distances from their place of origin. Certainly in the interpretation of the results of the NCMS, land cover changes in Scotland have resulted more from social, economic and political pessures than from ecological pressures. However, the role of agriculture, although large, is perhaps not as important as further south in the UK. The importance of forestry has to be recognised. As Anderson stated, 'it can scarcely be said that the so-called national policy in respect of forestry has been a satisfactory one, but a belated departure from the narrow one of building up a reserve of timber to meet a national emergency to one which aims at forestry taking its proper place in the national economy is to be welcomed'.[32] The emphasis has changed, from the creation of a strategic reserve of timber, to a multi-use policy incorporating also aspects such as biodiversity, public recreation[33] and the need to absorb carbon dioxide from the air.[34]

The predominance of agricultural change in the lowlands and afforestation in the uplands can be seen in the analyses of the Countryside Survey 1990 data by Potter and Lobley[35] and Potter *et al*.[36] In Great Britain as a whole, Potter and Lobley say 'the most significant gains and losses in environmental stock [took] place in pastoral landscapes, chiefly attributable to changes in grassland management' and 'overall, the pivotal role played by recent intensification on livestock farms underlines the critical importance of changes to the livestock support system as a factor in future environmental change'. Taken with the statement 'Government is making provision to spend £90 million supporting the expansion of tree cover over the three years 1994/95 to 1996/97, sufficient to assist the creation of some 60,000 hectares at present rates of grant for new woodlands and forests',[37] the importance of support mechanisms and grants is clearly seen. Small changes in these state-sponsored support mechanisms for land use can cause relatively rapid changes in land cover. These human-induced changes in land cover can clearly be seen in the results of the NCMS.

Consequences of change: the future, biodiversity and sustainability

Two of the reasons for undertaking the NCMS were to understand for the first time the changes that have taken place in the Scottish countryside during the last 50 years or so, and from this understanding to be able to contribute to policy formulation in the future. Although the Wildlife and Countryside Act 1981 was intended to help prevent the loss of countryside features important to nature conservation, habitat change continues to be a major concern. Against this background, the NCMS was planned to provide quantitative data against which past, present and future rural policy and legislation could be assessed for its effect on the structure and appearance of the countryside.

This book documents the changes that have taken place, both nationally and locally. The fact that the data are open to statistical analysis is a tremendous step forward in being able to attach a degree of certainty to the results obtained. A study of what has happened is important both as a baseline from which to assess future change, and as an historical record of the land cover and its changes during the latter half of the twentieth century. This book provides such a thorough documentation, but the book is also important since it provides the factual basis on which future developments can be assessed. Together with the Land Cover of Scotland in 1988,[38] and its integration with the NCMS[39] and the Countryside Survey 1990, Scotland is now one of the best-studied parts of the world, and can act as a model for understanding changes in land cover elsewhere.

For the future, there is a number of topics that are of particular importance. In a sense these relate to the various contributions to the UK's plan for sustainable development:[40] climate change, biodiversity, forestry, and monitoring or environmental audits.

First, the UK has produced a statement on climate change[41] which encapsulates the crux of the problem – the emission of the so-called 'greenhouse gases'. Suffice it to say here that the various studies and models indicate three particular changes to the Scottish climate. There will be a gradual warming effect, there is the probability that the environment will become wetter, and there is also the possibility that extreme events, such as gales, will become more frequent. Each of these changes is likely to drive ecological successions, as well as to create new opportunities, or to close current opportunities, for land uses. How each will affect the various land cover types is a matter of speculation, but Lombard[42] reminded us that each ecosystem is different, has different soil fauna, and will react in a different way. He concluded that 'all these differences must be taken into account when the effects of global change on species and landscapes are modelled'. This presents a considerable challenge in the environmental sciences where there are few 'laws', and where our ignorance of the functioning of systems is profound as compared with that in the physical sciences. Vitousek[43] said that ecologists should 'get active', 'get connected', 'get real', 'get involved in ecological societies', and 'must not get down'! These are good messages and it is up to the present generation of people to make the difference. Compounded with the effect of human society on climate are the problems of acidification (largely sulphur emissions) and eutrophication (largely nitrogen emissions) on both terrestrial and aquatic systems.[44] It is important that these pollution effects are studied together with climate change, and that an overview of environmental change is maintained rather than a piecemeal approach to individual problems.

Second, land cover change has an effect on biodiversity. This is made clear in the UK's Biodiversity Action Plan.[45] Again the Countryside Survey 1990 has provided a broad-brush review of such effects in Great Britain,[46] but it is the detail that is most important. Changes from one land cover type to another drastically affect the fauna and flora, visibly those that occur above ground but perhaps as dramatically those that live below ground and are responsible for so many of the ecosystem functions. Intensification of agriculture has dramatically affected the populations of some species of birds[47] and can affect both the diet and body weight of mammal species.[48] Fragmentation of land cover types can impose a metapopulation structure in which connectivity is a key to species' continued existence,[49] but attempts at restoration may provide a glimmer of hope for the future.[50] Perhaps there are two pointers for the long-term future in efforts at restoration and in natural resource accounting[51] but for the immediate future the establishment of simple guidelines for the conservation of biodiversity[52] is certainly helpful.

Third, there are clearly many questions raised by considering the position of forestry.[53] In terms of percentage changes, the NCMS has demonstrated that trees have had a major impact on the Scottish environment. The depletion of timber resources during the First World War, the creation in 1919 of the Forestry Commission, and then the further depletion of timber in the Second World War, left a situation where afforestation to create a strategic reserve of timber was the only viable option. At the start of the NCMS study period, in the late 1940s, only 5% of Scotland was wooded, and of this just over one-third was of coniferous plantation (the result of the work of the Forestry Commission during its first quarter century as well as of private foresters). By the late 1980s about 14% of Scotland was wooded, and about five-sixths of this was of plantation forestry with, in general, non-native coniferous species. Such changes have considerable knock-on effects. They change the landscape, creating distinctive landscape types that are either new or similar to those that existed centuries ago (as outlined, for example, in the landscape character assessment of Dumfries & Galloway).[54] They change the land cover from types dominated by natural and semi-natural vegetation to ones dominated by introduced coniferous species. Together with the declining area of natural and ancient broadleaved woodlands, they change the biodiversity from one of considerable species richness[55] to one that is considerably species-poorer. Again, restoration may be important here as there is now a strong research focus on ways of managing plantation forests to increase their biodiversity.[56] Forests and woodlands therefore have a very important role in the land use of Scotland, and this is a role that is likely to increase in the decades ahead.

Fourth, there is the whole subject of environmental monitoring and environmental audit. There is an increasing interest in maintaining statistics about the environment. In Scotland, both the public sector[57] and the voluntary sector[58] have compiled statistics on the Scottish environment for the purposes of their own policy development. Although the statistics may be used in different ways, it is important that such statistics are both accurate and up to date. More recently both Scottish Natural Heritage[59] and the Scottish Environment Protection Agency[60] have produced publications on the state of the Scottish environment. Again, such statements need to be both accurate and up to date. The system of environmental accounting is a part of the Countryside Surveys of Great Britain,[61] and could be developed from both the LCS88 and NCMS approaches.

Conclusions

In relation to Scotland, the NCMS has provided a factual basis for assessing the land cover and for quantifying the changes that have occurred since the Second World War. The value of the investment in this study will be determined by how the data in this book are used for the development of policy by Scottish Natural Heritage, the Scottish Office and others working in Scotland; how the data can be used in environmental audits or state-of-the-environment reports; the use of the data for educational purposes; and the contribution of the data to the use of resources in a more sustainable way in the future than in the past. All of these relate to the fact that the NCMS was designed to give information for Scotland as a whole, and within Scotland at the regional scale.

However, the book also has a wider relevance. It can be viewed as a case study, demonstrating methodology that could be used anywhere in the world. The fact that the statistical significance of the results can be assessed is very important since it is rare to have an estimate of the significance of amounts of change. The results of the NCMS can clearly assist in achieving the aims of the UK's Biodiversity Action Plan[62] and to contributing to understanding the dynamics of several of the broad habitat types recognised in the plan.[63]

More widely, the relationships between land cover and land use, and their dynamics, need to be understood if we are ever to achieve the goals of sustainable development and biodiversity conservation. These are linked because biodiversity includes all species, including the human species, and the search for sustainability is essential if all of these species are to survive into the future. Ramakrishnan[64] reminded us that sustainable development is a goal for all countries in the world, whatever their current state of development and wherever they are. The NCMS, focusing as a case study on Scotland, should assist us in achieving these global aims.

References

1   Skole, D.L. (1994). Data on global land-cover change: acquisition, assessment, and analysis. In *Changes in Land Use and Land Cover: a Global Perspective*, ed. by W.B. Meyer and B.L. Turner. Cambridge: Cambridge University Press, pp. 437–471.

2   Tansley, A.G. (1949). *Britain's Green Mantle: Past, Present and Future*. London: George Allen & Unwin.

3   Brown, A. (1992). *The UK Environment*. London: HMSO.

4   Rodwell, J.S. (1991 – *in press*). *British Plant Communities*, volumes 1–5. Cambridge: Cambridge University Press.

5   Anonymous (1994). *CORINE Land Cover Technical Guide*. Luxembourg: European Community.

6   Anonymous (1994). *The New Map of England: a Celebration of the South Western Landscape*. Cheltenham: Countryside Commission.

7   Anonymous (1996). *Biodiversity: the UK Steering Group Report. Volume 1: Meeting the Rio Challenge* and *Volume 2: Action Plans*. London: HMSO.

8   Anonymous (1993). *The Land Cover of Scotland 1988: Executive Summary*. Aberdeen: Macaulay Land Use Research Institute.

9   Barr, C.J., Bunce, R.G.H., Clarke, R.T., Fuller, R.M., Furse, M.T., Gillespie, M.K., Groom, G.B., Hallam, C.J., Hornung, M., Howard, D.C. and Ness, M.J. (1993). *Countryside Survey 1990: Main Report*. London: Department of the Environment.

10 Hills, G.A. (1961). *The Ecological Basis for Land-use Planning*. Ontario: Department of Lands and Forests, Research Report No. 46.

11 Barr, C.J., Bunce, R.G.H., Clarke, R.T., Fuller, R.M., Furse, M.T., Gillespie, M.K., Groom, G.B., Hallam, C.J., Hornung, M., Howard, D.C. and Ness, M.J. (1993). *Countryside Survey 1990: Main Report*. London: Department of the Environment.

12 Rodwell, J.S. (1991 – *in press*). *British Plant Communities*, volumes 1–5. Cambridge: Cambridge University Press.

13 Wyatt, B.K., Greatorex-Davies, J.N., Hill, M.O., Parr, T.W., Bunce, R.G.H. and Fuller, R.M. (1994). *Comparison of Land Cover Definitions*. London: Department of the Environment.

14 Weixelman, D.A., Zamudio, D.C., Zamudio, K.A. and Tausch, R.J. (1997). Classifying ecological types and evaluating site degradation. *Journal of Range Management* **50**, 315–321.

15 Skole, D.L. (1994). Data on global land-cover change: acquisition, assessment, and analysis. In *Changes in Land Use and Land Cover: a Global Perspective*, ed. by W.B. Meyer and B.L. Turner. Cambridge: Cambridge University Press, pp. 437–471.

16 Brown, A. (1992). *The UK Environment*. London: HMSO.

17 Campbell, J.B. (1996). *Introduction to Remote Sensing*. London: Taylor & Francis.

18 Bunce, R.G.H. and Last, F.T. (1981). How to characterise the habitats of Scotland. *Annual Report of the Edinburgh Centre of Rural Economy*, 1–14.

19 Anonymous (1997). *Biodiversity in the Euroregion: an Identification of Key Issues Concerning Wildlife Management in the Five Regions*. Brussels: g.e.i.e. Euroregion.

20 Anonymous (1994). *Climate Change: the UK Programme*. London: HMSO.

21 Connell, J.H. and Slatyer, R.O. (1977). Mechanisms of succession in natural communities and their role in community stability and organization. *American Naturalist* **111**, 1119–1144.

22 Miles, J. and Walton, D.W.H. (1993). *Primary Succession on Land*. Oxford: Blackwell.

23   Usher, M.B. (1992). Land use change and the environment: cause or effect? In *Land Use Change: the Causes and Consequences*, ed. by M.C. Whitby. pp. 28–36. London: HMSO.

24   Bennett, K., Bunting, M.J. and Fossitt, J.A. (1997). Long-term vegetation change in the Western and Northern Isles, Scotland. *Botanical Journal of Scotland* **49**, 127–140.

25   Huntley, B., Daniell, J.R.G. and Allen, J.R.M. (1997). Scottish vegetation history: the Highlands. *Botanical Journal of Scotland* **49**, 163–175.

26   Ramsay, S. and Dickson, J.A. (1997). Vegetational history of Central Scotland. *Botanical Journal of Scotland* **49**, 141–150.

27   Tipping, R. (1997). Vegetation history of Southern Scotland. *Botanical Journal of Scotland* **49**, 151–162.

28   Munton, R.J.C., Lowe, P. and Marsden, T. (1992). Forces driving land use change: the social, economic and political context. In *Land Use Change: the Causes and Consequences*, ed. by M.C. Whitby. pp. 15–27. London: HMSO.

29   Lowe, P., Ward, N. and Munton, R.J.C. (1992). Social analysis of land use change: the role of the farmer. In *Land Use Change: the Causes and Consequences*, ed. by M.C. Whitby. London: HMSO. pp. 42–51.

30   Brouwer, F.M., Thomas, A.J. and Chadwick, M.J. (eds) (1991). *Land Use Changes in Europe: Processes of Change, Environmental Transformations and Future Patterns*. Dordrecht: Kluwer Academic.

31   Skinner, J.A., Lewis, K.A., Bardon, K.S., Tucker, P., Cath, J.A. and Chambers, B.J. (1997). An overview of the environmental impact of agriculture in the U.K. *Journal of Environmental Management* **50**, 111–128.

32   Anderson, M. L. (1967). *A History of Scottish Forestry. Volume 2, from the Industrial Revolution to Modern Times*. London and Edinburgh: Thomas Nelson.

33   Anonymous (1992). *Forest Recreation Guidelines*. London: HMSO.

34   Anonymous (1994). *Climate Change: the UK Programme*. London: HMSO.

35   Potter, C. and Lobley, M. (1996). *Processes of Countryside Change in Britain*. London: Department of the Environment.

36   Potter, C., Barr, C. and Lobley, M. (1996). Environmental change in Britain's countryside: an analysis of recent patterns and socio-economic processes based on the Countryside Survey 1990. *Journal of Environmental Management* **48**, 169–186.

37   Anonymous (1994). *Climate Change: the UK Programme*. London: HMSO.

38   Anonymous (1993). *The Land Cover of Scotland 1988: Executive Summary*. Aberdeen: Macaulay Land Use Research Institute.

39   Brooker, N. (1998). The integration of land cover data from the National Countryside Monitoring Scheme with the Land Cover of Scotland 1988. Research, Survey and Monitoring Report No. 99. Perth: Scottish Natural Heritage.

40   Anonymous (1994). *Sustainable Development: the UK Strategy*. London: HMSO.

41   Anonymous (1994). *Climate Change: the UK Programme*. London: HMSO.

42   Lombard, A.T. (1996). Global change, biodiversity and ecosystem functioning. *South African Journal of Science* **92**, 115–116.

43   Vitousek, P.M. (1994). Beyond global warming: ecology and global change. *Ecology* **75**, 1861–1876.

44   Lee, J.A. (1998). Unintentional experiments with terrestrial ecosystems: ecological effects of sulphur and nitrogen pollutants. *Journal of Ecology* **86**, 1–12.

45   Anonymous (1994). *Biodiversity: the UK Action Plan*. London: HMSO.

46   Bunce, R.G.H., Howard, D.C., Hallam, C.J., Barr, C.J. and Benefield, C.B. (1993). *Ecological Consequences of Land Use Change*. London: Department of the Environment.

47   Pain, D.J., Hill, D. and McCracken, D.I. (1997). Impact of agricultural intensification of pastoral systems on bird distribution in Britain 1970–1990. *Agriculture, Ecosystems and Environment* **64**, 19–32.

48   Hulbert, I.A.R. and Iason, G.R. (1996). The possible effects of landscape change on diet composition and body weight of mountain hare *Lepus timidus*. *Wildlife Biology* **2**, 269–273.

49   Petit, S. and Burel, F. (1998). Connectivity in fragmented populations: *Abax parallelepipedus* in a hedgerow network landscape. *Comptes Rendus de l'Académie des Sciences, Life Sciences* **321**, 55–61.

50 Dobson, A.P., Bradshaw, A.D. and Baker, A.J.M. (1997). Hopes for the future: restoration ecology and conservation biology. *Science* **277**, 515–522.

51 Common, M.S. and Norton, T.W. (1995). Biodiversity, natural resource accounting and ecological monitoring. In *Biodiversity Conservation*, ed. by C.A. Perrings. Dordrecht: Kluwer Academic, pp. 87–110.

52 Small, E. (1997). Biodiversity priorities from the perspective of Canadian agriculture: ten commandments. *Canadian Field-Naturalist* **111**, 487–505.

53 Anonymous (1994). *Sustainable Forestry: the UK Programme*. London: HMSO.

54 Land Use Consultants. (1988). Dumfries and Galloway landscape assessment. Scottish Natural Heritage Review No. 94. Perth: Scottish Natural Heritage.

55 Peterken, G.F. (1996). *Natural Woodlands: Ecology and Conservation in Northern Temperate Regions*. Cambridge: Cambridge University Press.

56 Newton, A.C. and Humphrey, J.W. (1997). Forest management for biodiversity: perspectives on the policy context and current initiatives. In *Biodiversity in Scotland: Status, Trends and Initiatives*, ed. by L.V. Fleming, A.C. Newton, J.A Vickery and M.B. Usher. Edinburgh: The Stationery Office, pp. 179–197.

57 Anonymous (1991). *The Scottish Environment – Statistics*. Edinburgh: The Scottish Office.

58 Dargie, T.C.D. and Briggs, D.J. (1991). *State of the Scottish Environment 1991*. Perth: Scottish Wildlife and Countryside Link.

59 Mackey, E.C. (ed.) (1995). *The Natural Heritage of Scotland: an Overview*. Perth: Scottish Natural Heritage.

60 Anonymous (1996). *SEPA 96: State of the Environment Report*. Stirling: Scottish Environment Protection Agency.

61 Haines-Young, R.H., Watkins, C., Bunce, R.G.H. and Hallam, C.J. (1996). *Environmental Accounts for Land Cover*. London: Department of the Environment.

62 Anonymous (1994). *Biodiversity: the UK Action Plan*. London: HMSO.

63 Pienkowski, M.W., Bignal, E.M., Galbraith, C.A., McCracken, D.I., Stillman, R.A., Boobyer, M.G. and Curtis, D.J. (1996). A simplified classification of land-type zones to assist the integration of biodiversity objectives in land-use policies. *Biological Conservation* **75**, 11–25.

64 Ramakrishnan, P.S. (1992). *Shifting Agriculture and Sustainable Development: an Interdisciplinary Study from North-Eastern India*. Paris: UNESCO and Carnforth: Parthenon Publishing.

PART ONE

THE METHOD

1 WHY NCMS?

This book documents the results of a land cover monitoring study, known as the National Countryside Monitoring Scheme (NCMS). It is a study of land cover change in Scotland from the late 1940s (around 1947) to the early 1970s (around 1973) and then to the late 1980s (around 1988). The study thus witnessed four decades of urban growth, together with the transformation of agriculture and forestry in Scotland. In contrast to the imperative of socio-economic reconstruction in the aftermath of the Second World War, broader environmental concerns for sustainable development started to emerge from key sectoral policies in the 1980s. By revealing changes in its land cover, the NCMS casts new light upon this fascinating phase in Scotland's recent history.

It was through the policy shifts of the 1980s that the NCMS came into being. The Wildlife and Countryside Act 1981 extended environmental provisions embodied in the National Parks and Access to the Countryside Act 1949, thereby reflecting mounting concerns about ways in which the structure and appearance of the countryside had been affected by changes in farming, forestry and other land uses. The framing of the Act exposed a paucity of hard evidence in the form of robust quantitative information, and prompted more systematic investigations. In response, the NCMS was initiated in 1983 by the Nature Conservancy Council and, as land cover information was especially lacking north of the border, from 1986 onwards it was directed to focus on Scotland. Under the Natural Heritage (Scotland) Act 1991, the newly established Scottish Natural Heritage (SNH) inherited the study – this phase of which it has now brought to completion.

Motivated by a concern for the state of Scotland's natural heritage, a vital characteristic of the NCMS is that it has been able to look across the major land use sectors in order to provide a view of land cover change throughout Scotland from the late 1940s to the late 1980s. 'Land cover' refers to features of land surface, which may be natural, semi-natural, managed or created by humans. They are directly observable and in the case of NCMS remotely so from air photography. 'Land use', on the other hand, refers to activities such as agriculture, forestry or recreation. Not directly observable, inferences about land use can often be made from land cover. A reason for developing and maintaining a land cover monitoring study is to provide a consistent view of the stock and state of our natural and built resources as they change through time.

The NCMS is not the only source of land cover information about Scotland (other national-scale studies being the Land Cover of Scotland 1988 census[1] and the GB-wide Countryside Survey 1990[2]), but it uniquely describes key changes which have taken place over four decades, and at a range of geographical scales.

Its results have been presented here thematically according to the main land cover groups, as well as geographically for each of twelve regions. In drawing key results together in a sectoral analysis, Chapter 26 summarises evidence of urban development, intensification and specialisation of lowland agriculture, and land utilisation changes in the uplands. The time series thus contributes new information towards developing an improved understanding of interdependencies that exist between Scotland's changing land cover, its biodiversity, the importance of amenity, and the ways in which we utilise our natural resources.

As we look to the future, the NCMS fills an important gap in our knowledge about land cover change in Scotland from the late 1940s to the late 1980s. In pursuit of an attractive, productive, healthy and diverse environment, and thereby also the welfare of future generations, our strategies for sustainable development can be more fully informed towards developing more responsible attitudes to environmental management.

References

1   The Macaulay Land Use Research Institute (1993). *The Land Cover of Scotland 1988*. Aberdeen: MLURI.

2   Barr, C.J., Bunce, R.G.H., Clark, R.T., Fuller, R.M., Furse, M.T., Gillespie, M.K., Groom, G.B., Hallam, C.J., Hornung, M., Howard, D.C. and Ness, M.J. (1993). *Countryside Survey 1990: Main Report*. Eastcote: Department of the Environment.

2 THE MEASUREMENT OF CHANGE

2.1 Background

Established by the Nature Conservancy Council in June 1983, the National Countryside Monitoring Scheme (NCMS) was designed to provide estimates of land cover change. Piloted in Cumbria, it went on to utilise Scotland-wide aerial photography in order to compare Scotland's land cover of the late 1940s with that of the early 1970s. When photography for the late 1980s became available, Scottish Natural Heritage took the opportunity to extend the time series.

The study describes the extent of 31 areal and five linear components of the countryside, and their changes through time. In the interests of long-term continuity a stratified random sample approach was adopted with specified criteria of reliability in order to detect changes of 10% or more with 95% confidence. By aggregation, the study was capable of providing results at district, regional and national scales.

The NCMS took place during a period of rapid advances in remote sensing and geographical information systems (GIS) technology and was innovative in the utilisation of emergent information systems for the capture and processing of geographical information. Such capabilities were appreciably more powerful by the completion of the project than they had been at the start.

The NCMS design principles are outlined below.

2.2 Stratification

Within Britain there is a considerable range of geographical diversity in ecosystems, determined largely by major climatic gradients and geographical differences in physiography and geology, which in turn shape the pattern of variation in soil development, human activity and land use.[1] When the first generalised land utilisation map became available it was evident that, even with the most casual glance, 'one cannot fail to notice the extraordinary contrasts between one part of the country and another . . . it would be difficult to find any area of comparable size anywhere in the world which offers such amazing variety'.[2] With its varied climate and soils, such contrasts are especially evident in Scotland, a country of 'very considerable geologic and topographic and hence edaphic, floristic and vegetational diversity'.[3]

'Stratification' is the process of subdividing a varied area into more broadly similar geographical units. If the land cover within each stratum varies relatively little, precise area estimates can be obtained from a relatively small sample within it. Stratification helps also to ensure that the less common types of land cover are not under-represented. Fewer sampling points are required to obtain estimates to a given precision than would be the case for a simple random sample.

The stratification of Scotland as a whole is a considerable undertaking and only recently has a possible biogeographical zonation scheme been attempted.[4] When the NCMS was piloted in Cumbria in the early 1980s, environmental 'land classes' that had been developed by the Institute of Terrestrial Ecology provided a basis for stratification.[5-7] These had not been defined for Scotland when the study transferred to Grampian region in 1986. The NCMS stratification procedure therefore utilised Landsat Multi-Spectral Scanner (MSS) imagery. Although only about ten Landsat satellite MSS images are required for Scotland-wide coverage, 'owing to high incidence of cloud cover, it may be necessary to allow ± 2 years around a baseline to acquire complete cloud free imagery'.[8] The Landsat MSS images used for stratification in fact spanned seven years, from 1977 to 1984. The strata, being highly generalised, are unlikely to exhibit discernible change over such a time period and so this is not expected to have a bearing on results. More important is the effect of seasonal differences between images, which can result in wide variations in classification accuracy between scenes. No attempt was therefore made by the NCMS to generate a composite stratification scheme for Scotland as a whole. Instead, each Scottish region, as shown on the Ordnance Survey Local Government Areas map of 1984, was processed separately (Figure 2.1).

The absence of a biogeographical standard for stratification meant that the NCMS design became tied to the pre-April 1996 local authority region and district boundaries. This constraint was overcome subsequently to allow estimates to be generated for any area of interest, providing that sufficient sample squares are represented.

For each NCMS region, pixels from satellite imagery were classified into between two and five broad classes. Physiographic characteristics varied from region to region but generally 'upland' classes were predominantly mire, heather moorland and rough grassland; 'lowland' classes tended to be mainly arable and smooth grassland; and 'intermediate' classes included grassland, forestry and moorland. An 'urban' class was defined where appropriate. The geometrically corrected and classified pixel image was then converted into a 1 × 1 km grid by assigning to each Ordnance Survey grid square the most commonly occurring class. This initial classification was coarsened to 5 × 5 km squares for sampling.

2.3 Sampling

Initially a random sample of 5 × 5 km squares was selected in order to survey at least 10% of the area of each stratum within each district of any given region. The sampling intensity was designed to detect changes of 10% in the extent of commonly occurring habitats with 95% statistical confidence.

It became evident that such a sampling scheme might yield too few sample squares in small districts.[9] Following a review of the method the sample square size was reduced to 2.5 × 2.5 km and the number of squares sampled was

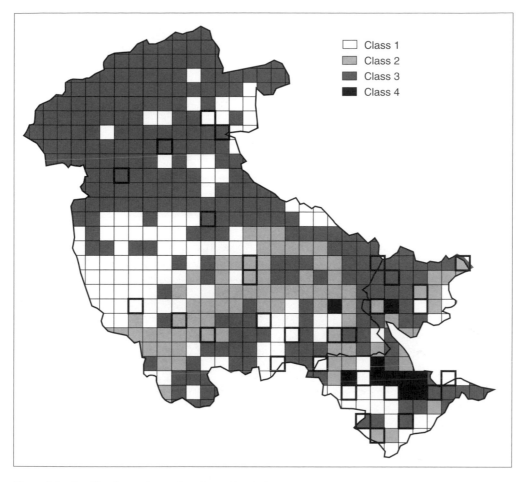

Figure 2.1   Stratification and sampling (Central region).

increased. In the revised design a minimum of five sample squares per stratum per district was selected, or all were selected where fewer than five squares were present. The NCMS sample for Scotland as a whole included 467 squares and covered approximately 7.5% of Scotland's land area (Figure 2.2).

2.4   Air photo interpretation

Scotland-wide air photography had been flown by the Royal Air Force after the Second World War and again by the Ordnance Survey in the early 1970s. These photo sets provided the coverage and consistency of land cover information which met NCMS requirements, and so enabled the 'first phase' of the study to assess land cover change from the late 1940s to the early 1970s. Further photographic coverage, which was commissioned by the Scottish Development Department in the late 1980s, then enabled the NCMS time series to be extended.

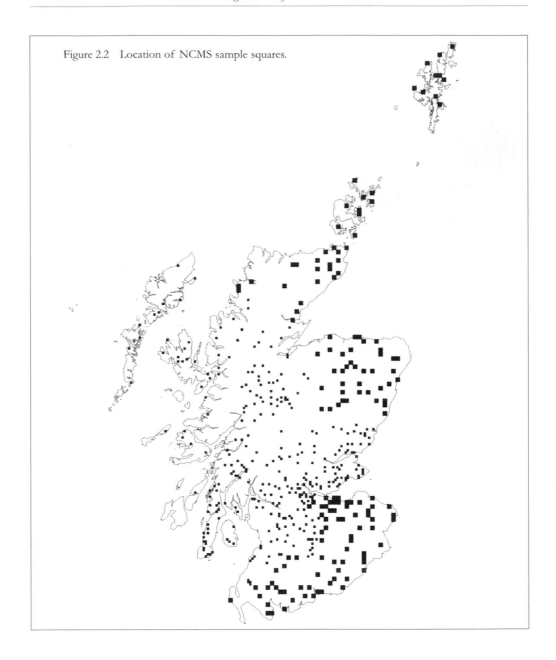

Figure 2.2   Location of NCMS sample squares.

Accurate and consistent interpretation was dependent on the textural quality and sharpness of pictures, as well as the knowledge and skill of interpreters. All photographs were viewed as stereo pairs, and land cover classification was made with reference to an interpretation key.[10] Each sample square was interpreted and mapped by one interpreter alone, and then checked and verified by at least one other. Any differences in the interpretation were noted and resolved, where necessary with field visits, prior to digitising.

Nevertheless, interpretation inaccuracy is inherent in the method because:

• photographic quality varied, especially between time periods;

• the scale of photography, although mainly of 1:24,000, varied from 1:10,000 to 1:30,000;

• it could be difficult to decide upon the dominance of one feature within a mosaic community, or to discriminate between features which had indistinct boundaries and/or which changed in form and colour seasonally;

• the classification of 'mire' (peat-forming vegetation) assumed the sub-surface presence of waterlogged peat, which could only be inferred from surface morphology; and

• subjective judgement in air photo interpretation, compounded by the turnover of interpreters during the project, meant that inconsistencies inevitably arose.

General interpretation problems were that:

• smooth grassland and cereals looked similar in late spring or early summer, when most of the photography was flown;

• leafless deciduous tree 'skeletons' were indistinct without shadow to betray their presence;

• discrimination between tall hedgerows, lines of trees, and vegetated dykes or banks was especially problematic where the photography was of poor quality or small scale;

• bracken, commonly evident within mosaics, was readily mistaken for rough grass in spring or low scrub in autumn;

• distinguishing 'broadleaved plantation' and 'mixed plantation' from similar categories of woodland was problematic;

• heterogeneous mosaics of heathland plant communities blended and merged, with indistinct boundaries for mapping; and

• low-lying or suppressed heather provided little textural information on air photographs and, especially where grass was present, could be difficult to distinguish from rough grassland.

A characteristic of Scotland's mires, which are permanently damp or waterlogged and thus peat-forming, is that they merge into periodically waterlogged wet heaths on shallow peat and humic mineral soils. Wet heaths in turn intergrade into dry heaths on more free-draining rankers, sands and podzols. While characteristic mire vegetation types (bryophytes, herbaceous plants and sub-shrubs of which *Calluna vulgaris* and *Erica tetralix* are the most widespread) occur on soils that are organic in character, they also occur on wet heath mineral profiles.[11-13] The lack of a distinct boundary between mire and moorland presented particular difficulties in

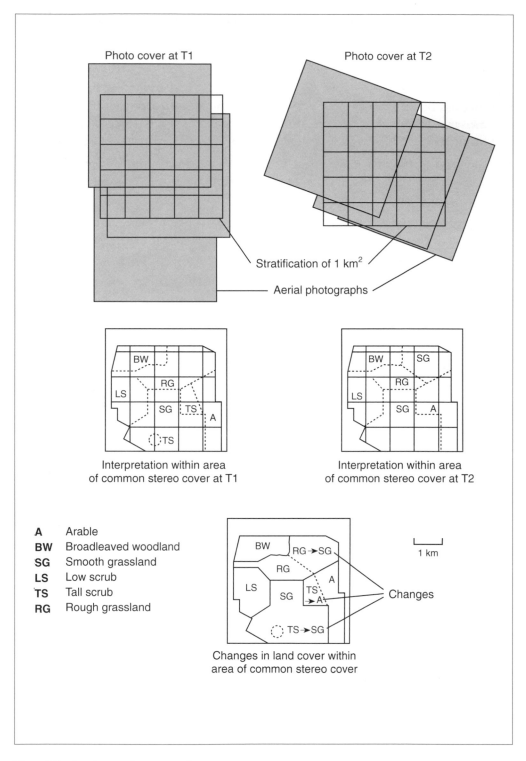

Figure 2.3   Land cover change mapping.

the interpretation, which required extensive checking and in some cases correction when 1980s photography was viewed.

Distinguishing heather-dominated or grass-dominated blanket mire from heather moorland or rough grassland relied upon visual evidence of 'hummock and hollow' morphology, peat lochans or hags, peat cutting or surface drainage. As it was no longer regarded as actively peat-forming, mire which had been drained (mainly associated with afforestation) was reclassified in the NCMS method according to its dominant surface vegetation of heather or rough grassland. In hindsight, it would have been more informative to recognise the qualitative distinction between those long-established habitats and the degradation of mire associated with drainage.

For each individual sample square, interpretation of the 1940s photography was followed by interpretation of the 1970s photography (Figure 2.3). The analysis and documentation of the 1940s and 1970s interpretation, region by region[14] and by aggregation for Scotland as a whole,[15] was termed the 'first phase' of the NCMS study. When air photography for the late 1980s became available, the study was extended into a 'second phase'.

2.5 Mapping

The NCMS classification distinguished between 31 areal features and five linear features (Table 2.1). In areas with little relief and abundant landmarks the interpretation was drawn onto transparent film overlaid onto the corresponding Ordnance Survey 1:10,000 map sheet. A Kern PG2 photogrammetric plotting machine was employed where there was significant relief or little topographic detail.

The smallest size of features which could be mapped (the 'minimum mappable area') was approximately 0.1 ha for areal features and 30 m for linear features. For such detailed mapping it proved to be impracticable to edit in changes from the 1940s onwards and so the entire sample for the 1940s, 1970s and 1980s was independently mapped and digitised. While this eliminated a potential source of interpretational bias through time, it also excluded a means of continuously check-ing the validity of changes between times. For areal features, re-mapping resulted in the creation of 'sliver polygons' where two supposedly co-incident lines did not exactly superimpose. Similar problems occurred in accurately digitising linear features which ran parallel and in close proximity to one another, such as a ditch running alongside a hedge. These caused non-systematic locational errors which tended to cancel out in the analysis.

Digital mapping software allowed map data to be captured via a digitising table or to be encoded from photogrammetric stereo plotting instruments.

Table 2.1 The NCMS classification of land cover features. Linear features are shown in italics.

	Land cover group	Feature type
1	Grassland	Rough grassland Intermediate grassland Smooth grassland
2	Mire	Heather-dominated blanket mire Grass-dominated blanket mire Lowland mire
3	Heather moorland	Heather moorland
4	Arable	Arable (cereal, horticultural and cultivated areas)
5	Woodland	Broadleaved woodland Mixed woodland Broadleaved plantation Parkland Coniferous woodland Young plantation Coniferous plantation Felled woodland
6	Fresh water	Lochs Reservoirs Rivers *Streams* Canals *Ditches* Marginal inundation Wet ground
7	Built and bare ground	Built land Recreational land Transport corridor *Tracks* Quarry Rock/cliff Bare ground
8	Bracken and scrub	Bracken Low scrub Tall scrub
9	Hedgerows and trees	*Hedgerow* *Lines of trees*

2.6 Interpretational accuracy

Numerous sources of error are inherent in land cover studies.[16,17] A key requirement is to assess the accuracy of the interpretation, which is subject to two types of error:

- 'error of omission' is where a feature is under-estimated by its incorrect interpretation as other features; and

- 'error of commission' is where a validated feature is over-estimated by the incorrect inclusion of other features.

Nevertheless, it has been judged that overall levels of accuracy of between 80 and 90% can be routinely obtained by air photo interpretation using skilled personnel.[18]

Due to the sequence of interpretation, field checking for accuracy assessment could not be undertaken until several years after the 1988 photography had been flown. In 1995, an exercise to assess the accuracy of the NCMS air photo interpretation independently was undertaken.[19] That involved the field checking of 1.25 × 1.25 km validation squares within a random sample of 150 NCMS sample squares. Within each validation square an example of each interpreted feature was selected at random for comparison with the 1980s air photo interpretation.

Site visits were made to validate the pre-selected features, taking account of possible changes since the land was photographed in the late 1980s. Field observations provided reliable data on 1,068 areal features and 313 linear features. Confusion rates, which quantify the disagreement between validator and interpreter, were calculated for each feature in the classification.

Results indicate that bracken, mire, rough grassland, heather moorland, as well as hedgerows, were all subject to interpretational difficulties. The visual regularity of built features, arable land and coniferous plantation made their interpretation more reliable (Table 2.2).

Confusion arose particularly among visually similar groups of features, which may have indistinct boundaries or which may occur as mosaics (mixtures below the minimum mappable area):

- bracken, blanket mire, heather moorland and rough grassland; and
- broadleaved woodland, mixed woodland, tall scrub and coniferous woodland.

Countering the effect of misclassification on the estimates, it was found that confusion between any two features tended to be mutually cancelling (i.e. occurred in both directions) and confusion declined with increasing polygon size (i.e. large polygons were less prone to error of interpretation than small ones).

The relatively small validation sample size means that confidence intervals for the confusion rates tend to be wide. Although this precludes correction of the NCMS area estimates for misclassification, results suggest that:

- blanket mire and rough grassland were over-estimated at the expense of bracken and heather moorland;
- young plantation was over-estimated at the expense of mixed woodland and coniferous plantation; and
- rough grassland was over-estimated at the expense of rock.

Table 2.2   Summary of main confusions (features for which adequate validation data were available, and in order of least to most confused).

Interpreted feature	Main confusions
Areal features	
Built	–
Arable	–
Smooth grassland	–
Coniferous plantation	–
Lochs	Reservoirs
Bare ground	Quarry
Wet ground	Rough grassland
Young (coniferous) plantation	Mixed woodland, coniferous plantation
Rock	Rough grassland
Broadleaved woodland	Mixed woodland
Intermediate grassland	Smooth grassland
Transport corridor	Tracks
Mixed woodland	Broadleaved woodland, coniferous plantation
Heather moorland	Rough grassland, blanket mire
Grass-dominated blanket mire	Rough grassland, heather-dominated blanket mire
Rough grassland	Grass-dominated blanket mire, bracken
Tall scrub	Broadleaved woodland, low scrub
Low scrub	Tall scrub
Heather-dominated blanket mire	Heather moorland, grass-dominated mire, rough grassland
Bracken	Rough grassland, low scrub
Linear features	
Treeline	–
Tracks	–
Ditches	–
Streams	Ditches
Hedgerow	Tracks

Further analysis has assessed the accuracy of change estimates. If the assumption is valid that misclassification rates were constant throughout the study period, the following main points emerge from the analysis:

- As mire appears to have been over-estimated at the expense of heather moorland, so an estimated 21% reduction in the area of mire from the 1940s to the 1980s may be nearer to 18%.

- Similarly, the estimated 23% reduction of heather moorland from the 1940s to the 1980s may be closer to 24%. These results may be associated with definitional difficulties of distinguishing between mosaic features in the uplands.

- Due to its confusion with young and coniferous plantation, the estimated 37% reduction of mixed woodland appears to be unreliable.

- Due to confusion with heather moorland and rough grassland, the bracken area appears to have been under-estimated throughout the study. This was especially so in the 1940s and 1970s, resulting in an over-estimate of the expansion of bracken from the 1970s to the 1980s. Bracken is likely to be more extensive than NCMS results suggest and not to have changed as greatly.

Accuracy rates of 80% or higher were achieved for about half of the features for which adequate data were available. In view of the quality of photography available to the study, this suggests that the NCMS classification and mapping resolution stretched the limits of air photo interpretation. Nevertheless, comparison of NCMS with the Land Cover of Scotland 1988 (LCS88) census has shown that 'misclassification rates estimated by this study agree broadly with those found for LCS88, although methodological differences prevent an exact comparison'.[20]

2.7 Data processing

Data processing software in a geographical information system was employed to build vector data files. Automated error checking and manual correction were repeated until no known digitising errors remained.

While line plots and measurements could be produced for any given square, the desktop-PC technology of the mid 1980s could not process the vector data volumes involved in an overlay analysis of two time periods. Digitised vector data were therefore converted to a raster format of 10-m pixels for analysis. Comparison matrices for the 1940s–1970s, 1970s–1980s and 1940s–1980s were then generated for each sample square.

District and regional results were calculated by statistical software using stratification information to extrapolate from sample square data. Statistical outputs were checked automatically and visually for suspect results, such as out-of-range or improbable values. If found, the original interpretation and digitised maps would be re-examined to resolve any problems.

2.8 GIS developments

During the course of the study there was a migration across three GIS platforms. While the final NCMS dataset only occupies about 200 MB of disk space, operational files require about 2 GB of GIS workstation hard disk. When the study originated in the 1980s, with customised software for running on stand-alone 8088/8086 personal computers, managing such a large dataset was problematical. When the original CP/M format files for the 1940s and 1970s were first converted to DOS format and backed up, they occupied more than 1,500 5¼-inch floppy disks.

Table 2.3 Considerations for improving the NCMS method.

NCMS method	GIS approach
Air-photo interpretation from stereo-pairs, mapping by hand, digitising	Orthorectified digital photography interpreted and digitised directly on 'head-up' display screens
Limited access to information on paper maps	Within a GIS environment, other datasets or supporting visual information could aid interpretation in real time
Entire sample square interpreted for each time period	Masking to select only the overlapping cover for interpretation
Time-consuming validation steps only identify errors after all data have been entered, and can still fail to detect misclassified features and erroneous codes	Error correction and validation incorporated in the capture procedure
Vector dataset rasterised prior to GIS overlay analysis	Stock and interchange would be computed from the digitised vector data; although checks on GRID v Vector in NCMS have shown that there is little difference in results (because the grid size is the same as the minimum mappable unit), avoiding rasterisation eliminates a step and overcomes the need to reclassify cells containing more than one feature type
5 × 5 km sample squares split into 25 separate 1 km squares for PC-based statistical analysis	Sample squares would be processed as single units on the GIS
Linear interchange is impossible because of the inability to match lines between time periods exactly; net change is calculated by processing them as raster features	Buffering would allow linear features to be treated as areal features; in effect a 10 m buffer is the same as a 10 m square, except the buffer replicates the shape of the line better
Difficult to undertake field validation	GPS, data loggers, digital cameras and field GIS systems would be feasible, allowing surveyors to carry a subset of the digital NCMS data with them into the field
Statistical program requires GIS output to be in the form of sequential ASCII files	Redesign interface between the statistics program and the GIS so that it does not limit the power of the GIS
Access to results reliant on paper reports	Being a wholly digital product, NCMS would be suited to electronic publication
Reliance on air photography and associated technology	Advances in satellite remote sensing and image processing may in future bypass the need for air photo interpretation and digitising

In 1992 the project upgraded to an Intergraph workstation environment, in which improved GIS performance was constrained by the requirement for downward compatibility with the predecessor system. Although improvements were achieved in the automation of data transfer, the statistics program governed the GIS output format.

In 1997 the individual NCMS sample files were for the first time assembled on an ArcInfo workstation as single data layers for each of the three time periods. This simplified data management and made results more accessible for viewing and analysis. Stratification information, formerly held only as data files for input to the statistics program, was also digitised to provide greater flexibility in the presentation and use of NCMS results.

The NCMS was completed in 1998. During its 14 years, GIS technology and experience in land cover studies have advanced greatly. The NCMS was an innovative and ambitious project which has created an important Scotland-wide time series of land cover change. If it was repeated, many technical improvements could be incorporated (Table 2.3).

References

1   Ratcliffe, D.A. (ed.) (1977). The ecological background to site selection. In *A Nature Conservation Review*. Vol.1. Cambridge: Cambridge University Press.

2   Stamp, L.D. (1962). *The Land of Britain – Its Use and Misuse*. Third Edition. London: Longmans, Green & Co. Ltd.

3   Birks, H.J.B. (1996). Great Britain – Scotland. In Berglund, B.E., Birks, H.J.B., Ralska-Jasiewiczowa and Wright, H.E. (eds) *Paleoecological Events During the Last 15,000 Years: Regional Synthesis of Lakes and Mires in Europe*. Chichester: John Wiley & Sons Ltd.

4   Carey, P.D., Dring, J.C.M., Hill, M.O., Preston, C.D. and Wright, S.M. (1994). *Biogeographical Zones in Scotland*. Scottish Natural Heritage Research, Survey and Monitoring Report No 26. Perth: Scottish Natural Heritage.

5   Bunce, R.G.H., Barr, C.J. and Whittaker, H. (1981). A stratification system for ecological sampling. In Fuller, R.M. (ed.). *Ecological Mapping from Ground, Air and Space*. Institute of Terrestrial Ecology Symposium No. 10. Cambridge: ITE.

6   Benefield, C.B. and Bunce, R.G.H. (1982). *A Preliminary Visual Presentation of Land Classes in Britain*. Merlewood Research and Development Paper No. 91. Cumbria: Institute of Terrestrial Ecology.

7   Bunce, R.G.H., Lane, A.M.J., Howard, D.C. and Clarke, R.T. (1991). *ITE Land Classification: the classification of all 1 km squares in GB*. Report to the Department of the Environment by the Institute of Terrestrial Ecology. Grange-over-Sands: ITE.

8   Dunn, R. (1995). *Evaluation of the Land Cover of Scotland 1988 Project*. Edinburgh: The Scottish Office Central Research Unit. HMSO.

9   Kershaw, C.D. (1988). *A Review of Statistical Aspects of the NCMS*. Nature Conservancy Council internal communication.

10   Nature Conservancy Council (1987). *Aerial Photograph Interpretation: the National Countryside Monitoring Scheme*. NCC unpublished report.

11   Rodwell, J.S. (ed.) (1991). *British Plant Communities Volume 2: Mires and Heaths*. Cambridge: Cambridge University Press.

12   Gimingham, C.H. (1975). *An Introduction to Heathland Ecology*. Edinburgh: Oliver & Boyd.

13   Usher, M.B. and Thompson, D.B.A. (1993). Variation in upland heathlands in Great Britain: conservation importance. *Biological Conservation* **66**, 69–81.

14   Nature Conservancy Council and Countryside Commission for Scotland (1988). *National Countryside Monitoring Scheme Scotland : Grampian*. Edinburgh: NCC and CCS. A complete series of 11 reports was produced, since 1992 by Scottish Natural Heritage.

15   Tudor, G.J., Mackey, E.C. and Underwood, F.M. (1994). *The National Countryside Monitoring Scheme: The Changing Face of Scotland: Main Report*. Perth: Scottish Natural Heritage.

16   Burrough, P.A. (1986). Data quality, errors, and natural variation. In *Principles of Geographical Information Systems for Land Resource Assessment*. Monographs on Soil and Resources Survey No 12. Oxford: Oxford University Press.

17   Chrisman, N.R. (1991). The Error Component in Spatial Data. In Maguire, D.J., Goodchild, M.F. and Rhind, D.W. (eds). *Geographical Information Systems*. Harlow: Longman Scientific & Technical.

18   Dunn, R. (1995). *Evaluation of the Land Cover of Scotland 1988 Project*. Edinburgh: The Scottish Office Central Research Unit. HMSO.

19   Elston, D.A., Gauld, J.H. and Miller, J.A. (in prep.). *The National Countryside Monitoring Scheme Accuracy Assessment*. Scottish Natural Heritage Research, Survey and Monitoring Report. Perth: Scottish Natural Heritage.

20   *Ibid.*

3 THE PRESENTATION OF RESULTS

Land cover data can be examined from a number of angles: for instance, as tables quantifying land cover stock and change, as charts of rates of change, as flow diagrams of interchange, or as maps of geographical variation. All are applied in Chapter 4 to summarise the main study findings across Scotland as a whole.

Subsequent chapters explore these findings more fully – thematically according to land cover type in Chapters 5 to 13, and according to geographical region in Chapters 14 to 25. The discussion in Chapter 26 draws together key findings to examine evidence of change in key land use sectors.

As NCMS estimates were obtained by extrapolation from a sample, results are subject to sampling variation. This uncertainty is reflected in the use of 'confidence intervals' for estimates, which define the range of values within which a true area or length is likely to lie. Confidence intervals are particularly important for estimates of change, indicating the strength of evidence that land cover change in the sample is a reflection of change across the country. The 'null hypothesis' must always be that no real change took place across the country. The likelihood that the null hypothesis holds true can be tested from changes found in the sample squares. If the confidence interval does not span zero, i.e. does not go from a negative to a positive value, we can be fairly confident that a real change has taken place.[1] Wherever possible a distinction is made in the tables, figures and text between results which are statistically significant and those which are not.

The NCMS is, of course, an abstraction of the real world. It applies decision rules, objective and subjective, to the differentiation of non-homogeneous habitats. As with any conventional mapping method, NCMS places discrete lines over fuzzy boundaries. Inevitably, boundary differences arise in mapping different periods, leading to spurious minor gains and losses. This effect can be especially severe for small features which have large boundaries relative to area, and for long thin features for which a slight digitising mismatch can result in substantial but mutually cancelling differences between two time periods. Consequently, only net change was calculated for linear features.

The dynamics of change can be illustrated by gains and losses, or 'interchanges', between pairs of features. For example, it was estimated that 273 km² of heather moorland was lost to bracken between the 1940s and 1980s, but heather moorland also expanded on to bracken by 44 km² over the same period. There was thus a dynamic interchange, real and methodological, between the two features. The result was a net loss of 229 km² of heather moorland to bracken. It is inherent in the method that gains and losses will tend to be over-estimated, and consequently that the unchanged extent will tend to be under-estimated. Where there is no systematic bias, the net change figure should be largely unaffected. The statistical significance of net interchanges between features has not been assessed and so those results should be viewed accordingly.

The key purpose of the analysis is to describe and explain land cover changes which have taken place, and the interactions between different land cover types.

3.1 National results

The aim in Chapter 4 is to provide a readily accessible summary of key findings for Scotland as a whole. The discussion focuses on NCMS findings, with summary boxes of key points. Results are expressed in tables and diagrams of land cover stock, change and interchange.

3.2 Thematic results

The NCMS classified Scotland's land cover into 31 areal and five linear features. For presentation, alike features are brought together into feature 'groups'. Chapter 9 on 'woodland', for instance, includes the eight types of woodland in the NCMS classification. There are eight NCMS land cover groupings of this kind and the sequence of Chapters 5 to 12 is broadly from largest to smallest, according to the 1940s group area. Chapter 13 covers the linear features of hedgerows and trees.

Although the NCMS is a sample survey it would be helpful to visualise the geographical distribution of its features throughout Scotland. This has been partly achieved by the 'density mapping' of each NCMS region according to the proportion of the area accounted for by any given feature. While that is an aid to comparing broad geographical differences, it provides only a general impression of feature distribution.

A comparison of the Land Cover of Scotland 1988 (LCS88) census with the NCMS sample has enabled distribution maps to be projected for NCMS features.[2] The smaller NCMS mapping resolution means that LCS88 polygons generally contain several NCMS polygons, but by averaging over all NCMS sample squares a 'typical' NCMS composition of each LCS88 feature can be determined. For illustrative simplicity, the distribution maps in the thematic chapters show the 'most abundant' NCMS feature distribution (i.e. where NCMS features would be most commonly found, but not their every location). The method allows also for projecting 'probability of occurrence' and 'relative abundance', which, although graphically complex, more closely replicate the NCMS results.

3.3 Geographical results

Chapters 14 to 25 present results geographically. The NCMS sample design was originally developed to provide results for Scottish administrative regions (Figure 3.1). As the optimal basis for comparing and contrasting land cover change across Scotland, the sequence of nine regional chapters is alphabetical, followed by results for the three island councils.

3.4 Discussion

Key findings are brought together in a discussion of factors which have influenced the course of land cover change in Scotland from the late 1940s to the late 1980s.

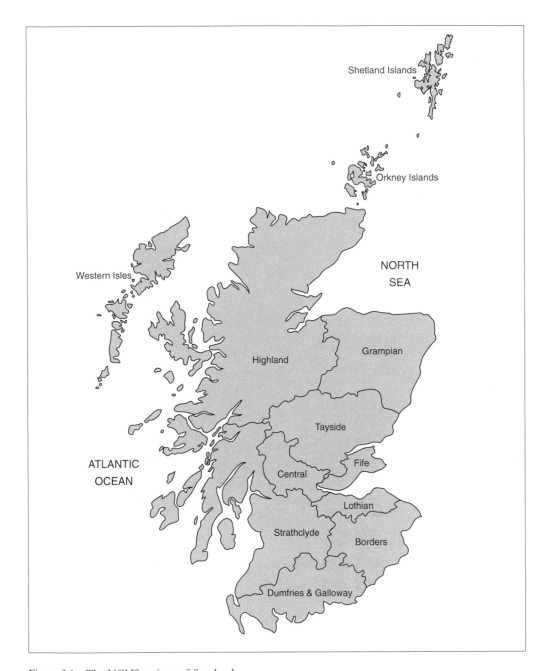

Figure 3.1   The NCMS regions of Scotland.

References

1   Bhattacharyya, G.K. and Johnson, R.A. (1977). Statistical Concepts and Methods. New York: Wiley.
2   Brooker, N. (1998). The Integration of Land Cover Data from the National Countryside Monitoring Scheme with the Land Cover of Scotland 1988. Scottish Natural Heritage Research, Survey and Monitoring Report No. 99. Perth: Scottish Natural Heritage.

PART TWO

OVERVIEW OF KEY FINDINGS

4 LAND COVER CHANGE IN SCOTLAND

Land use and resulting landscapes are products of history and of 'myriad decisions' by land managers, influenced by prevailing land use policies.[1] Over recent decades, appreciable changes in the character of rural land in the UK have been brought about by urban growth, agricultural modernisation, afforestation and quasi-urban uses such as recreation and reservoir development.

4.1 Land cover stock

In the 1940s (Figure 4.1, Table 4.1), 30% of Scotland was covered by grassland, half of which was rough grassland. Blanket mire covered a similar area, characterised by grass and sedge vegetation cover to the west, becoming more heather-rich to the east. Heather moorland accounted for a fifth of the land area; and one-tenth was under arable production. Overall, these accounted for nearly nine-tenths of Scotland. The remaining area was composed mainly of woodland or scrub, fresh water, or built features such as settlements and roads.

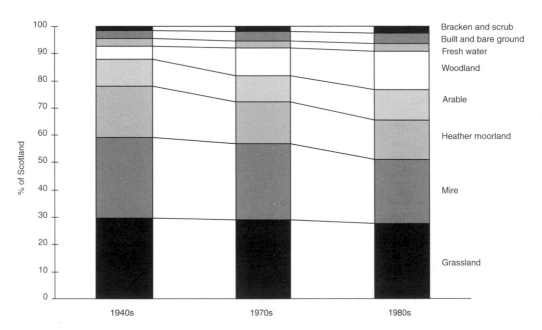

Figure 4.1   Summary of land cover change in Scotland.

Table 4.1 Land cover stock estimates for Scotland (total area: 77,837 km²).

Areal features

Feature group	Feature type	1940s (km²)	(%)	1970s (km²)	(%)	1980s (km²)	(%)
Grassland	Rough grassland	12331	16	11052	14	11130	14
	Intermediate grassland	3278	4	3726	5	3757	5
	Smooth grassland	7543	10	7970	10	6738	9
	Group total	23151	30	22748	29	21625	28
Mire	Blanket mire – heather-dominated	13967	18	12782	16	10132	13
	Blanket mire – grass-dominated	8749	11	8599	11	7798	10
	Lowland mire	229	0	166	0	127	0
	Group total	22945	29	21547	28	18057	23
Heather moorland	Heather moorland	14615	19	11820	15	11294	15
	Group total	14615	19	11820	15	11294	15
Arable	Arable	7745	10	7453	10	8593	11
	Group total	7745	10	7453	10	8593	11
Woodland	Broadleaved woodland	1509	2	1297	2	1164	1
	Mixed woodland	542	1	501	1	341	0
	Broadleaved plantation	33	0	38	0	38	0
	Parkland	78	0	70	0	73	0
	Coniferous woodland	206	0	107	0	108	0
	Young plantation	430	1	2877	4	4426	6
	Coniferous plantation	837	1	2972	4	4705	6
	Felled woodland	29	0	75	0	108	0
	Group total	3665	5	7936	10	10963	14
Fresh water	Lochs	1193	2	1102	1	1078	1
	Reservoirs	150	0	288	0	323	0
	Rivers	229	0	224	0	224	0
	Canals	7	0	8	0	7	0
	Marginal inundation	46	0	51	0	56	0
	Wet ground	572	1	525	1	680	1
	Group total	2196	3	2199	3	2368	3
Built and bare ground	Built	897	1	1214	2	1312	2
	Recreation	71	0	140	0	168	0
	Transport corridor	669	1	750	1	816	1
	Quarry	45	0	71	0	92	0
	Rock	450	1	451	1	377	0
	Bare ground	42	0	70	0	219	0
	Group total	2175	3	2696	3	2984	4
Bracken and scrub	Bracken	710	1	776	1	1268	2
	Low scrub	442	1	441	1	446	1
	Tall scrub	192	0	220	0	240	0
	Group total	1343	2	1437	2	1954	3

continued

Table 4.1 – *continued*

Linear features

Feature type	1940s (km)	(km/km²)	1970s (km)	(km/km²)	1980s (km)	(km/km²)
Hedgerows	42556	0.5	25282	0.3	19463	0.3
Treeline	17611	0.2	15946	0.2	17471	0.2
Streams	129579	1.7	127937	1.6	131058	1.7
Ditches	49478	0.6	62432	0.8	99621	1.3
Tracks	29258	0.4	35952	0.5	37760	0.5

Notes
  • The total area is calculated from the number of 1 km² stratification squares.
  • All areas are rounded to the nearest square kilometre.
  • Percentages are of the total area of Scotland.
  • All lengths are rounded to the nearest kilometre.
  • The km/km² column shows the average length of the feature per square kilometre of Scotland.

4.2   Land cover change

From the 1940s to the 1980s (see also Table 4.2) the areas of mire and heather moorland were reduced by a fifth. The woodland area expanded to three times its former extent. The built area grew by 50% and features associated with land disturbance or urban development also expanded.

Hedgerow length was reduced from more than 42,000 km in the 1940s to less than 20,000 km in the 1980s (see also Table 4.3). The length of ditches, mainly associated with land preparation for afforestation, doubled. The length of tracks, often penetrating formerly inaccessible parts of the countryside and perhaps associated with forestry or sporting estates, extended from less than 30,000 km to nearly 40,000 km.

When the magnitude and significance of results are considered (Table 4.4) it becomes clear that features associated with economic development expanded while long-established or semi-natural features contracted.

4.3   Rates of change

The study investigated changes across 26 intervening years from around 1947 to around 1973, and a further 15 intervening years to 1988. Mean annual rates of change provide insights into the main trends from the 1940s to the 1970s and through to the 1980s.

The greatest area increase (Figure 4.2) was associated with afforestation, which progressed at a continuous rate. The rate of mire loss increased from the 1970s to the 1980s, but the rates of rough grassland and heather moorland loss were seemingly reduced. In fact the results are inter-related, because drained mire was reclassified in the NCMS method according to its dominant surface vegetation of rough grassland or heather moorland. When the effect of mire drainage, commonly associated with land preparation for coniferous afforestation, was taken into account the rates of rough grassland and heather moorland loss were

Table 4.2   Net change estimates for Scotland – areal features.

Feature group	Feature type	1940s–1970s			1970s–1980s			1940s–1980s		
		Lower	(km²)	Upper	Lower	(km²)	Upper	Lower	(km²)	Upper
Grassland	Rough grassland	−1916	**−1279**	−642	−662	78	817	−2149	**−1201**	−253
	Intermediate grassland	191	**448**	705	−452	32	515	29	**479**	929
	Smooth grassland	−52	428	907	−1864	**−1232**	−601	−1502	**−805**	−108
	Group total		−404			−1123			−1527	
Mire	Blanket mire:									
	heather-dominated	−1662	**−1185**	−708	−4185	**−2650**	−1115	−5554	**−3835**	−2117
	grass-dominated	−491	**−150**	190	−2331	**−800**	730	−2561	**−951**	660
	Lowland mire	−98	**−62**	−26	−70	**−39**	−9	−164	**−102**	−40
	Group total		−1398			−3490			−4888	
Heather moorland	Heather moorland	−3524	**−2795**	−2065	−1366	**−526**	313	−4428	**−3321**	−2214
	Group total		−2795			−526			−3321	
Arable	Arable	−754	**−292**	169	550	**1140**	1730	207	**848**	1488
	Group total		−292			1140			848	
Woodland	Broadleaved woodland	−280	**−213**	−145	−209	**−133**	−56	−450	**−345**	−241
	Mixed woodland	−105	**−41**	22	−244	**−160**	−76	−295	**−201**	−108
	Broadleaved plantation	−7	5	17	−15	0	15	−14	5	25
	Parkland	−32	−9	14	−19	4	27	−33	−5	23
	Coniferous woodland	−188	**−99**	−10	−38	2	41	−212	−97	17
	Young plantation	1743	**2447**	3151	488	**1549**	2610	3040	**3996**	4953
	Coniferous plantation	1651	**2135**	2618	1245	**1733**	2221	3241	**3868**	4494
	Felled woodland	−9	46	101	−35	33	101	23	**79**	134
	Group total		4271			3027			7298	
Fresh water	Lochs	−179	**−90**	−2	−74	−24	25	−215	**−115**	−15
	Reservoirs	22	**138**	254	−17	35	86	47	**172**	298
	Rivers	−10	−5	1	−13	0	12	−20	−5	10
	Canals	0	**1**	3	−4	−2	1	−3	0	2
	Marginal inundation	−7	6	19	−15	5	24	−5	11	26
	Wet ground	−121	−46	28	24	**155**	287	−47	109	265
	Group total		3			168			171	
Built and bare ground	Built	229	**317**	404	58	**98**	138	299	**415**	530
	Recreation	34	**70**	105	15	**28**	41	57	**98**	138
	Transport corridor	32	**80**	129	33	**66**	98	106	**146**	186
	Quarry	4	**26**	47	−49	21	91	−34	47	127
	Rock	−5	1	7	−177	−74	28	−176	−73	29
	Bare ground	10	**28**	45	34	**149**	265	59	**177**	295
	Group total		522			287			809	
Bracken and scrub	Bracken	−59	66	192	201	**492**	782	256	**558**	860
	Low scrub	−72	−1	70	−54	5	64	−69	4	77
	Tall scrub	−18	28	74	−25	21	66	9	**48**	88
	Group total		94			517			611	

Notes
- All areas are rounded to the nearest square kilometre.
- The lower and upper limits define a range of values which contains the true area with 95% confidence.
- Changes that are statistically significant at the 5% level are in bold. These are changes for which the likelihood that no change took place is less than .05.

Table 4.3 Net change estimates for Scotland – linear features.

Feature type	1940s–1970s			1970s–1980s			1940s–1980s		
	Lower	(km)	Upper	Lower	(km)	Upper	Lower	(km)	Upper
Hedgerows	−21610	**−17274**	−12939	−8539	**−5819**	−3099	−28987	**−23093**	−17200
Treeline	−2888	**−1665**	−443	72	**1525**	2978	−1398	**−140**	1118
Streams	−3021	**−1641**	−265	−2406	3121	8648	−4197	1480	7157
Ditches	7794	**12954**	18114	23313	**37189**	51065	34843	**50143**	65444
Tracks	4215	**6693**	9171	−1748	1808	5364	4656	**8501**	12347

Notes
- All lengths are rounded to the nearest kilometre.
- The lower and upper limits define a range of values that contains the true length with 95% confidence.
- Changes that are statistically significant at the 5% level are in bold. These are changes for which the likelihood that no change took place is less than .05.

Table 4.4 Land cover change in Scotland, 1940s–1980s. Features ordered by magnitude of change (with statistically significant change judged at the 5% level).

Areal features

Feature type	Lower (km²)	Change (km²)	Upper (km²)	(%)
Significant increases				
Young plantation	3040	3996	4953	929
Coniferous plantation	3241	3868	4494	462
Arable	207	848	1488	11
Bracken	256	558	860	79
Intermediate grassland	29	479	929	15
Built	299	415	530	46
Bare ground	59	177	295	418
Reservoirs	47	172	298	115
Transport corridor	106	146	186	22
Recreation	57	98	138	138
Felled woodland	23	79	134	267
Tall scrub	9	48	88	25
Non-significant increases				
Wet ground	−47	109	265	19
Quarry	−34	47	127	104
Marginal inundation	−5	11	26	23
Broadleaved plantation	−14	5	25	16
Low scrub	−69	4	77	1
Non-significant decreases				
Canals	−3	0	2	−5
Rivers	−20	−5	10	−2
Parkland	−33	−5	23	−7
Rock	−176	−73	29	−16
Coniferous woodland	−212	−97	17	−47
Blanket mire – grass-dominated	−2561	−951	660	−11
Significant decreases				
Lowland mire	−164	−102	−40	−44
Lochs	−215	−115	−15	−10
Mixed woodland	−295	−201	−108	−37

continued

Table 4.4 – *continued*

Feature type	Lower (km^2)	Change (km^2)	Upper (km^2)	(%)
Significant decreases (continued)				
Broadleaved woodland	−450	−345	−241	−23
Smooth grassland	−1502	−805	−108	−11
Rough grassland	−2149	−1201	−253	−10
Heather moorland	−4428	−3321	−2214	−23
Blanket mire – heather-dominated	−5554	−3835	−2117	−27

Linear features	Lower (km)	Change (km)	Upper (km)	(%)
Significant increases				
Ditches	34843	50143	65444	101
Tracks	4656	8501	12347	29
Non-significant increases				
Streams	−4197	1480	7157	1
Non-significant decreases				
Treeline	−1398	−140	1118	−1
Significant decreases				
Hedgerows	−28987	−23093	−17200	−54

Notes
- All areas are rounded to the nearest square kilometre and lengths to the nearest kilometre.
- Significant changes are defined as those for which the likelihood that no change took place is less than .05.
- Non-significant changes should be treated with caution as they may be a product of 'sampling error'.
- The lower and upper limits define a range of values that contains the true area or length with 95% confidence.
- Percentages show the increase or reduction of the feature as a percentage of its 1940s extent.
- An asterisk (*) indicates that a value could not be calculated.

comparable for the two periods. From the 1970s to the 1980s the arable area expanded, mainly at the expense of smooth grassland.

Among features of intermediate extent (Figure 4.3), broadleaved and mixed woodland were reduced. Reservoir expansion, most rapid from the 1940s to the 1970s, raised former lochs levels and inundated heather moorland and rough grassland. Built land and transport corridor expanded, mainly on to smooth grassland or arable land. Bracken, which had increased by 10% from the 1940s to the 1970s, doubled in extent from the 1970s to the 1980s, mainly on to rough grassland and heather moorland.

Among the less-extensive features (Figure 4.4), lowland mire was reduced to about half its 1940s extent. A decrease in coniferous woodland from the 1940s to the 1970s (significant change) was arrested from the 1970s to the 1980s, while features associated with urban development, recreation and land disturbance increased.

Corresponding figures for linear features indicate that hedgerows continued to be removed, albeit less rapidly from the 1970s to the 1980s (Figure 4.5). The length of lines of trees remained largely unaltered throughout the study period. Land drainage, taken to be the conversion of mire to grassland or moorland,

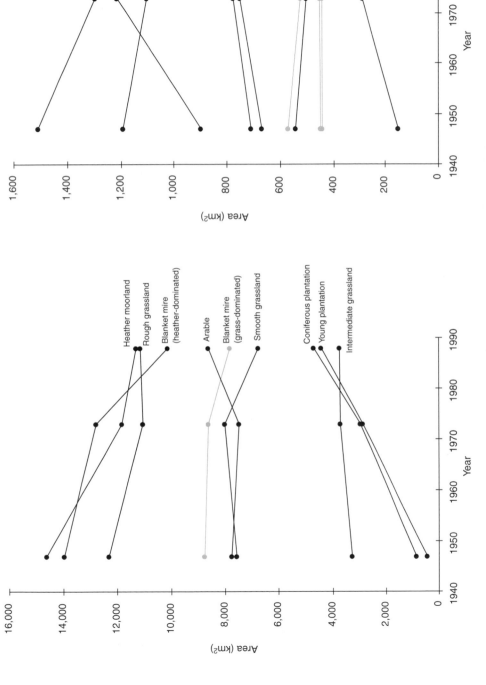

Figure 4.2 Trends in area: features greater than 2000 km² extent in the 1980s. Bold lines indicate that the 1940s–1980s change is statistically significant at the 5% level.

Figure 4.3 Trends in area: features of 300–2000 km² extent in the 1980s. Bold lines indicate that the 1940s–1980s change is statistically significant at the 5% level.

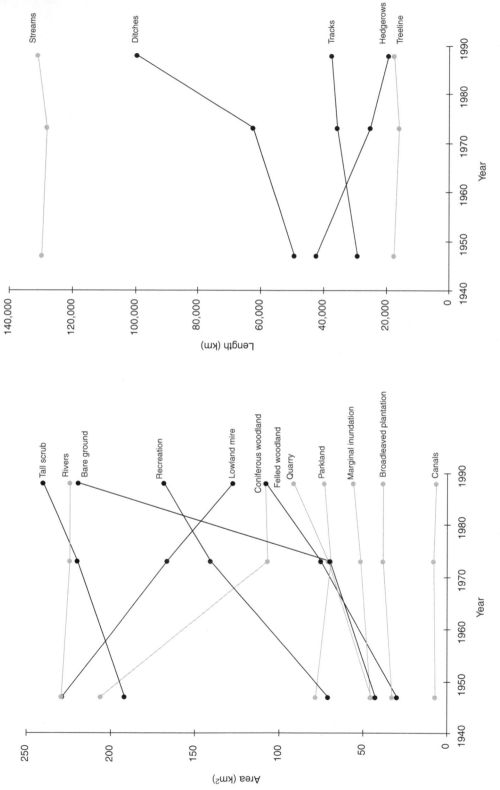

Figure 4.4   Trends in area: features less than 300 km² extent in the 1980s. Bold lines indicate that the 1940s–1980s change is statistically significant at the 5% level.

Figure 4.5   Trends in length: linear features. Bold lines indicate that the 1940s–1980s change is statistically significant at the 5% level.

expanded from the 1940s to the 1970s and increased by nearly 60% from the 1970s to the 1980s.

4.4 Interchange between features

Within ecological limits, any feature from the 1940s may be converted into any other feature in the 1970s, and similarly so from the 1970s to the 1980s. Although the significance of net interchange has not been tested, viewing the dynamics of change over 26 years from the survey base years of 1947 and 1973 (Figure 4.6) illustrates that:

- heather moorland, blanket mire and rough grassland were reduced in area by an expanding coniferous plantation forest;
- bi-directional interchange between heather moorland and rough grassland was in favour of rough grassland;
- there was a tendency to grassland improvement; and
- a high degree of interchange between smooth grassland and arable had little net effect on their respective areas.

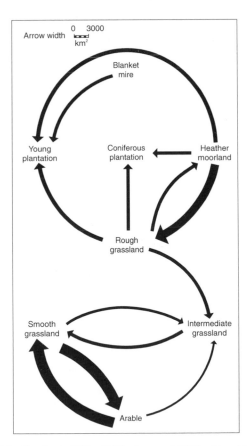

Figure 4.6   Scotland: 1940s–1970s changes >0.5% of total land area.

It should be noted that the scale of Figure 4.6 depicts only changes of, or exceeding, 0.5% of the total land area of Scotland. Due to the small initial extent of young plantation in the 1940s, its maturing into coniferous plantation or subsequent felling by the 1970s fell below the scale threshold of the diagram (i.e. there is no arrow from young plantation to coniferous plantation). Conversely, conifers planted after the 1940s photography was taken had time to mature, so that unforested rough grassland and heather moorland in the 1940s became coniferous plantation in the 1970s (i.e. without a young plantation transition).

Changes over 15 years between the survey base years of 1973 and 1988 (Figure 4.7) also illustrate:

• mire, heather moorland and rough grassland conversion to young plantation;

• the maturing of young plantation;

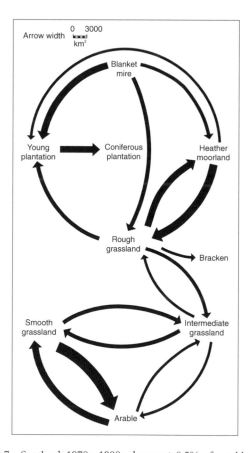

Figure 4.7   Scotland: 1970s–1980s changes >0.5% of total land area.

- mire conversion to heather moorland or rough grassland (due to the reclassification of drained mire to its dominant surface vegetation);

- bracken expansion;

- net conversion of rough grassland to intermediate grassland; and

- a net conversion of smooth grassland to arable.

The net result from the 1940s to the 1980s (Figure 4.8) was:

- a reduction of blanket mire due to afforestation and drainage;

- a reduction of rough grassland and heather moorland to afforestation, partly offset by the effect of mire drainage;

- interchange between rough grassland and heather moorland, favouring grassland at the expense of heather;

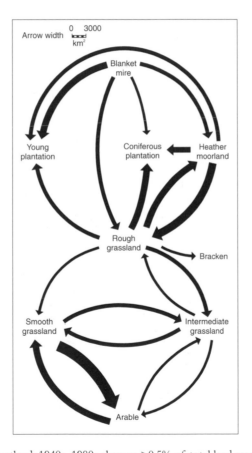

Figure 4.8   Scotland: 1940s–1980s changes >0.5% of total land area.

Land cover summary

1940s baseline

- 30% of the area of Scotland was grassland (53% rough, 14% intermediate, 33% smooth)

- 29% mire (61% heather-dominant, 38% grass-dominant)

- 19% heather moorland

- 10% arable

- 5% woodland, 3% water, 3% built and bare ground, 2% bracken and scrub

- more than 42,000 km hedgerow

1940s–1980s change

- 20% reduction in the area of mire

- 23% reduction in the area of heather moorland

- conifer plantation woodland expanded from 1,267 km^2 to 9,131 km^2, but semi-natural woodland was reduced

- a reduction in the loch area of 115 km^2 accompanied by an expansion of the reservoir area by 172 km^2 is associated with the conversion and extension of lochs to reservoirs for hydro-power and/or water supply

- built land expanded by nearly 50%, transport corridor by 22%, bare ground by 418% and recreational land by 138%

- bracken expanded by 79%

- 23,093 km reduction in hedgerow length (–54%); expansion in ditches (101%) and tracks (29%)

1980s outcome

- 28% of the area of Scotland was grassland (51% rough, 17% intermediate, 31% smooth)

- 23% mire (56% heather-dominant, 43% grass-dominant)

- 15% heather moorland

- 11% arable

- 14% woodland, 3% water, 4% built and bare ground, 3% bracken and scrub

- less than 20,000 km hedgerow remaining

- bracken expansion;

- grassland improvement; and

- a net conversion of grassland to arable.

Thus throughout the study period there was a net expansion of features associated with urbanisation, agricultural intensification and afforestation, and a consequent reduction of long-established or semi-natural features.

References

1   Parry, M.L., Hossell, J.E. and Wright, L.J. (1992). Land use in the United Kingdom. In Whitby, M.C. (ed.). *Land Use Change: The Causes and Consequences*. Institute of Terrestrial Ecology Symposium No. 27. London: HMSO.

PART THREE

THEMATIC ANALYSIS OF LAND COVER GROUPS

5 GRASSLAND

Three-quarters of Scotland is classed as agricultural land, much of which is grassland. Agricultural grasslands can be differentiated according to function and use,[1] where 'rough grazing' is associated with relatively low stocking intensity and semi-natural vegetation in the uplands. 'Permanent pastures', predominantly in the lowlands, are graded according to the degree of sward improvement. Under suitable management, including drainage, liming, fertiliser application and surface treatment, most pastures can be transformed into a grade of better quality to provide higher livestock output. Temporary 'leys', associated with arable farming as a break crop to help control pests and disease, are included in the NCMS classification as 'arable'.

5.1 Historical background

Commercial sheep farming commenced in the Borders in the 1760s, with the introduction of black-faced and Cheviot breeds.[2] It progressively displaced the less-profitable farming of Highland sheep and cattle, so that by the end of the eighteenth century it had spread throughout much of Scotland. To make way for new sheep-rearing practices, the farming population was also displaced. In the northern and western Highlands, the coastal kelp and fishing industries at that time offered employment, thereby establishing the crofting system.

Refrigeration and the importation of lamb and mutton from Australia and New Zealand around the 1870s brought an end to the commercial sheep farming boom. As deer stalking became fashionable and sheep farming less profitable, large tracts of the more marginal sheep farms were converted to deer forests in the late nineteenth century. Deer forest had extended to 1.5 million ha (20% of Scotland) by 1912.[3]

Rough grasslands in the uplands remain important today for sheep rearing, sport and recreation. A characteristic feature of sheep farming in Scotland is that it is 'stratified'. Hardy, pure-bred hill stock supply lambs for lowland cross-breeding and thence the production of meat-producing 'fat' lambs. In the uplands red deer (*Cervus elaphus*) share much of their range with sheep. Both have a strong preference for *Agrostis–Festuca* grasslands, with deer tending to utilise higher-altitude summer grazing.

Beef cattle production is mainly associated with lowland pastures and arable leys, although it can utilise the more fertile upland grazing. Dairying requires intensive grassland management in the lowlands, including the application of nitrogen fertiliser and the production of silage for winter feeding.

5.2 The character of Scottish grasslands

Except at high altitude, on exposed coasts or in extreme northern areas where climate limits the growth of trees, grasslands in Scotland would undergo natural succession to woodland if ungrazed by livestock or deer.[4]

Owing to its isolation from the continental land mass and to its glacial history, Britain has a naturally impoverished grassland flora.[5] Several grassland communities are confined to Britain,[6] including some which are restricted to Scotland. The character of grassland communities, in terms of the range and abundance of plant and animal species, is governed in large part by soil type and drainage, as well as by the degree of disturbance or alteration through land management. In the uplands, grazing and browsing by sheep and deer, as well as the 'muirburn' of purple moor grass in the West Highlands, have had a dominant effect on the composition of plant communities.[7]

Grasslands have been variously classified in terms of their appearance (rough, smooth), from their soil types (acid or *calcifugous*, neutral or *mesotrophic*, calcareous or *calcicolous*), from their human influence (improved, semi-improved, unimproved), or from their plant communities.[8]

Particular types of grassland are sometimes referred to by reference to location (e.g. maritime, coastal, lowland), soil moisture (e.g. dry, damp, wet, marshy), soil or rock type (e.g. alluvial, serpentine), or floristic composition (e.g. *Agrostis–Festuca*). Sometimes qualifying descriptive terms (e.g. herb-rich, species-rich, orchid-rich, species-poor) or management terms (e.g. grazed, mown) are applied.[9]

The NCMS classification relied upon air photographic characteristics of tone, texture and contrast. Three broad classes of grassland were differentiated as 'rough' (mainly uplands), 'intermediate' (partly improved) and 'smooth' (improved pasture). Transition from rough to smooth implies an increasing intensity of land management associated with grassland improvement.

5.3 NCMS findings

Grassland was widely distributed throughout Scotland, especially to the southwest and less so to the northwest (Figure 5.1). From the 1940s to the 1980s there was a tendency towards grassland improvement. This was accompanied from the 1970s to the 1980s by a net conversion of grassland to arable, reflecting agricultural policy around the time of UK entry into the European Economic Community in 1973.[10]

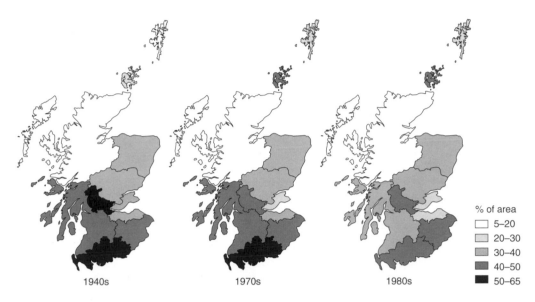

Figure 5.1   The pattern of geographical change for grassland.

There was thus a net decline in the overall extent of grassland from the 1940s to the 1980s (Table 5.1, Figure 5.2) due to a reduction in the area of rough grassland (partly to afforestation) and a reduction in the area of smooth grassland (mainly through conversion to arable).

Grassland group summary *(see Table 5.1, Figure 5.2)*

1940s baseline

- 30% of the area of Scotland was grassland

- of the total grassland area about half was rough, a third smooth and the rest intermediate

1940s–1980s change

- estimated 7% reduction in grassland extent

- an increase in area of intermediate grassland was offset by declines in the areas of rough and smooth grassland

1980s outcome

- 28% of Scotland was grassland

5.3.1 Rough grassland

When viewed on air photographs, rank or tussocky grassland has a rough texture. Interpretation notes state that it may appear to have been drained, regularly grazed or treated with farm manure. It should not, however, have been so improved by fertiliser or herbicides as to have altered the sward composition greatly. Rough grassland is associated with unenclosed uplands, lowland sites with poor access, or wet areas. It may include roadside verges.

Table 5.1   Grassland group: area estimates.

| | Area estimates | | | | | | Net change | | |
| | 1940s | | 1970s | | 1980s | | 1940s–1980s | | |
Feature	(km²)	(%)	(km²)	(%)	(km²)	(%)	(km²)	(% of 40s)	Sig.
Rough grassland	12331	16	11052	14	11130	14	−1201	−10	*
Intermediate grassland	3278	4	3726	5	3757	5	479	15	*
Smooth grassland	7543	10	7970	10	6738	9	−805	−11	*
Group total	23151	30	22748	29	21625	28	−1527	−7	na

Notes
- Asterisks indicate the statistical significance of change: $*$ $p < .05$, $**$ $p < .01$, $***$ $p < .001$. Thus one asterisk indicates that the probability that no change in the feature's extent has taken place is less than .05.
- Features showing significant change ($p < .05$) have been shown in italics. Significance was not calculated for the group total (na).
- All areas are rounded to the nearest square kilometre.
- Area percentages are of the total area of Scotland.
- Net change percentages show the increase or decrease in the feature as a percentage of its 1940s extent.

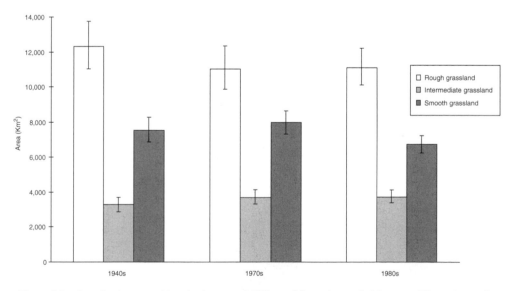

Figure 5.2   Grassland composition (estimate and 95% confidence interval). Note: confidence intervals for area estimates cannot be used to assess the significance of net changes – refer to the relevant tables for net changes.

Rough grassland is uncultivated and in the main composed of native species, albeit modified in community structure by land management. Using the Land Cover of Scotland 1988 census map, the NCMS sample can be projected to illustrate where rough grassland should be most commonly found in the 1980s (Figure 5.3).

The NCMS definition of rough grasslands would include acidic or calci-fugous grasslands (the most extensive rough grassland throughout Scotland),

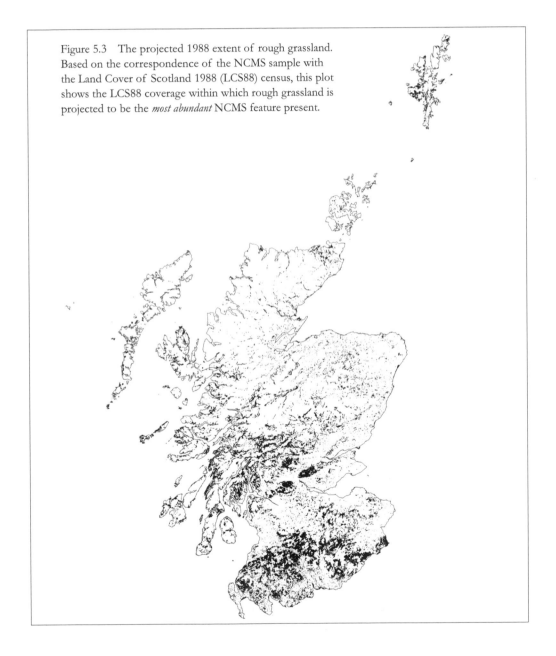

Figure 5.3   The projected 1988 extent of rough grassland. Based on the correspondence of the NCMS sample with the Land Cover of Scotland 1988 (LCS88) census, this plot shows the LCS88 coverage within which rough grassland is projected to be the *most abundant* NCMS feature present.

characterised by a few prominent species. These include sheep's fescue (*Festuca ovina*), red fescue (*F. rubra*), common bent (*Agrostis capillaris*), sweet vernal-grass (*Anthoxanthum odoratum*), wavy hair-grass (*Deschampsia flexuosa*), and mat-grass (*Nardus stricta*). Other species tend to be less prominent but may include tormentil (*Potentilla erecta)* and heath bedstraw (*Galium saxatile*). The presence of heather (*Calluna vulgaris*) and bilberry (*Vaccinium myrtillus*) would be indicative of grassland derived from heath.

Neutral or mesotrophic grasslands are usually found throughout lowland areas on moderate to nutrient-rich soils with a pH of 4.5–5.5. The National Vegetation Classification (NVC) has identified 13 neutral grassland communities, which are characterised by grasses such as cock's-foot (*Dactylis glomerata*), meadow fescue (*Festuca pratensis*), red fescue (*F. rubra*), Yorkshire fog (*Holcus lanatus*), and smooth meadow-grass (*Poa pratensis*). Other flowering plants include common mouse-ear (*Cerastium fontanum*), ribwort plantain (*Plantago lanceolata*), meadow buttercup (*Ranunculus acris*), and white clover (*Trifolium repens*).

Lime-loving or calcicolous grasslands establish on soils derived from chalk or limestone. They generally contain sheep's fescue (*Festuca ovina*), and are some of the most species-rich plant communities in Britain. In Scotland the most

Table 5.2   Rough grassland: regional estimates.

Region	Regional area (km²)	1940s (km²)	1940s (%)	1970s (km²)	1970s (%)	1980s (km²)	1980s (%)	Net change 1940s–1980s (km²)	Net change 1940s–1980s (% of 40s)	Sig.
Borders	4695	1174	25	879	19	760	16	−414	−35	**
Central	2716	944	35	877	32	770	28	−174	−18	*
Dumfries & Galloway	6342	2047	32	1526	24	1264	20	−783	−38	***
Fife	1377	88	6	73	5	51	4	−37	−42	***
Grampian	8686	608	7	607	7	688	8	79	13	
Highland	24611	925	4	1062	4	2222	9	1297	140	***
Lothian	1814	317	17	320	18	209	12	−108	−34	*
Strathclyde	14430	3811	26	3453	24	2705	19	−1107	−29	***
Tayside	7394	1799	24	1621	22	1819	25	20	1	
Orkney Islands	1115	114	10	109	10	75	7	−39	−34	
Shetland Islands	1810	260	14	271	15	246	14	−14	−5	
Western Isles	2847	244	9	254	9	320	11	76	31	
Scotland	77837	12331	16	11052	14	11130	14	−1201	−10	*
Drained mire				202		1093	·			
Adjusted total		12331	16	10850	14	10036	13	−2295	−19	*

Notes
- Asterisks indicate the statistical significance of change: * $p < .05$, ** $p < .01$, *** $p < .001$. Thus one asterisk indicates that the probability that no change in the feature's extent has taken place is less than .05.
- Regions showing significant change ($p < .05$) are shown in italics.
- All areas are rounded to the nearest square kilometre.
- Area percentages show the percentage of the region occupied by the feature.
- Net change percentages show the increase or decrease in the feature as a percentage of its 1940s extent.
- The adjusted total removes the estimated area gained through drainage of mire.

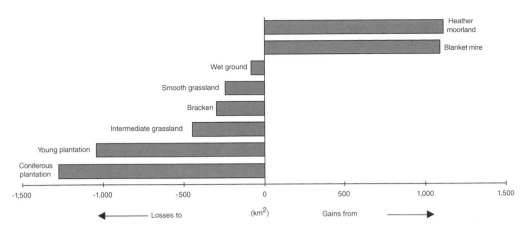

Figure 5.4   Rough grassland gains and losses, 1940s–1980s (from matrices of interchange). Note: the graph shows the main features from which there were net gains and to which there were net losses (net changes less than 10 km² were automatically excluded). Thus the largest net loss of rough grassland was to coniferous plantation and the largest net gain was from heather moorland.

significant areas are in Durness, Inchnadamph, Skye, Caenlochan-Glen Clova and Breadalbane.

Machair is a semi-natural calcicolous grassland confined mainly to the north-west coast, including the Western Isles and parts of Orkney and Shetland.[11] Traditionally managed by low-intensity grazing, mowing or arable use, a mosaic of plant communities develops on gently sloping coastal plains formed by wind-blown calcareous shell sand. Machair incorporates a range of habitats including species-rich grassland and fens, with dunes towards the sea, and blackland on peat soils further inland.

Throughout the study, about half of the grassland area for Scotland as a whole was classified as rough grassland. The extent of rough grassland was reduced (Table 5.2) by afforestation and grassland improvement (Figure 5.4). The reduction was partly offset by conversion of heather moorland to rough grassland, as well as the drainage of grass-dominated blanket mire (which was reclassified as rough grassland).

Although rough grassland was encountered throughout Scotland, relative to regional area it was predominant in the southern half of Scotland (Figure 5.5) where it exhibited significant declines in extent from the 1940s to the 1980s.

5.3.2 Intermediate – between rough and smooth grassland

Where the textural characteristics of air photography could not categorise grassland decisively as rough or smooth, the NCMS adopted an 'intermediate' class, which implied a degree of grassland improvement. In comparison with rough grassland, the sward composition of intermediate grassland may appear to have been modified to a greater degree by land management practices such as the application of fertiliser or herbicide, heavy grazing pressure or land drainage.

Rough grassland summary *(see Table 5.2, Figure 5.4)*

1940s baseline

- 16% of the area of Scotland was rough grassland
- relatively most abundant in Central (35% of region) and Dumfries & Galloway (32%), least so in Highland (4%) and Fife (6%)

1940s–1980s change

- 10% reduction in area
- notable reductions in Dumfries & Galloway (38%), Borders (35%), Lothian (34%) and Strathclyde (29%)
- notable increase in Highland (140%)

Dynamics of change

- biggest reductions to afforestation and grassland improvement
- biggest gains from conversion of heather moorland and drainage of grass-dominated blanket mire

1980s outcome

- 14% of the area of Scotland was rough grassland
- relatively most abundant in Central (28%) and Tayside (25%), least so in Fife (4%)

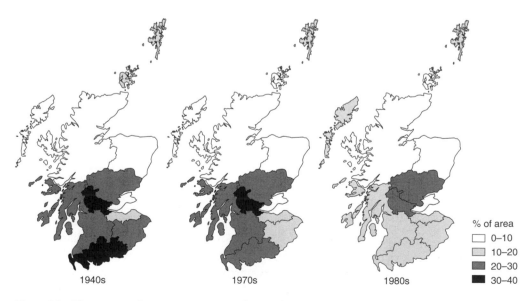

% of area
0–10
10–20
20–30
30–40

1940s   1970s   1980s

Figure 5.5   The pattern of geographical change for rough grassland.

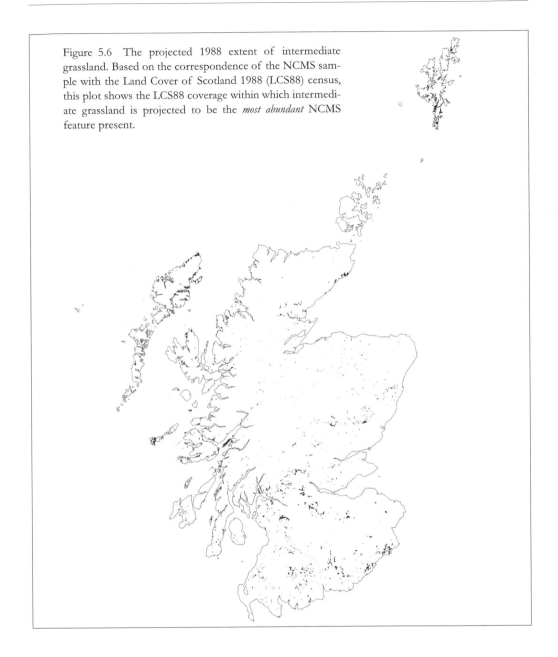

Figure 5.6 The projected 1988 extent of intermediate grassland. Based on the correspondence of the NCMS sample with the Land Cover of Scotland 1988 (LCS88) census, this plot shows the LCS88 coverage within which intermediate grassland is projected to be the *most abundant* NCMS feature present.

Projecting the NCMS sample illustrates the expected 1980s distribution of intermediate grassland (Figure 5.6).

Grassland improvement, afforestation and urban development reduced the extent of intermediate grassland (Table 5.3, Figure 5.7). This was offset by conversion of rough grassland and heather moorland to intermediate grassland, and by the drainage of blanket mire. Qualitatively, all of these shifts represent threats to semi-natural plant communities.

Table 5.3   Intermediate grassland: regional estimates (see Table 5.2 for explanation).

Region	Regional area (km²)	1940s (km²)	1940s (%)	1970s (km²)	1970s (%)	1980s (km²)	1980s (%)	Net change 1940s–1980s (km²)	Net change 1940s–1980s (% of 40s)	Sig.
Borders	4695	351	7	393	8	524	11	173	49	**
Central	2716	90	3	84	3	110	4	20	23	
Dumf. & Gall.	6342	685	11	702	11	555	9	−130	−19	
Fife	1377	87	6	60	4	117	9	30	35	**
Grampian	8686	237	3	263	3	639	7	402	170	***
Highland	24611	365	1	446	2	337	1	−28	−8	
Lothian	1814	128	7	125	7	133	7	5	4	
Strathclyde	14430	729	5	838	6	749	5	20	3	
Tayside	7394	375	5	474	6	284	4	−92	−24	
Orkney Islands	1115	60	5	120	11	138	12	77	128	***
Shetland Islands	1810	61	3	112	6	100	6	39	64	
Western Isles	2847	110	4	108	4	72	3	−38	−35	
Scotland	77837	3278	4	3726	5	3757	5	479	15	*

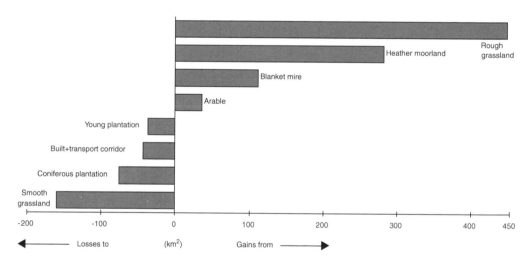

Figure 5.7   Intermediate grassland net gains and losses, 1940s–1980s (from matrices of interchange). See Figure 5.4 for explanation.

Geographically, intermediate grassland was widely encountered (Figure 5.8). Overall it increased significantly in extent, and notably in the Orkney Islands, Grampian and Fife.

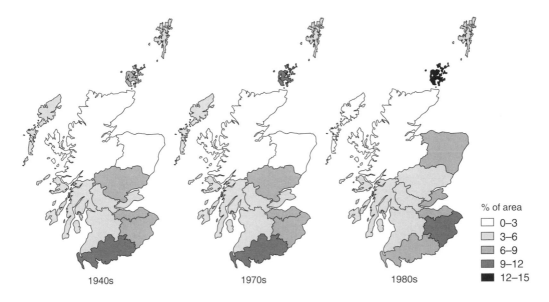

Figure 5.8   The pattern of geographical change for intermediate grassland.

Intermediate grassland summary *(see Table 5.3, Figure 5.7)*

1940s baseline

- 4% of the area of Scotland was classed as intermediate grassland
- relatively most abundant in Dumfries & Galloway (11% of region), least so in Highland (1%)

1940s–1980s change

- overall increase in area of 15%
- biggest regional increases in Grampian (170%) and the Orkney Islands (128%)
- apparent losses in Tayside (24%) and Dumfries & Galloway (19%)

Dynamics of change

- biggest reductions to grassland improvement, afforestation and urban development
- biggest gains from rough grassland, heather moorland and the drainage of grass-dominated blanket mire

1980s outcome

- 5% of the area of Scotland was intermediate grassland
- relatively most abundant in the Orkney Islands (12%) and Borders (11%), least so in Highland (1%)

5.3.3 Smooth grassland

Highly managed grasslands contain a limited number of plant species and relatively few animals. Agricultural grasses include perennial rye-grass (*Lolium perenne*), cock's-foot (*Dactylis glomerata*), and timothy (*Phleum pratense*).

In the NCMS classification, smooth grassland may include areas that have been heavily modified by the application of fertilisers and/or herbicides, and may have been reseeded. Temporary grassland ley within an arable rotation was classed as

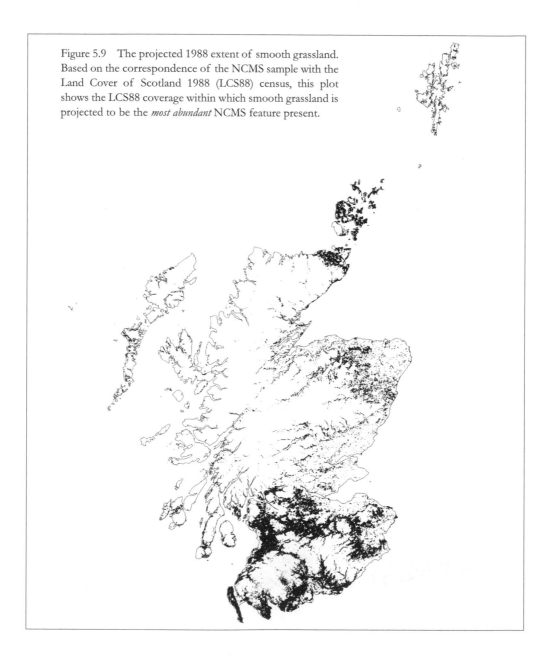

Figure 5.9   The projected 1988 extent of smooth grassland. Based on the correspondence of the NCMS sample with the Land Cover of Scotland 1988 (LCS88) census, this plot shows the LCS88 coverage within which smooth grassland is projected to be the *most abundant* NCMS feature present.

Table 5.4   Smooth grassland: regional estimates (see Table 5.2 for explanation).

Region	Regional area (km²)	1940s (km²)	(%)	1970s (km²)	(%)	1980s (km²)	(%)	1940s–1980s (km²)	(% of 40s)	Sig.
Borders	4695	581	12	676	14	755	16	174	30	
Central	2716	332	12	338	12	340	13	8	2	
Dumfries & Galloway	6342	1363	21	1372	22	1019	16	−343	−25	*
Fife	1377	269	20	219	16	151	11	−118	−44	***
Grampian	8686	2231	26	2045	24	1323	15	−908	−41	***
Highland	24611	345	1	387	2	410	2	64	19	
Lothian	1814	164	9	175	10	163	9	−1	−1	
Strathclyde	14430	1441	10	1703	12	1445	10	4	0	
Tayside	7394	665	9	707	10	723	10	58	9	
Orkney Islands	1115	131	12	302	27	301	27	170	130	*
Shetland Islands	1810	15	1	18	1	53	3	38	250	**
Western Isles	2847	5	0	28	1	54	2	49	972	*
Scotland	77837	7543	10	7970	10	6738	9	−805	−11	*

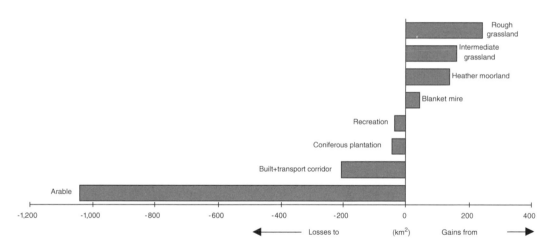

Figure 5.10   Smooth grassland net gains and losses, 1940s–1980s (from matrices of interchange). See Figure 5.4 for explanation.

'arable', distinguished from smooth grassland by contextual detail. Projecting the NCMS sample illustrates where smooth grassland would be expected to be most commonly found in the 1980s (Figure 5.9).

The study indicates an expansion of smooth grassland from the 1940s to the 1970s, followed by a reduction from the 1970s to the 1980s (Table 5.4). The net result was an overall reduction in the area of smooth grassland, mainly due to arable expansion and urban development (Figure 5.10). Smaller gains arose from grassland improvement and the conversion of heather moorland and blanket mire.

Smooth grassland summary *(see Table 5.4, Figure 5.10)*

1940s baseline

* 10% of the area of Scotland was classed as smooth grassland
* relatively most abundant in Grampian (26% of region), least so in the Western Isles (less than 0.5%), the Shetland Islands and Highland (both 1%)

1940s–1980s change

* small increase 1940s–1970s was reversed 1970s–1980s, resulting in an overall decline in area of 11%
* biggest regional reductions in Fife (44%), Grampian (41%) and Dumfries & Galloway (25%)
* small area increases in the Orkney Islands (130%), the Shetland Islands (250%) and the Western Isles (972%)

Dynamics of change

* biggest reductions from conversion to arable
* biggest gains from formerly rough and intermediate grassland

1980s outcome

* 9% of the area of Scotland was smooth grassland
* relatively most abundant in the Orkney Islands (27%) and Borders (16%), least so in the Western Isles, Highland (both 2%) and the Shetland Islands (3%)

Geographically, smooth grassland was widely encountered. Relative to regional area there was little in the Shetland Islands, Western Isles or Highland region. Reduced in extent overall, it increased significantly in the Outer Isles. Significant declines were in Grampian, Fife and Dumfries & Galloway (Figure 5.11).

5.3.4 Summary of changes in the composition of grassland

Within the three NCMS grassland categories, increases and decreases occurred. Summary estimates of overall extent can, however, mask qualitative changes among vegetation communities (Table 5.5, Figure 5.12).

Interchange among habitats illustrates that some rough grassland was converted to heather moorland but a greater expanse of heather moorland was converted to rough grassland. There was thus a net conversion of heather moorland to rough grassland. Conversion of rough grassland to coniferous plantation (which reduced the grassland area) and the drainage of blanket mire (which increased the grassland area) were distinctly uni-directional.

Interchange also took place among the grassland types themselves, with a tendency towards grassland improvement. Interchange between arable and smooth grassland resulted in a net expansion of the arable area at the expense of smooth grassland.

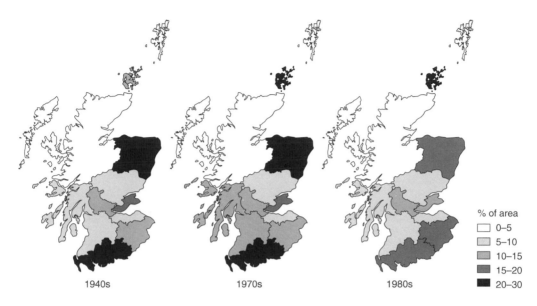

Figure 5.11   The pattern of geographical change for smooth grassland.

Table 5.5   Grassland compositional change, 1940s–1980s.

	Rough		Intermediate		Smooth	
	1940s went to (km²)	1980s came from (km²)	1940s went to (km²)	1980s came from (km²)	1940s went to (km²)	1980s came from (km²)
Rough grassland			447	895	287	530
Intermediate grassland	895	447			853	1014
Smooth grassland	530	287	1014	853		
Blanket mire		1200				
Heather moorland	1525	2636		313		
Arable			503	540	3222	2181
Young + coniferous plantation	2505					
Built + transport corridor					302	
Bracken	501					
Others	1046	1230	599	441	388	522
(Unchanged area)	(5329)	(5329)	(715)	(715)	(2491)	(2491)
Total area	12331	11130	3278	3757	7543	6738

Notes
- For each grassland feature the area lost to, and gained from, other features is shown. Gains and losses of less than 250 km² have been grouped into 'Others'.
- The figures in brackets estimate the area that was unchanged between the 1940s and 1980s.
- All areas are rounded to the nearest square kilometre.

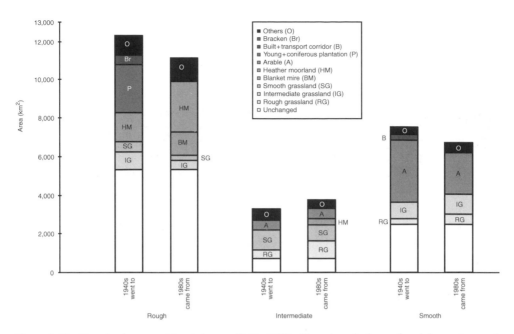

Figure 5.12   Grassland compositional change, 1940s–1980s. Note that: the base of each bar estimates the area of the feature that was unchanged between the 1940s and the 1980s; the remainder of each bar shows the main features to which area was lost and from which area was gained; gains and losses of less than 250 km^2 have been grouped into 'Others'; the heights of the bars show the area of the feature in the 1940s and the 1980s; and measured change is made up of (a) real change, and (b) inaccuracies inherent in the method. See Chapter 3 for details.

These results expose difficulties in distinguishing between visually similar tones and textures on the air photography, but they also reflect a dynamic character in Scotland's grasslands. Less than half of the 1940s rough grassland area appeared unaltered in the 1980s, compared with one-third of smooth grassland and one-fifth of intermediate grassland.

References

1   Ministry of Agriculture, Fisheries and Food (1966). *Grass and Grassland*. Bulletin No. 154. London: HMSO.

2   Whyte, I. and Whyte, K. (1991). *The Changing Scottish Landscape 1500–1800*. London: Routledge.

3   Scottish Natural Heritage (1994). *Red Deer and the Natural Heritage: SNH Policy Paper*. Perth: Scottish Natural Heritage.

4   McVean, D.N. and Ratcliffe, D.A. (1962). Forest and scrub. In *Plant Communities of the Scottish Highlands*. Monographs of the Nature Conservancy Number One, London: HMSO.

5   Hubbard, C.E. (1985). *Grasses, A Guide to Their Structure, Identification, Uses and Distribution in the British Isles*. Middlesex: Penguin Books.

6   Pigott, C.D., Ratcliffe, D.A., Malloch, A.J.C., Birks, H.J.B., Proctor, M.C.F., Shimwell, D.W., Huntley, J.P., Radford, E., Wiggington, M.J. and Wilkins, P. (1992). *British Plant Communities Volume 3: Grasslands and Montane Communities*. Edited by Rodwell, J.S. Cambridge: Cambridge University Press.

7   Scottish Natural Heritage (1994). *Red Deer and the Natural Heritage: SNH Policy Paper*. Perth: Scottish Natural Heritage.

A case study in grassland compositional change

An NCMS sample square from the Borders provides an example of grassland improvement during the study period.

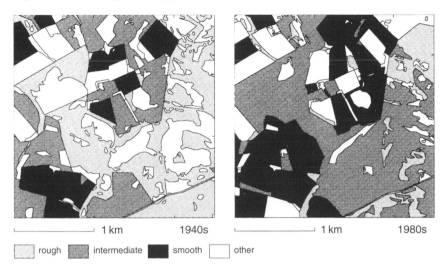

In the case study around half of the grassland area was classed as rough grassland in the 1940s, mainly in a moorland mosaic with patches of heather (mapped here as 'other'). Rough grassland expanded at the expense of the heather from the 1940s to the 1970s, but then became converted to intermediate grassland by the 1980s. Similarly, much of the formerly intermediate grassland changed to smooth grassland.

Overall, grassland expanded at the expense of heather and a varied scene was transformed into one of mainly managed grassland in the 1980s.

8   Gilbert, G. and Gibbons, D.W. (1996). *A Review of Habitat, Land Cover and Land-Use Survey and Monitoring in the United Kingdom*. Bedfordshire: Royal Society for the Protection of Birds.

9   Ward, S.D. (1996). *Grassland Management Agreements: A Guide to Assist SNH Staff in the Review or Negotiation of Grassland Management Agreements Based Upon Best Practice Derived from the Agreed Management Policies Contained in Existing Agreements*. Scottish Natural Heritage Review No 73. Perth: Scottish Natural Heritage.

10   Carter, E.S. and Stansfield, J.M. (1994). *British Farming: Changing Policies and Production Systems*. Ipswich: Farming Press Books.

11   Angus, S. (1994). The conservation importance of machair systems of the Scottish islands, with particular reference to the Outer Hebrides. In Baxter, J.M. and Usher, M.B. (eds) *The Islands of Scotland, A Living Marine Heritage*. Edinburgh: HMSO.

6   MIRE

'Mire' is the generic term for a wetland which supports vegetation that is capable of peat formation. Through incomplete decay and steady accumulation of dead material in a largely waterlogged and anaerobic environment, a variety of plants can lay down peat, such as *Sphagnum* mosses or cotton and deer grasses in bogs, or sedges, reeds and trees in fens.

6.1   Mire types

'Fens' are mires which form where water flow is impeded. They vary in scale, from springs and flushes which are prevalent in the Scottish uplands to basins where topography permits and flood-plains in the lowlands. Although widespread in Scotland, apart from notable exceptions such as the Insh marshes, they are rarely extensive. With nutrients supplied by disparate water sources including groundwater, fens are represented by a diversity of wetland types, including wet woodland (carr), swamp (e.g. reedbeds), as well as short and tall herb and sedge wet grassland. In some instances fens have developed into bogs. Many open sedge fenlands in Scotland have been actively managed, traditionally by grazing as well as for peat or marl (limey clay) extraction. Without grazing there would typically be invasion by scrub and carr woodland. The NCMS classification did not uniquely identify fen as a feature in its own right, but mapped it according to its surface vegetation. This would include woodland or grassland, as well as 'blanket mire' or 'lowland mire' with which fen is often, though not always, associated.

'Bogs' are the most extensive form of mire in Scotland. Receiving nutrients mainly from precipitation (ombrotrophic), they represent some of the most nutrient-poor and acidic environments for plant growth. With available nitrogen and phosphorus in short supply, bog plants are adapted to tight nutrient cycling, exemplified in the carnivorous sundew (*Drosera* spp.).

The geographical distribution of Scottish bogs reflects climatic differences. With increasing altitude, latitude and oceanicity, summers remain cool. Where topography permits, conditions become favourable for the development of a continuous mantle of peat, termed 'blanket mire' in which 'blanket bog' is the main constituent. Very large expanses of blanket bog, including the most intact examples, occur in Caithness and Sutherland. Under low-intensity management of sheep grazing, sport (deer, grouse and salmon) and local small-scale peat cutting, the conservation interest in these areas has largely survived.[1]

In the lowlands, where a summer moisture deficit is more pronounced, topography and restricted drainage may be conducive to the much scarcer formation of 'raised bog'. Pinched by agricultural improvement, peat cutting and other developments, raised bogs occur most distinctively as dome-shaped 'islands' of peat, with vegetation reflecting the position of the water table. Lowland raised bog is scattered mainly across the central belt, the Grampian coastal plain and the Solway shore, with transitional forms which intergrade into blanket bog. Especially vulnerable to exploitation by farming, forestry and peat extraction, no raised bog in Britain now bears a completely natural vegetation. Less than one-tenth of the raised bog habitat in Scotland remains in a relatively unaltered state.[2]

'Blanket mire' and 'lowland mire' were mapped by NCMS, representing the two main types of bog.

6.2 Historical background

Peat-forming ecosystems preserve a sequential record of their own development and, embodied within that, evidence and features of their contemporary environment. Within layers of peat is the preserved pollen record of climatic conditions over the past 3,000 to 7,000 years. Many Scottish blanket bogs contain stumps of former Scots pine woodland, enveloped by mire formation as conditions became cooler and wetter, or strata exhibiting phases of woodland cover, such as birch. A growing peat tends also to preserve a record of its cationic environment and can thus be an important archive of changing atmospheric inputs of, for example, pollutant heavy metals and radionuclides.

Under the prevailing climate and grazing regime most bogs in Scotland are treeless. Tree growth on bogs becomes less likely with exposure in the north and northwest, and at altitude. Under the extreme oceanic climate of the Northern Isles, Western Isles and at high altitude, bogs may be naturally treeless, thus representing a post-glacial climax vegetation formation.[3] Elsewhere, grazing and burning may have contributed to a restricted tree cover. In the absence of grazing and with hydrological interference trees can establish. Trees occur on many lowland raised bogs, from low-density scrub to closed canopy woodland.

Scottish mire systems have, to varying degrees, been modified by human activity. Together with effects of acid deposition, the communities of plants and animals associated with bogs may be greatly altered by land management and drainage, resulting in a floristic convergence of vegetation types,[4] erosion and associated impacts on water courses.[5]

On a global scale during the Holocene, northern peatlands were a major carbon dioxide (CO_2) sink and methane (CH_4) source in the biosphere. The overall radiative forcing effect on climate is uncertain. It is suggested that CO_2 uptake through peat accumulation and biomass production may compensate for the warming effect of CH_4 emissions; however, the balance of uptake and emission changes over time. Land use practices (notably agriculture and forestry, in which water table level is the critical factor) and global changes (acid load, climate warming), can alter fluxes and thus the radiative influence of the northern peatlands.[6]

Low-intensity land uses can be sustainable, where grazing, sporting estate management, burning and domestic peat cutting have only limited and localised effects. More intensive forms of exploitation, including mechanised drainage, enrichment with fertilisers, ploughing and afforestation have been more damaging. Although the impact of past and present commercial-scale peat extraction in Scotland is extensive, especially in the lowlands of the central belt and the Grampian plain, many exploitable reserves occur in areas which are not economically viable, are under forestry, or are demarcated for nature conservation.

A backdrop for the 1980s debate about the 'flow country' of Caithness and Sutherland was a growing appreciation of the global significance of peatland. Recognised to be of very high conservation importance and as distinctive habitats for many rare plants and animals, Scottish mires are nowadays valued much more highly for a range of environmental 'goods and services', including their aesthetic attraction, wildlife importance, the peat archive (archaeology, palaeoecology) and contribution to wild land.

6.3 The peatland habitat

Peatlands provide habitat for many characteristic plants and animals of Scotland, including invertebrates, amphibians and reptiles, birds and mammals. Extensive blanket bog may appear relatively uniform and featureless, but small variations in surface morphology and hydrology provide environmental gradients which allow distinct vegetation communities to develop. Bogs which support pools provide ecological niches for an especially rich diversity of plants, invertebrates and wetland birds.

A floristic distinction between blanket mire and heaths is the presence of cotton grass (*Eriophorum vaginatum*) in blanket mire, often co-dominant with heather (*Calluna vulgaris*). Hummock-building bog mosses (typically *Sphagnum papillosum* and *S. capillifolium*) are also more abundant and characteristic of blanket mire than heathland. *Sphagnum* mosses are essential to the continued accrual of peat in bog peatlands, keeping the surface sufficiently moist and forming acids which help prevent the decay of plant remains. The drier hummocks between pools may support a variety of heath shrubs such as heather (*Calluna vulgaris*), bilberry (*Vaccinium myrtillus*), and crowberry (*Empetrum nigrum*), as well as bog cotton (*Eriophorum* spp.), feather mosses and the woolly hair moss (*Racomitrium lanuginosum*). Ridges may support cranberry (*Vaccinium oxycoccus*), cross-leaved heath (*Erica tetralix*) and deer grass (*Trichophorum cespitosum*). Shallow pools may contain mud sedge (*Carex limosa*), bogbean (*Menyanthes trifoliata*) and, in the deeper pools, intermediate bladderwort (*Utricularia intermedia*).[7]

A marked gradient in the input of aerial nutrients arises from ions from the sea, to some extent mirroring the rainfall pattern from west to east. These combine to encourage purple moor grass (*Molinia caerulea*) and bog myrtle (*Myrica gale*) in the west, whereas heather and bearberry (*Arctostaphylos uva-ursi*) become more common to the east. This distinction was recognised during the NCMS analysis of photography for the 1940s and 1970s, when the NCMS classification of blanket mire became subdivided into 'grass-dominated' and 'heather-dominated'.

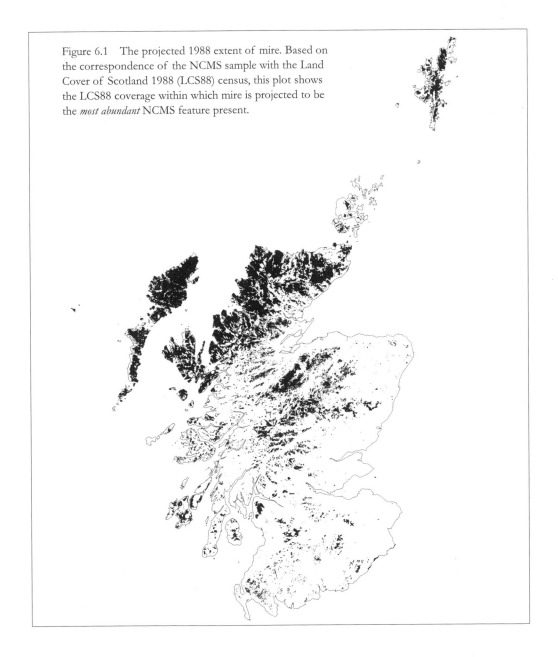

Figure 6.1   The projected 1988 extent of mire. Based on the correspondence of the NCMS sample with the Land Cover of Scotland 1988 (LCS88) census, this plot shows the LCS88 coverage within which mire is projected to be the *most abundant* NCMS feature present.

6.4 NCMS findings

The projected NCMS distribution of mire is especially distinctive in the west and north (Figure 6.1). The overall extent was reduced by about a fifth during the study period (Table 6.1, Figure 6.2).

Table 6.1 Mire group: area estimates (see Table 5.1 for explanation).

Feature	1940s (km²)	(%)	1970s (km²)	(%)	1980s (km²)	(%)	Net change 1940s–1980s (km²)	(% of 40s)	Sig.
Heather-dominated blanket mire	13967	18	12782	16	10132	13	−3835	−27	*
Grass-dominated blanket mire	8749	11	8599	11	7798	10	−951	−11	
Lowland mire	229	0	166	0	127	0	−102	−44	*
Group total	22945	29	21547	28	18057	23	−4888	−21	na

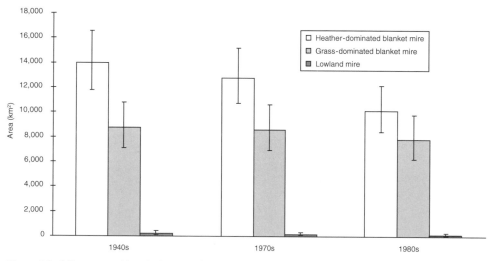

Figure 6.2 Mire composition (estimate and 95% confidence interval). Note: confidence intervals for area estimates cannot be used to assess the significance of net changes – refer to the relevant tables for net changes.

6.4.1 Blanket mire

The NCMS interpretation of blanket mire used landscape form and vegetation cover, together with surface evidence (such as peat exposures, cuttings, hags, hummock-hollow morphology) to infer the sub-surface presence of wet acidic peat. The classification initially recognised only heather-dominated mire, but as the study progressed into Highland, Strathclyde and the Western Isles, grass-dominated mire was commonly encountered. The classification of blanket mire was thus sub-divided into 'grass-dominated' and 'heather-dominated' (and this applied to all regions in the 1980s interpretation).

Mire group summary *(see Table 6.1, Figure 6.2)*

1940s baseline

- almost 30% of the area of Scotland was mire

- of the total mire area, 61% was heather-dominated blanket mire, 38% was grass-dominated blanket mire, and less than 0.5% was lowland mire

1940s–1980s change

- estimated 21% reduction in overall area

- a suggested decline in grass-dominated blanket mire was less marked than the much greater reduction of heather-dominated blanket mire

- relatively small in extent, lowland mire showed a marked reduction in area

1980s outcome

- less than a quarter of Scotland was mire

- of the total mire area, 56% was heather-dominated blanket mire, 43% was grass-dominated blanket mire, and less than 0.5% was lowland mire

Table 6.2   Blanket mire: regional estimates.

Region	Regional area (km²)	1940s (km²)	1940s (%)	1970s (km²)	1970s (%)	1980s (km²)	1980s (%)	Net change 1940s–1980s (km²)	Net change (% of 40s)	Sig.
Borders	4695	332	7	145	3	96	2	−236	−71	*
Central	2716	81	3	76	3	76	3	−5	−6	
Dumf. & Gall.	6342	660	10	523	8	333	5	−328	−50	
Fife	1377	0	0	0	0	0	0	0	0	
Grampian	8686	406	5	397	5	355	4	−51	−13	
Highland	24611	15119	61	14593	59	12446	51	−2672	−18	*
Lothian	1814	27	1	20	1	13	1	−14	−53	
Strathclyde	14430	2460	17	2117	15	1385	10	−1075	−44	***
Tayside	7394	730	10	737	10	731	10	1	0	
Orkney Islands	1115	272	24	240	22	202	18	−70	−26	*
Shetland Islands	1810	913	50	859	47	740	41	−173	−19	**
Western Isles	2847	1717	60	1675	59	1553	55	−164	−10	
Scotland	77837	22716	29	21381	27	17930	23	−4786	−21	***

Notes   • See Table 5.2 for explanation.
   • Apparent increase in area of mire in Tayside due to anomalies in air-photo interpretation.

In the presence of drainage ditches, mire was reclassified according to its dominant surface vegetation as rough grassland or heather moorland. While it has

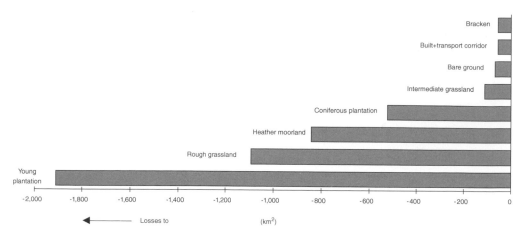

Figure 6.3   1940s–1980s blanket mire net gains and losses (from matrices of interchange). See Figure 5.4 for explanation.

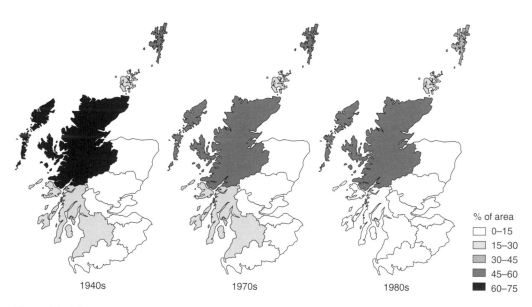

Figure 6.4   The pattern of geographical change for blanket mire.

thus been possible to infer the extent of mire drainage through mire conversion to rough grassland or heather moorland, a better approach would have been to recognise 'drained mire' as a distinct land cover class. When mire was stripped of its surface vegetation it was classified as 'bare ground'. Similarly, 'bare peat' would have been more informative.

During the study period the extent of blanket mire was reduced throughout Scotland (Table 6.2, Figure 6.3, Figure 6.4), with the greatest reductions in

Blanket mire summary *(see Table 6.2, Figure 6.3)*

1940s baseline

- 29% of the area of Scotland was blanket mire

- substantial regional variation, with blanket mire comprising over 50% of Highland, the Shetland Islands and the Western Isles, but not found at all in Fife

1940s–1980s change

- 21% reduction in area

- greatest reduction in extent in Highland (18%) and Strathclyde (44%)

- relative to regional area, proportionally large reductions also in Borders (71%) and Dumfries & Galloway (50%)

Dynamics of change

- biggest reductions to afforestation and (through drainage) to rough grassland and heather moorland

1980s outcome

- 23% of the area of Scotland was blanket mire

- still relatively most abundant in the Western Isles (55%), Highland (51%) and the Shetland Islands (41%)

Table 6.3   Lowland mire: regional estimates (see Table 5.2 for explanation).

Region	Regional area (km²)	1940s (km²)	1940s (%)	1970s (km²)	1970s (%)	1980s (km²)	1980s (%)	Net change 1940s–1980s (km²)	(% of 40s)	Sig.
Borders	4695	13	0	10	0	8	0	−5	−37	*
Central	2716	51	2	42	2	31	1	−20	−39	
Dumfries & Galloway	6342	48	1	20	0	9	0	−39	−81	*
Fife	1377	2	0	1	0	0	0	−2	−85	*
Grampian	8686	7	0	5	0	2	0	−6	−77	
Highland	24611	17	0	12	0	9	0	−9	−50	
Lothian	1814	3	0	2	0	2	0	−1	−24	
Strathclyde	14430	86	1	72	0	64	0	−22	−26	
Tayside	7394	0	0	0	0	0	0	0	0	
Orkney Islands	1115	3	0	3	0	3	0	0	9	
Shetland Islands	1810	0	0	0	0	0	0	0	0	
Western Isles	2847	0	0	0	0	0	0	0	0	
Scotland	77837	229	0	166	0	127	0	−102	−44	**

Highland and Strathclyde. Afforestation and mire conversion to rough grassland or heather moorland, associated with drainage in preparation for tree planting, were mainly responsible. The rate of loss was greatest from the 1970s to the 1980s.

6.4.2 Lowland mire

The NCMS classification of lowland mire generally related to dome formations of raised bog, but also included unwooded fens.

By the late 1980s, lowland mire had been reduced to about half of its 1940s extent (Table 6.3). Reductions were due largely to afforestation and conversion to other uses, generally associated with drainage (Figure 6.5). Significant reductions were in Borders and Dumfries & Galloway (Figure 6.6).

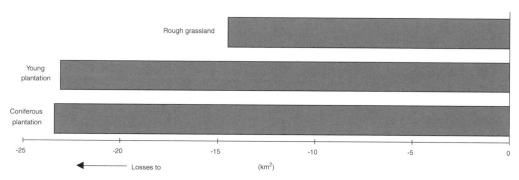

Figure 6.5   1940s–1980s lowland mire net gains and losses (from matrices of interchange). See Figure 5.4 for explanation.

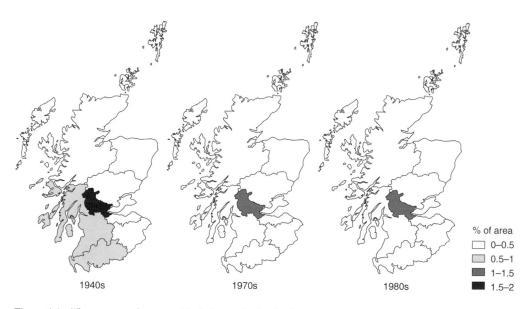

Figure 6.6   The pattern of geographical change for lowland mire.

Lowland mire summary *(see Table 6.3, Figure 6.5)*

1940s baseline

- less than 0.3% of the area of Scotland was lowland mire

- largest areas of lowland mire in Strathclyde, Central and Dumfries & Galloway

1940s–1980s change

- 44% reduction in area

- notable area reductions in Dumfries & Galloway (81%)

- apparent reductions in Strathclyde (26%) and Central (39%)

Dynamics of change

- biggest losses to afforestation and (through drainage) to rough grassland

1980s outcome

- less than 0.2% of the area of Scotland was lowland mire

- main remaining extent of lowland mire in Strathclyde (64 km²) and Central (31 km²)

6.4.3 Summary of changes in the composition of mire

Within the two NCMS mire categories, reductions in area occurred (Table 6.4, Figure 6.7). Apparent minor gains reflect difficulties inherent in the mapping of unenclosed landscape features which can be visually similar and have

Table 6.4   Mire compositional changes, 1940s–1980s.

	Blanket		Lowland	
	1940s went to (km²)	1980s came from (km²)	1940s went to (km²)	1980s came from (km²)
Rough grassland	1200			
Heather moorland	989			
Young + coniferous plantation	2437			
Others	616	460	115	15
(Unchanged area)	(17470)	(17470)	(114)	(114)
Total area	22712	17930	229	129

Notes   • Gains and losses of less than 150 km² have been grouped into 'Others'.
• Apparent gains are due to difficulties in the interpretation of mire from aerial photography.
• See Table 5.5 for full explanation.

indistinct boundaries. Nevertheless, the summary illustrates contrasts of scale between the extensive blanket mire and the more restricted lowland mire and the high proportion of lowland mire which was affected by land cover change.

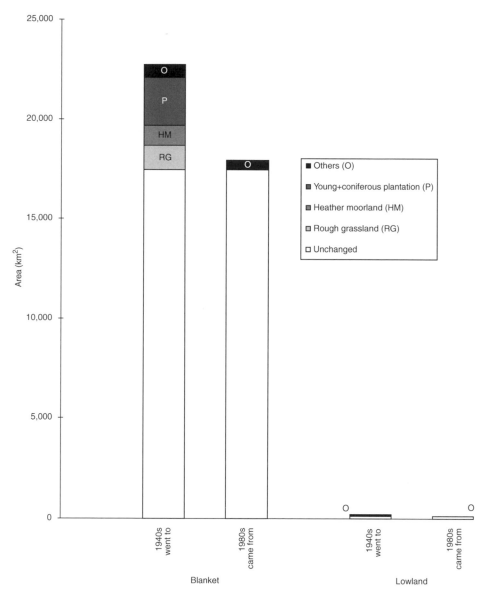

Figure 6.7 Mire compositional changes, 1940s–1980s. Note that gains and losses of less than 150 km^2 have been grouped into 'Others', and that apparent gains are due to difficulties in the interpretation of mire from aerial photography. See Figure 5.12 for full explanation.

Case study in the composition of mire

A Caithness sample square provides an example of mire drainage and subsequent afforestation.

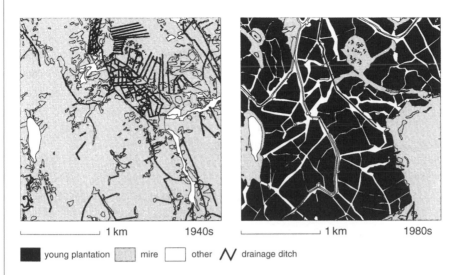

| | 1 km | 1940s | | 1 km | 1980s |

■ young plantation ▨ mire □ other /\/ drainage ditch

Mire covered more than 85% of the sample square as a whole in the 1940s. By the late 1980s there had been some conversion to grassland but the main reason for a reduction in the mire area was afforestation. Preparation for this can be seen as drainage ditches in the 1940s scene. Planting took place mainly between the early 1970s and the late 1980s.

References

1   Burton, R. (1965). The peat resources of Great Britain. In Lappalainen, E. (ed.). *Global Peat Resources.* Jyska, Finland: International Peat Society.

2   Lindsay, R. and Immirzi, P. (1996). *An Inventory of Lowland Raised Bogs in Great Britain.* Scottish Natural Heritage Research, Survey and Monitoring Report No. 78. Perth: Scottish Natural Heritage.

3   Lindsay, R. (1995). *The Ecology, Classification and Conservation of Ombrotrophic Mires.* Perth: Scottish Natural Heritage.

4   Rodwell, J.S. (ed.) (1991). *British Plant Communities Volume 2: Mires and Heaths.* Cambridge: Cambridge University Press.

5   Lindsay, R.A., Charman, D.J., Everingham, F., O'Reilly, R.M., Palmer, M.A., Rowell, T.A. and Stroud, D.A. (1988). *The Flow Country: The Peatlands of Caithness and Sutherland.* Peterborough: Nature Conservancy Council.

6   Martikainen, P.J. (1996). The fluxes of greenhouse gases and N_2O in northern peatlands. In Lappalainen, E. *Global Peat Resources.* Jyska, Finland: International Peat Society.

7   Stroud, D.A., Reed, T.M., Pienkowski, M.W. and Lindsay, R.A. (1987). *Birds, Bogs and Forestry: The Peatlands of Caithness and Sutherland.* Peterborough: Nature Conservancy Council.

7   HEATHER MOORLAND

For much of the post-glacial period heathland has been a feature of northwest European landscapes. With few extensive areas left outside Great Britain, heather moorland is considered to be of 'considerable economic, nature conservation, landscape, aesthetic and tourism-related value'.[1] In Scotland it occurs predominantly in the sub-montane zone between the former natural treeline and enclosed agricultural land, supporting a rich assemblage of moorland invertebrates, birds and mammals.

Apart from heaths at high altitudes and on exposed coastal areas, heathland plant species composition has been modified over thousands of years of land management by grazing and fire to provide habitat for domestic stock. Heather moorland is maintained especially for sheep (*Ovis aries*), red grouse (*Lagopus lagopus*) and red deer (*Cervus elaphus*). Semi-natural in character, heath is composed mainly of native species derived from former scrub and woodland climax cover. It is sustained by appropriate grazing and burning regimes, and may thus revert to scrub and woodland where the pressure of grazing and burning is insufficient, or be pushed towards grassland dominance where it is too intensive.[2, 3]

7.1   Historical background

During the first half of the nineteenth century, red grouse were an abundant yet incidental inhabitant of the hill sheep farm. Moorland was burnt by the farmer and hill shepherd to maintain a vigorous growth of palatable fresh green heather, required by sheep and grouse alike. From around 1870 onwards, the importation of sheep products led to a fall in the grazing value of Scottish hill land.

The advent of the railway, improved guns, increased wealth and fashion made the sporting value of grouse approach or exceed that of the grazing value of the farm. Conflicting views of moorland management for sport and grazing arose. Following decimation of grouse numbers in 1872/73, the Game Laws Commission came down in favour of methods of burning to maximise food supply, especially in early spring. Patch burning at that time was thought to segregate birds and thereby to lessen risks of infection.[4]

Whereas sheep are wide-ranging, grouse are territorial (*c.* 2 ha) and so require a patchwork of young growth for feeding, as well as older growth for nesting and cover within their territories.[5] Short burning cycles, or fires which burn too hot, at high altitudes or on steep slopes, can retard regeneration of palatable species and increase the risk of soil erosion. Unpalatable grasses such as *Molinia* and sedge-like species *Eriophorum* and *Trichophorum* can spread at the expense of the dwarf shrubs which provide an important part of the winter diet of red deer and red grouse.[6]

The economic value of grouse moors and grouse bags fell into decline from the 1930s onwards. With fewer gamekeepers to manage the sporting interest, rising sheep numbers and falling standards of burning resulted in a decline in the heather cover upon which grouse rely.[7]

Nowadays, heaths and moorland dominated by heather (*Calluna vulgaris*) and other dwarf shrubs remain a major component of Scotland's landscape, either as dominant communities or as mosaics with other vegetation types. Nevertheless,

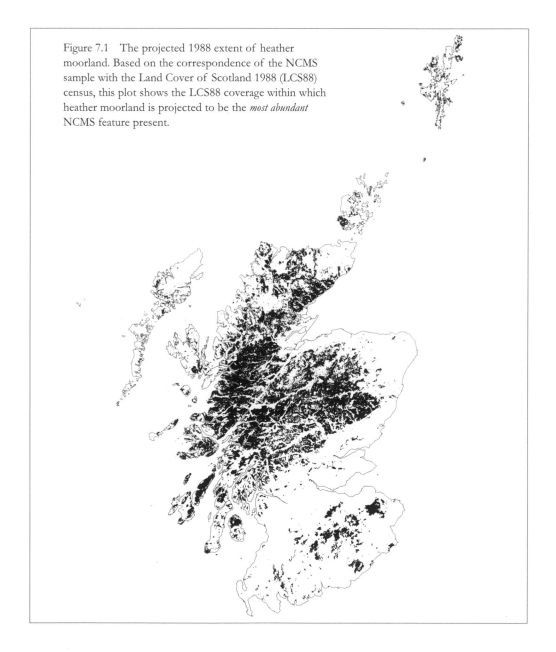

Figure 7.1   The projected 1988 extent of heather moorland. Based on the correspondence of the NCMS sample with the Land Cover of Scotland 1988 (LCS88) census, this plot shows the LCS88 coverage within which heather moorland is projected to be the *most abundant* NCMS feature present.

during the NCMS study period heathlands were under intense pressure from over-grazing, over-burning, increased nitrogen deposition and afforestation.[8]

7.2 The character of heather moorland

Heaths below the natural treeline have been derived mostly from woodland. Through grazing and burning management they persist in a dynamic state of apparent equilibrium. In countering the natural tendency to revert to woodland, intensive grazing and to a lesser degree burning can push regeneration towards grassland.[9] Thus, without appropriate management, heaths and moorland below the natural treeline could either revert to woodland and scrub or be converted to acid grasslands.[10]

Due to changes in soil moisture conditions, blanket mires, wet heaths and dry heaths grade into each other.[11, 12] Both blanket mire and wet heath are typically dominated by mixtures of dwarf shrubs such as *Calluna vulgaris* and *Erica tetralix* and grasses or sedges such as *Eriophorum vaginatum*, *Scirpus cespitosus* or *Molinia caerulea*. Dry heaths are usually characterised by overwhelming dominance of dwarf shrubs such as *Calluna vulgaris* and *Erica cinerea* but under heavy grazing there may be an invasion of grasses such as mat grass (*Nardus stricta*). In western Scotland the oceanic, cool, wet climate favours the widespread development of wet heaths, for example on slopes that would support dry heath in the east. A floristic difference between wet and dry heaths is the presence of *Erica tetralix* in wet heath, which is characteristic of wet peaty soils. In all cases, with increased burning or grazing, the relative abundance of the grasses and sedges tends to increase and the abundance of dwarf shrubs to decrease. However, under light grazing and burning regimes, dwarf-shrub cover (especially *Calluna vulgaris*) may increase.

Maritime heaths occur on coastal cliff tops and dunes, where the vegetation is influenced by exposure and salt spray. Heather (*Calluna vulgaris*) is usually dominant in more sheltered parts, with bell heather (*Erica cinerea*) also common. Cross-leaved heather (*Erica tetralix*) and crowberry (*Empetrum nigrum*) are found around the cooler and wetter coasts of northern and western Scotland.

The NCMS classification for heather moorland included areas where dwarf shrubs and regenerating burnt patches dominated the ground cover. The projected NCMS distribution of heather moorland most commonly occurs in all upland areas, but notably in the Southern Uplands and to the north of the Highland boundary fault (Figure 7.1).

7.3 NCMS findings

Heather moorland covered nearly a fifth of Scotland in the 1940s (Table 7.1, Figure 7.2), but was reduced to 15% by the mid 1970s. Due to the reclassification of drained mire as heather moorland, little apparent change in the heather moorland extent from the 1970s to the late 1980s conceals an underlying trend in afforestation and conversion to grassland during that period. Consequently, there are even some (non-significant) regional increases within the broad pattern of heather moorland loss throughout Scotland (Figure 7.3).

Bracken and heather have been shown to have a cyclical relationship, in which bracken can invade heather stands in pioneer and degenerate phases when

Table 7.1   Heather moorland: regional estimates.

Region	Regional area (km²)	1940s (km²)	(%)	1970s (km²)	(%)	1980s (km²)	(%)	Net change 1940s–1980s (km²)	(% of 40s)	Sig.
				Area estimates						
Borders	4695	939	20	742	16	546	12	−394	−42	**
Central	2716	519	19	498	18	449	17	−71	−14	*
Dumfries & Galloway	6342	601	9	208	3	240	4	−361	−60	*
Fife	1377	15	1	5	0	5	0	−10	−66	*
Grampian	8686	2536	29	1809	21	1647	19	−889	−35	***
Highland	24611	5222	21	4603	19	4249	17	−973	−19	**
Lothian	1814	194	11	158	9	231	13	36	19	
Strathclyde	14430	1832	13	1321	9	1697	12	−135	−7	
Tayside	7394	1796	24	1564	21	1170	16	−626	−35	**
Orkney Islands	1115	94	8	80	7	64	6	−30	−32	
Shetland Islands	1810	405	22	370	20	474	26	69	17	
Western Isles	2847	462	16	464	16	525	18	63	14	
Scotland	77837	14615	19	11820	15	11294	15	−3321	−23	***
Drained mire				192		839				
Adjusted total		14615	19	11628	15	10455	13	−4160	−28	***

Notes • See Table 5.2 for explanation.
      • The adjusted total removes the estimated area gained through drainage of mire.

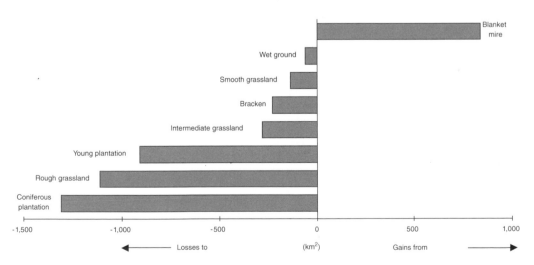

Figure 7.2   Heather moorland net gains and losses, 1940s–1980s (from matrices of interchange). See Figure 5.4 for explanation.

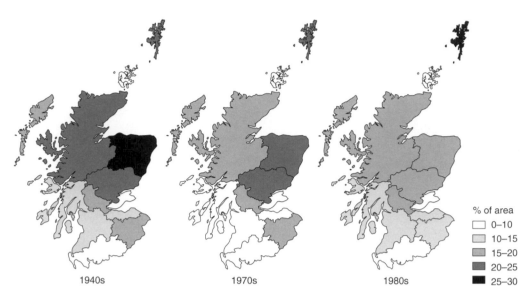

Figure 7.3   The pattern of geographical change for heather moorland.

Heather moorland summary *(see Table 7.1, Figure 7.2)*

1940s baseline

- nearly a fifth of the area of Scotland was heather moorland
- relatively most abundant in upland regions of Grampian (29%), Tayside (24%), the Shetland Islands (22%) and Highland (21%)
- least abundant in Fife (1%) and the Orkney Islands (8%)

1940s–1980s change

- 23% reduction in the area of heather moorland
- greatest area reductions in Highland (19%), Grampian (35%) and Tayside (35%)

Dynamics of change

- biggest reductions to afforestation and conversion to rough grassland
- gains from the drainage of blanket mire

1980s outcome

- 15% of the area of Scotland was heather moorland
- most abundant in the Shetland Islands (26%), Grampian (19%) and Western Isles (18%)
- least abundant in Fife (less than 0.4%), Dumfries & Galloway (4%) and the Orkney Islands (6%)

Table 7.2   Heather moorland compositional changes, 1940s–1980s.

	Heather moorland	
	1940s went to (km^2)	1980s came from (km^2)
Rough grassland	2636	1525
Intermediate grassland	313	
Blanket mire		989
Young + coniferous plantation	2245	
Bracken	273	
Others	777	404
(Unchanged area)	(8377)	(8377)
Total area	14621	11294

Notes   • Gains and losses of less than 150 km^2 have been grouped into 'Others'.
   • See Table 5.5 for explanation.

competition is weak, but may retreat when competition from *Calluna* is strongest in its building and mature phases.[13] Bracken infestation may be negligible on some heather moorlands because of unfavourable soils or management which favours heather.[14] Bracken expansion was evident in the NCMS results from the 1940s to the 1970s and from the 1970s to the 1980s.

7.3.1 Summary of changes in the composition of heather moorland

Taking account of the dynamics of change (Table 7.2, Figure 7.4), it is estimated that around 60% of the 1940s heather moorland remained unaltered in the 1980s. As much as 40% of the 1940s heather moorland was reduced by afforestation and grassland expansion.

The reduction in area was partly compensated for by an expansion of heather moorland on former rough grassland. More importantly, drained heather-dominated blanket mire accounted for nearly one-tenth of the NCMS heather moorland estimate for the 1980s.

References

1   Thompson, D.B.A., MacDonald, A.J., Marsden, J.H. and Galbraith, C.A. (1995). Upland heather moorland in Great Britain: a review of international importance, vegetation change and some objectives for nature conservation. *Biological Conservation* **71**, 163–178.

2   Bunce, R.G.H. and Heal, O.W. (1984). Landscape evaluation and the impact of changing land-use on the rural environment: the problem and the approach. In Roberts, R.D. and Roberts, T.M. (eds). *Planning and Ecology*. London: Chapman & Hall.

3   Miles, J. (1985). The pedogenic effect of different species and vegetation types and the implications of succession. *Journal of Soil Science* **36**, 571–584.

4   Leslie, A.S. and Shipley, A.E. (eds) (1912). *The Grouse in Health and Disease*. London: Smith, Elder & Co.

5   Watson, A. and Miller, G.R. (1976). *Grouse Management. The Game Conservancy Booklet 12*. Banchory: Institute of Terrestrial Ecology.

6   Scottish Natural Heritage (1994). *Red Deer and the Natural Heritage: SNH Policy Paper*. Perth: Scottish Natural Heritage.

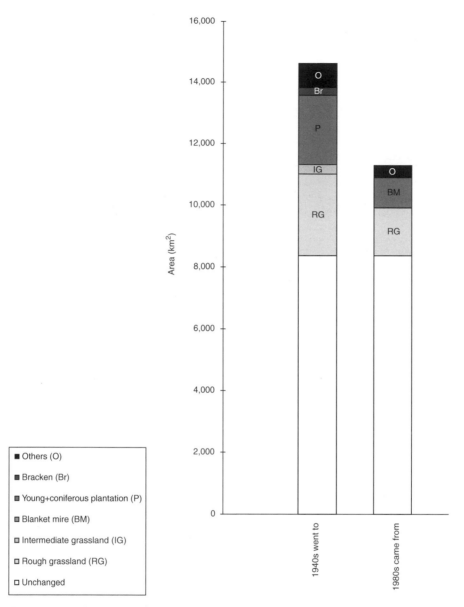

Figure 7.4   Heather moorland compositional changes, 1940s–1980s. Note that gains and losses of less than 150 km² have been grouped into 'Others'. See Figure 5.12 for full explanation.

7   Watson, A. and Lance, A.N. (1984). Ecological aspects of game shooting and upland conservation. *ECOS* **5(3)**, 2–7.

8   Stevenson, A.C. and Birks, H.J.B. (1995). Heaths and moorland: long-term ecological changes, and interactions with climate and people. In Thompson, D.B.A., Hester, A.J. and Usher, M.B. (eds). *Heaths and Moorland: Cultural Landscapes*. Edinburgh: HMSO.

9   Legg, C. (1995). Heathland dynamics: a matter of scale. In Thompson, D.B.A., Hester, A.J. and Usher, M.B. (eds). *Heaths and Moorland: Cultural Landscapes*. Edinburgh: HMSO.

Case study on the conversion of heather moorland to grassland

A Tayside sample square provides an example of how relatively uniform stands of heather could become patchy and fragmented, and reduced in extent by pasture encroachment. With arable and pasture to the northern and southern margins of the case study, heather moorland was dominant in the 1940s square. Rough grassland was confined mainly to stream courses. The 1980s scene shows heather moorland reduced in area and patchy.

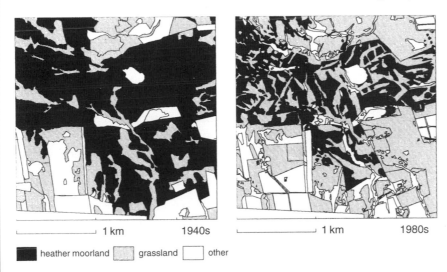

| 1 km | 1940s | | 1 km | 1980s |

■ heather moorland ▨ grassland □ other

Heather moorland was reduced by farmland encroachment. Rough grassland expanded from the 1940s to the 1970s and was in turn converted to smooth grassland from the 1970s to 1980s. Patches of rough grassland within the remaining heather moorland appeared from the 1970s to the 1980s, as did bracken.

The net outcome in this case was that the area of heather moorland, which had covered 54% of the square in the 1940s, was halved. Fragmentation also occurred, with the number of distinct vegetation 'patches' increasing from 82 in the 1940s square (minimum mappable area 0.1 ha) to 407 in the 1980s.

10 Ward, S.D., MacDonald, A.J. and Matthew, E.M. (1995). Scottish heaths and moorland: how should conservation be taken forward? In Thompson, D.B.A., Hester, A.J. and Usher, M.B. (eds). *Heaths and Moorland: Cultural Landscapes*. Edinburgh: HMSO.

11 Rodwell, J.S. (ed.) (1991). *British Plant Communities Volume 2: Mires and Heaths*. Cambridge: Cambridge University Press.

12 Gimmingham, C.H. (1975). *An Introduction to Heathland Ecology*. Edinburgh: Oliver & Boyd.

13 Marrs, R.H. and Pakeman, R.J. (1995). Bracken invasion: lessons from the past and prospects for the future. In Thompson, D.B.A., Hester, A.J. and Usher, M.B. (eds). *Heaths and Moorland: Cultural Landscapes*. Edinburgh: HMSO.

14 Miles, J. (1985). The pedogenic effect of different species and vegetation types and the implications of succession. *Journal of Soil Science* **36**, 571–584.

8   ARABLE

Topography and climate limit intensive crop production in Scotland to the more fertile soils in lower rainfall areas, mainly in the eastern lowlands.

8.1   Historical background

Arable farming in pre-improvement Scotland was organised around an open-field system, with continuous arable cultivation of the best land nearest to the farming settlement households (the so called 'infield' land) and intermittent cultivation of land further away ('outfield').[1] Ridge and furrow ploughing to assist land drainage survived until the adoption of sub-surface tile drainage in the nineteenth century.[2] A prominent boundary was the 'head dyke', which enclosed both the infield and outfield, from more extensive rough grazing beyond.[3]

The improving movement of the latter part of the eighteenth century brought about major changes in the Scottish countryside. These included the laying out of extensive enclosed gardens, parkland and woodland ('policies') around country houses and the introduction of a new settlement pattern in the form of the planned village estate. Land reclamation and advances in liming, plough design, tile drainage and agricultural enclosure transformed lowland areas. With a growing urban industrial workforce, and as wool was supplemented by cotton for clothing, so relatively more land was required for arable production.[4]

Competition from overseas imports from the late nineteenth century onwards had serious consequences for sheep farming in the highlands. The lowlands were able to adapt more successfully by transferring out of arable production in order to concentrate on stock raising and dairy farming. In the inter-war years even these sectors became depressed. Revival of the arable sector, as of farming generally, did not get going until the Second World War and its aftermath. A main thrust in the Agriculture Act 1947 and subsequent developments was to increase arable production.

Mechanisation reduced the drudgery of farm work and replaced labour-intensive farming systems. The introduction of selective herbicides replaced weed control measures of crop rotation, cultivation and hand weeding. A better understanding of agronomy (including seed dressing, fertiliser requirements, improved crop varieties and the chemical control of pests and diseases) increased yields. Further gains arose from the breeding of more productive short-strawed cereals and crop varieties with pest and disease resistance. Arable farming was transformed by specialisation and intensification. Mechanisation countered the vagaries of weather, and replaced labour with high-speed operations of sowing

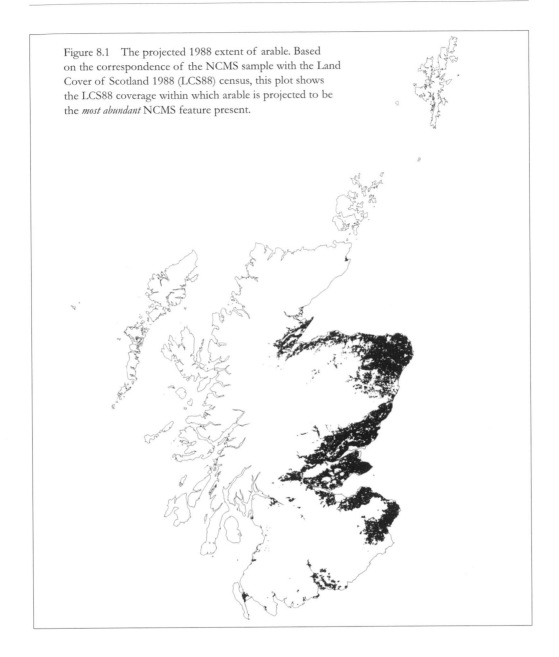

Figure 8.1   The projected 1988 extent of arable. Based
on the correspondence of the NCMS sample with the Land
Cover of Scotland 1988 (LCS88) census, this plot shows
the LCS88 coverage within which arable is projected to be
the *most abundant* NCMS feature present.

and harvesting. On-farm storage, driers, chillers and conditioners, together with
processing, marketing and transport, became integral to meeting more demanding
standards.[5]

The lighter soils and lower rainfall areas are the most suitable for arable cropping. The land use pattern which emerged in the latter half of the twentieth
century was predominantly rough grazing to the northwest, and crops and grass

Table 8.1   Arable: regional estimates (see Table 5.2 for explanation).

Region	Regional area (km²)	1940s (km²)	1940s (%)	1970s (km²)	1970s (%)	1980s (km²)	1980s (%)	Net change 1940s–1980s (km²)	Net change (% of 40s)	Sig.
Borders	4695	933	20	1010	22	946	20	13	1	
Central	2716	294	11	270	10	286	11	−8	−3	
Dumfries & Galloway	6342	414	7	456	7	900	14	486	118	***
Fife	1377	637	46	706	51	732	53	95	15	**
Grampian	8686	1595	18	1803	21	2036	23	441	28	*
Highland	24611	195	1	165	1	226	1	31	16	
Lothian	1814	617	34	559	31	530	29	−87	−14	*
Strathclyde	14430	1519	11	1140	8	1185	8	−334	−22	
Tayside	7394	1095	15	1080	15	1420	19	325	30	*
Orkney Islands	1115	388	35	209	19	276	25	−113	−29	
Shetland Islands	1810	17	1	10	1	14	1	−3	−17	
Western Isles	2847	43	2	43	2	43	2	0	0	
Scotland	77837	7745	10	7453	10	8593	11	848	11	**

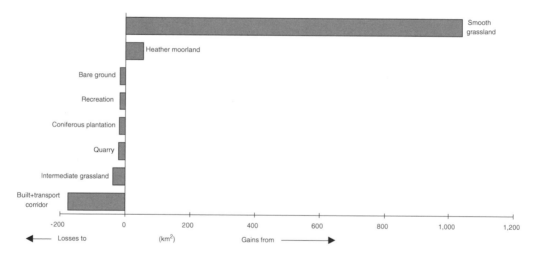

Figure 8.2   Arable net gains and losses, 1940s–1980s (from matrices of interchange). See Figure 5.4 for explanation.

in the central and eastern lowlands.[6] Three major trends in recent decades have been the intensification of farming, the increasing scale of farm operations and its increasing specialisation by farm and by area. 'The arable east has become more arable, the pastoral west has become less arable'.[7]

In addition to altering the appearance of the countryside, intensification removed habitats for wild plants and animals, such as hedges and field margins. Higher-yielding autumn-sown wheat and barley eliminated feeding grounds of winter stubble. Concern was expressed in the 1970s that the steady elimination of non-productive land, and the increased efficiency of production, posed threats to nature conservation.[8]

8.2 NCMS findings

Without differentiating between crops, the NCMS classification of 'arable' land included cereals, rotational grassland ley and horticulture. The projected NCMS distribution of arable land most commonly occurs in the eastern lowlands (Figure 8.1).

The arable area remained essentially unchanged from the 1940s to the 1970s. Entry into the European Economic Community in 1973, which favoured arable production, is reflected in arable expansion from the 1970s to the 1980s at the expense of smooth grassland (Table 8.1, Figure 8.2). To a lesser extent, arable land was reduced by urban and related developments.

The overall trend was of arable expansion, especially in the south and east, with evidence of contraction in parts of the west (Figure 8.3).

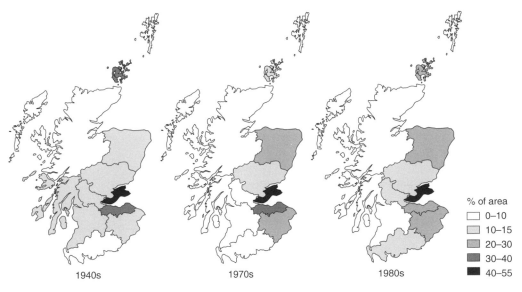

Figure 8.3   The pattern of geographical change for arable.

8.2.1 Summary of changes in the composition of arable land

Taking account of the dynamics of change (Table 8.2, Figure 8.4), around 60% of the 1940s arable land remained so in the 1980s. Within the other 40% there was an appreciable interchange between arable and grassland, with a net expansion of the arable area.

Case study of arable expansion on smooth grassland

Changes that were replicated throughout much of Scotland can be seen in an example from a Grampian square.

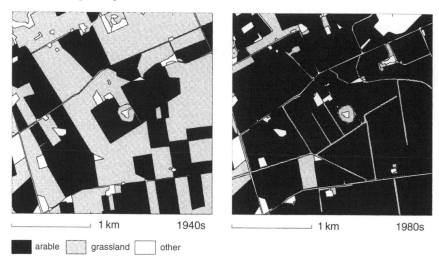

In the 1940s nearly half of the square was smooth grassland and one-third was arable. In the 1980s it was nearly two-thirds arable and only one-tenth smooth grassland. At the same time, the length of hedgerow was reduced by more than half, while the length of ditches increased fourfold.

Table 8.2   Arable compositional changes, 1940s–1980s.

	Arable	
	1940s went to (km²)	1980s came from (km²)
Rough grassland	167	176
Intermediate grassland	540	503
Smooth grassland	2181	3222
Built + transport corridor	262	
Others	203	300
(Unchanged area)	(4392)	(4392)
Total area	7745	8593

Notes   • Gains and losses of less than 100 km² have been grouped into 'Others'.
   • See Table 5.5 for explanation.

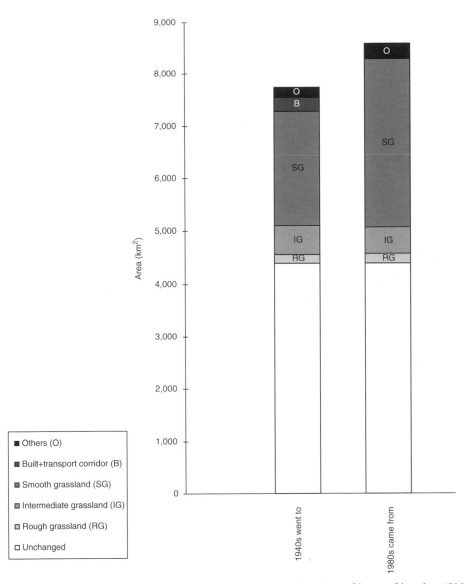

Figure 8.4   Arable compositional changes, 1940s–1980s. Note that gains and losses of less than 150 km² have been grouped into 'Others'. See Figure 5.12 for full explanation.

References

1   Fenton, A. (1991). The farming of the land. In Magnusson, M. and White, G. (eds). *The Nature of Scotland: Landscape, Wildlife and People*. Edinburgh: Canongate.

2   Foster, S. and Smout, T.C. (eds) (1994). *A History of Soils and Field Systems*. Aberdeen: Scottish Cultural Press.

3   Whyte, I. and Whyte, K. (1991). *The Changing Scottish Landscape 1500–1800*. London: Routledge.

Arable summary *(see Table 8.1, Figure 8.2)*

1940s baseline

- 10% of the area of Scotland was arable
- relatively most abundant in the lowland regions of Fife (46%), Lothian (34%) and the Orkney Islands (35%)
- least abundant in Highland and the Shetland Islands (both 1%)

1940s–1980s change

- slight 1940s to 1970s reduction was reversed from 1970s to 1980s, resulting in a net area increase of 11%
- biggest percentage gains in Dumfries & Galloway (118%), Tayside (30%) and Grampian (28%)
- significant reduction in Lothian (14%)

Dynamics of change

- biggest gain from smooth grassland
- biggest reduction to urban development

1980s outcome

- 11% of the area of Scotland was arable
- still relatively most abundant in the lowland regions of Fife (53%), Lothian (29%) and the Orkney Islands (25%)
- least abundant in Highland and the Shetland Islands (both 1%)

4   Pollard, E., Hooper, M.D. and Moor, N.W. (1974). *Hedges*. London: Collins.

5   Carter, E.S. and Stansfield, J.M. (1994). *British Farming: Changing Policies and Production Systems*. Ipswich: Farming Press Books.

6   Coppock, J.T. (1976). *An Agricultural Atlas of Scotland*. Edinburgh: John Donald Publishers Ltd.

7   Parry, M.L., Hossell, J.E. and Wright, L.J. (1992). Land use in the United Kingdom. In Whitby, M.C. (ed.). *Land Use Change: The Causes and Consequences*. ITE Symposium No. 27. London: HMSO.

8   Ratcliffe, D.A. (ed.) (1977). *A Nature Conservation Review*. Cambridge: Cambridge University Press.

9 WOODLAND

The species composition of Scottish woodland is influenced by climate, physical and chemical soil conditions, and the history of management. The ecological character of a woodland can be considered in terms of the tree layer, the shrub layer (greatly affected by grazing), the woodland floor or field layer (of small trees, shrubs, herbs and ferns) and the ground layer of tree litter, bryophytes and lichens.[1] Undisturbed soils are becoming increasingly recognised also for their natural heritage importance.[2] The nature conservation value of woodland, for plants and animals as well as for amenity, is highest for ancient semi-natural woodland and lowest for monoculture plantations of introduced trees.[3]

In an unaltered state Scotland would be mainly wooded, except on mires where the ground is too waterlogged for tree growth and on mountain tops and coastal margins where exposure imposes altitudinal and latitudinal limits. Brown earth soils south of the Highland boundary would favour ash (*Fraxinus* spp.) and oak (*Quercus* spp.), with pine (*Pinus sylvestris*) colonising the podzols and peats to the north. Hardier hazel (*Corylus avellana*), rowan (*Sorbus* spp.), birch (*Betula* spp.) and juniper (*Juniperus* spp.) would extend on to the upper slopes, and to the northwest.[4]

9.1 Historical background

That Scotland today is mainly deforested is largely a legacy of land clearance for agriculture since Neolithic times, around 5,000 years ago. The arrival of Celtic peoples around 2,500 years ago heralded the Iron Age, creating a demand for fuel timber and the technology for more extensive forest clearance. By medieval times, 1,000 years ago, much of the country was denuded of trees.

Eighteenth-century coppicing of oak woods for charcoal or tan bark gave a commercial incentive to the preservation and management of broadleaved woodland. In the nineteenth century, as iron furnaces replaced charcoal with coal, and as chemical substitutes were found for the natural tannin in oak bark, the oak woods lost their commercial value and fell into neglect.

In the eastern pinewoods, foresters were employed by estates to supervise the exploitation and maintenance of the woods as a sustainable resource. Lumbering gave purpose for the preservation and renewal of the Caledonian pinewoods, until competition from Norwegian, Swedish and Baltic suppliers of pine and spruce timber displaced domestic production. Surviving woods were variously turned over to sport or pasture, suppressing natural regeneration by browsing deer, cattle, goats and sheep.[5]

The industrial revolution gave impetus to afforestation, partly based on European species of larch (*Larix* spp.) and Norway spruce (*Picea abies*) in the late eighteenth century. North American species of Sitka spruce, (*Picea sitchensis*) and Douglas fir (*Pseudotsuga menziesii*) were introduced in the nineteenth century.[6] However, in the face of cheap timber imports from Europe and Canada, afforestation failed to develop as widely as in continental Europe. Thus, by the outbreak of the First World War, only around 5% of the land area was under tree cover, much the same as it had been in 1750. Domestic timber production accounted for less than one-tenth of needs.

In the aftermath of the First World War the Forestry Commission was established to create a strategic timber reserve and to reduce the nation's dependence on imported timber. However, economic depression in the 1920s and 1930s meant that few private landowners were in a position to make long-term investments in forestry. Commission planting was restricted to non-arable land, such as lowland heath, coastal dunes and hill grazing land.

With inter-war plantings still immature at the outbreak of the Second World War, which resulted again in heavy felling, speedy and large-scale action was required to replace growing stocks and to increase the area under woodland. The Forestry Act of 1945 thus introduced financial support for 'dedicating' private woodlands to the growing of timber into perpetuity, as well as grant aid for new planting. Expansion soon got underway, such that 'the 1950s will best be remembered as boom years for forestry, both Commission and private'.[7]

To avoid competition with agriculture, forest expansion was directed into marginal upland areas, with a view to diversification of employment and establishing a balance of land use between agriculture and forestry. Although infertile soils, difficult terrain and harsh climate were least satisfactory for tree growth, the sale of large estates helped to supply land for forestry.[8] The development of the Cuthbertson plough in the 1930s allowed blanket peat to be 'moor-gripped', or drained, and the introduction of the 'humpy' plough in the 1960s enabled the ploughing of deeper peat areas.

The main pre-war timber market had been for pit-props. As plantations came into production so new markets opened up, notably for chipboard and pulp. Investment by timber-using industries in the 1960s included the Fort William pulp and paper mill, and so the planting programme was accelerated in Scotland.

Despite apparent success, forestry remained unprofitable when subject to economic appraisal. As new schemes in the 1970s became subject to a required 3% rate of return, forestry policy looked to additional social benefits of stemming depopulation in fragile areas and environmental gains to landscape, wildlife and recreation.[9]

Planting continued to expand in the public and private sectors, but from the early 1980s the Forestry Commission was required to divest itself of a proportion of its woodlands and plantable land. With the introduction of a new Forestry Grant Scheme and continuing tax incentives, private planting out-paced state forestry in the 1980s.

While forest cover in the UK as a whole remained low relative to most of Europe, unease over the appropriateness of conifer planting in the uplands and peatlands of Scotland was growing. Characterised by dense, even-aged, regimented blocks (commonly of non-native Sitka spruce and lodgepole pine (*Pinus contorta*) and to a lesser extent Norway spruce, Douglas fir and larches) there was often little that was natural to Scotland in the appearance or composition of conifer plantations. Natural heritage considerations became more firmly enshrined in forestry policy in the mid-1980s. The amendment of the Wildlife and Countryside Act in 1985 required a reasonable balance to be struck between the development of afforestation and forest management for timber supply on the one hand, and the conservation and enhancement of natural beauty and the conservation of flora, fauna and geological or physiographical features of special interest on the other.[10]

Controversy erupted over the detrimental effects of blanket afforestation to nature conservation,[11] most prominently in the 'flow country' of Caithness and Sutherland.[12] Natural heritage concerns, coupled with public unease over tax arrangements, contributed to the removal of forestry from the scope of Income Tax and Corporation Tax relief in the March 1988 budget, to be replaced by a new Woodland Grant Scheme.

9.2 NCMS findings

The NCMS broadly reflected the classification of British forests according to continuity of forest cover on a site (ancient or secondary), whether the forests have been planted (semi-natural or planted) and whether they are composed of predominantly broadleaf or conifer species.[13]

Due to a rapid expansion in coniferous afforestation, the extent of woodland in

Table 9.1   Woodland group (see Table 5.1 for explanation).

Feature	1940s (km²)	(%)	1970s (km²)	(%)	1980s (km²)	(%)	1940s–1980s (km²)	(% of 40s)	Sig.
Broadleaved woodland	1509	2	1297	2	1164	1	−345	−23	***
Mixed woodland	542	1	501	1	341	0	−201	−37	***
Broadleaved plantation	33	0	38	0	38	0	5	16	
Parkland	78	0	70	0	73	0	−5	−7	
Coniferous woodland	206	0	107	0	108	0	−97	−47	
Young plantation	430	1	2877	4	4426	6	3996	929	***
Coniferous plantation	837	1	2972	4	4705	6	3868	462	***
Felled woodland	29	0	75	0	108	0	79	267	**
Group total	3665	5	7936	10	10963	14	7298	199	na

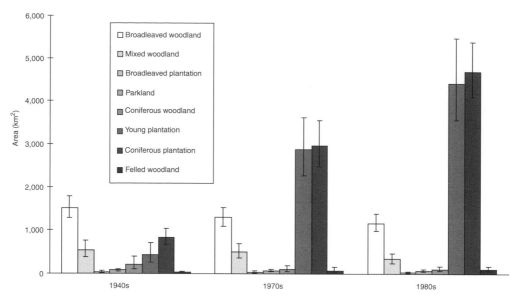

Figure 9.1   Woodland composition (estimate and 95% confidence interval). Note: confidence intervals for area estimates cannot be used to assess the significance of net changes – refer to the relevant tables for net changes.

Woodland group summary *(see Table 9.1, Figure 9.1)*

1940s baseline

- 5% of the area of Scotland was woodland

- of the total woodland area, 59% was broadleaved, 35% coniferous plantation and 6% coniferous woodland

1940s–1980s change

- more than doubled in overall area

- a seven-fold increase in coniferous plantation was partially offset by declines in the areas of broadleaved and coniferous woodland

1980s outcome

- 14% of Scotland was woodland

- of the total woodland area, 84% was coniferous plantation, 14% was broadleaved and 1% coniferous woodland

Scotland increased from around 5% of the land area in the 1940s to 14% of the land area in the 1980s. In contrast, remnants of long-established or semi-natural woodland decreased in extent (Table 9.1, Figure 9.1).

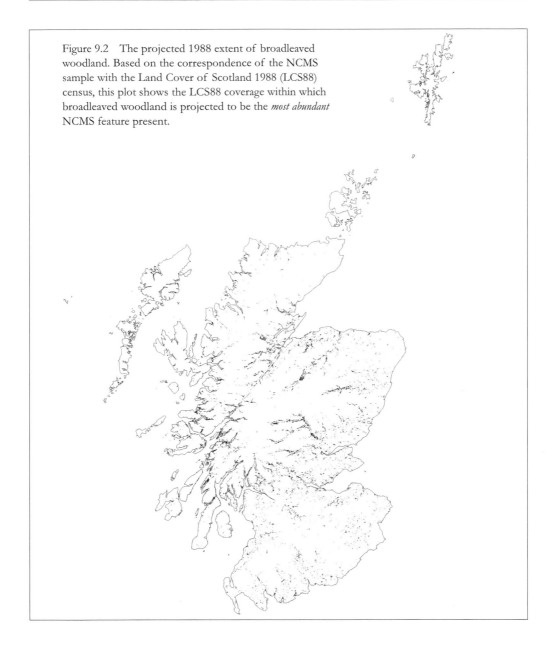

Figure 9.2   The projected 1988 extent of broadleaved woodland. Based on the correspondence of the NCMS sample with the Land Cover of Scotland 1988 (LCS88) census, this plot shows the LCS88 coverage within which broadleaved woodland is projected to be the *most abundant* NCMS feature present.

9.2.1 Broadleaved woodland

Broadleaved trees and woodland are an important feature of much of the British landscape. Of 33 tree species that are generally accepted as native, 30 are broadleaved. Retaining representative examples of natural woodland types is of great conservation importance.[14]

From the projected NCMS distribution, broadleaved woodland classes commonly occurred throughout the lowlands and straths of Scotland in the late 1980s (Figure 9.2). Differentiated in the NCMS classification are broadleaved woodland, mixed woodland, broadleaved plantation and parkland.

The NCMS definition of broadleaved woodland was where broadleaved crowns dominated the canopy and there was less than 25% coniferous cover. This definition would encompass native broadleaved woodland, such as the Argyll oakwoods, as well as eighteenth- and nineteenth-century plantings, including woods dominated by non-native sycamore and beech. The overall extent of broadleaved woodland was reduced by a quarter from the late 1940s to the late 1980s, especially in Highland, Strathclyde and Grampian. The reduction was due mainly to under-planting or replacement with conifers (Table 9.2, Figure 9.3).

Table 9.2   Broadleaved woodland: regional estimates (see Table 5.2 for explanation).

Region	Regional area (km²)	1940s (km²)	(%)	1970s (km²)	(%)	1980s (km²)	(%)	Net change 1940s–1980s (km²)	(% of 40s)	Sig.
Borders	4695	64	1	54	1	51	1	−14	−21	
Central	2716	60	2	62	2	64	2	4	7	
Dumf. & Gall.	6342	91	1	72	1	91	1	0	0	
Fife	1377	30	2	25	2	21	2	−10	−32	***
Grampian	8686	180	2	129	1	113	1	−67	−37	***
Highland	24611	507	2	458	2	356	1	−151	−30	***
Lothian	1814	65	4	48	3	46	3	−20	−30	***
Strathclyde	14430	409	3	346	2	339	2	−70	−17	**
Tayside	7394	103	1	103	1	83	1	−20	−19	
Orkney Islands	1115	0	0	0	0	0	0	0	0	
Shetland Islands	1810	0	0	0	0	0	0	0	0	
Western Isles	2847	0	0	0	0	0	0	0	0	
Scotland	77837	1509	2	1297	2	1164	1	−345	−23	***

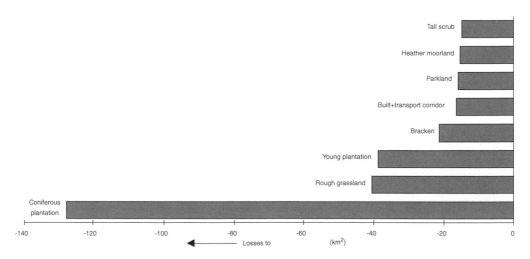

Figure 9.3   Broadleaved woodland net gains and losses, 1940s–1980s (from matrices of interchange). See Figure 5.4 for explanation.

Broadleaved woodland summary *(see Table 9.2, Figure 9.3)*

1940s baseline

- 2% of Scotland was broadleaved woodland

- relatively most abundant in Lothian (4%), and Strathclyde (3%)

- little or none found in the Orkney Islands, the Shetland Islands or the Western Isles

1940s–1980s change

- 23% reduction in area

- notable reductions in Highland (30%) Strathclyde (17%), Grampian (37%), Lothian (30%), and Fife (32%)

Dynamics of change

- biggest reductions to coniferous afforestation and clearance

1980s outcome

- about 1% of the area of Scotland was broadleaved woodland

- relatively most abundant in Lothian (3%), Strathclyde, Central and Fife (all 2%), little or none found in the Orkney Islands, the Shetland Islands or the Western Isles

---

Mixed woodland summary *(see Table 9.3, Figure 9.4)*

1940s baseline

- about 0.7% of the area of Scotland

- most abundant in Tayside (2%)

- not found in the Orkney Islands, the Shetland Islands and the Western Isles

1940s–1980s change

- overall decline in area of 37%

- notable reductions in Highland (60%), Tayside (50%) and Dumfries & Galloway (45%)

Dynamics of change

- losses due to felling and conversion to plantation

1980s outcome

- about 0.4% of the area of Scotland

The NCMS definition of mixed woodland was where coniferous and broadleaved trees each constituted at least 25% of the tree cover. It included 'policy' woodland if conifers and broadleaved trees were present. The extent of mixed woodland in the 1940s was estimated to be about one-third that of broadleaved woodland. It was reduced by a third over the study period, notably in Highland, Tayside and Dumfries & Galloway, and mainly through conversion to coniferous plantation (Table 9.3, Figure 9.4). In the interpretation, mixed woodland was especially confused with young and coniferous plantation and so the estimated reduction should be treated with caution.

The NCMS definition of broadleaved plantation was even-aged stands of planted broadleaved trees, usually dominated by one species. It was a very minor feature in Scotland during the study period and changed little in overall extent (Table 9.4).

Table 9.3   Mixed woodland: regional estimates (see Table 5.2 for explanation).

Region	Regional area (km²)	1940s (km²)	1940s (%)	1970s (km²)	1970s (%)	1980s (km²)	1980s (%)	Net change 1940s–1980s (km²)	Net change 1940s–1980s (% of 40s)	Sig.
Borders	4695	33	1	26	1	24	1	−9	−27	
Central	2716	23	1	20	1	22	1	−1	−5	
Dumfries & Galloway	6342	52	1	49	1	29	0	−23	−45	***
Fife	1377	16	1	11	1	12	1	−3	−22	
Grampian	8686	66	1	49	1	67	1	1	1	
Highland	24611	120	0	108	0	48	0	−72	−60	*
Lothian	1814	9	1	8	0	8	0	−1	−12	
Strathclyde	14430	90	1	104	1	63	0	−27	−30	
Tayside	7394	132	2	126	2	66	1	−66	−50	*
Orkney Islands	1115	0	0	0	0	0	0	0	0	
Shetland Islands	1810	0	0	0	0	0	0	0	0	
Western Isles	2847	0	0	0	0	0	0	0	0	
Scotland	77837	542	1	501	1	341	0	−201	−37	***

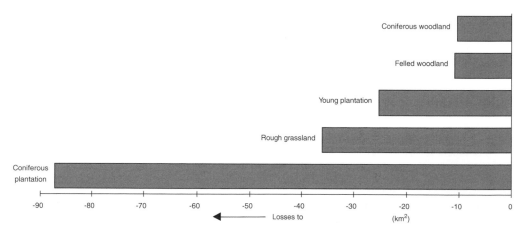

Figure 9.4   Mixed woodland net gains and losses, 1940s–1980s (from matrices of interchange). See Figure 5.4 for explanation.

Table 9.4 Broadleaved plantation: regional estimates (see Table 5.2 for explanation).

Region	Regional area (km²)	1940s (km²)	(%)	1970s (km²)	(%)	1980s (km²)	(%)	Net change 1940s–1980s (km²)	(% of 40s)	Sig.
Borders	4695	0	0	1	0	1	0	1	1463	*
Central	2716	4	0	8	0	8	0	4	108	***
Dumfries & Galloway	6342	1	0	4	0	6	0	5	511	*
Fife	1377	4	0	5	0	4	0	0	12	
Grampian	8686	1	0	1	0	3	0	2	373	
Highland	24611	1	0	2	0	4	0	3	476	
Lothian	1814	0	0	0	0	1	0	1	179	
Strathclyde	14430	11	0	8	0	7	0	−4	−33	
Tayside	7394	12	0	9	0	3	0	−8	−70	
Orkney Islands	1115	0	0	0	0	0	0	0	0	
Shetland Islands	1810	0	0	0	0	0	0	0	0	
Western Isles	2847	0	0	0	0	0	0	0	−100	
Scotland	77837	33	0	38	0	38	0	5	16	

Broadleaved plantation summary *(see Table 9.4)*

1940s baseline

- very small amounts found in Scotland
- most found in Strathclyde and Tayside

1940s–1980s change

- little overall change in area
- apparent increases in Dumfries & Galloway, Borders and Central but all areas and changes are very small and at the limit of the NCMS mapping resolution.

Dynamics of change

- little change

1980s outcome

- little overall change since the 1940s

The NCMS definition of parkland was a grouping of scattered trees (coniferous or broadleaved) providing 10 to 50% cover. It was a very minor feature, predominantly on grassland. Gains (notably from woodland) and losses (to farmland) were consistent with a general reduction in tree cover (Table 9.5, Figure 9.5).

Overall, broadleaved woodland was reduced in extent throughout Scotland, with the possible exception of Central region (Figure 9.6).

Table 9.5 Parkland: regional estimates (see Table 5.2 for explanation).

Region	Regional area (km²)	1940s (km²)	(%)	1970s (km²)	(%)	1980s (km²)	(%)	Net change 1940s–1980s (km²)	(% of 40s)	Sig.
				Area estimates				Net change 1940s–1980s		
Borders	4695	5	0	2	0	3	0	−3	−50	
Central	2716	5	0	1	0	2	0	−3	−53	
Dumfries & Galloway	6342	19	0	12	0	2	0	−17	−89	**
Fife	1377	4	0	1	0	1	0	−3	−64	*
Grampian	8686	9	0	25	0	22	0	12	131	**
Highland	24611	1	0	1	0	22	0	21	1992	**
Lothian	1814	11	1	8	0	2	0	−9	−80	**
Strathclyde	14430	23	0	12	0	8	0	−14	−64	
Tayside	7394	1	0	8	0	10	0	9	731	*
Orkney Islands	1115	0	0	0	0	0	0	0	0	
Shetland Islands	1810	0	0	0	0	0	0	0	0	
Western Isles	2847	0	0	0	0	0	0	0	−100	
Scotland	77837	78	0	70	0	73	0	−5	−7	

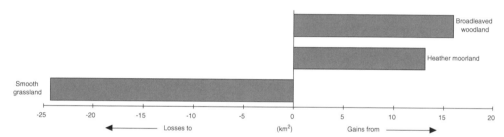

Figure 9.5 Net gains and losses for parkland, 1940s–1980s (from matrices of interchange). See Figure 5.4 for explanation.

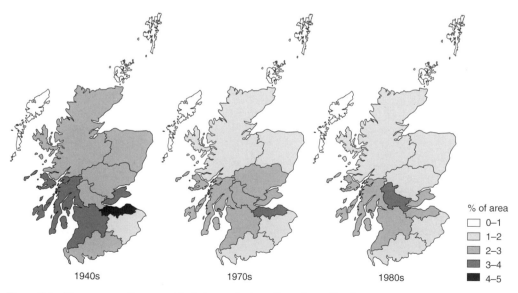

Figure 9.6 The pattern of geographical change for broadleaved woodland.

Parkland summary *(see Table 9.5, Figure 9.5)*

1940s baseline

- about 0.1% of the area of Scotland

- most found in Strathclyde, Dumfries & Galloway and Lothian

1940s–1980s change

- little change in total area

- increased in Highland, Grampian and Tayside

- reduced in Dumfries & Galloway and Lothian

Dynamics of change

- gains from woodland and heather moorland

- losses to farmland

1980s outcome

- about 0.1% of the area of Scotland

- mostly found in Grampian, Highland and Tayside

9.2.2 Coniferous woodland

Although geographically isolated, Scottish pinewoods are an integral part of a much more extensive and complex pattern of woodland variation across Eurasia.[15] Lying beyond the natural western limit of Norway spruce, the distinctive and diverse floristic character of native Scottish pinewoods is influenced both by the oceanic climate of the Atlantic seaboard and by the boreal climate akin to northern-continental Scandinavia. Relative to other tree species, Scots pine performs best on highly impoverished, sharply draining soils. At lower altitudes and on more fertile soils, competition and co-dominance with oak and birch are the norm. Remnant stands of native Scottish pinewoods are fragmentary and scattered into separate geographical groupings. They are of very great conservation importance and 'make a unique contribution to the landscape in terms of their species composition, structure and scenic character'.[16]

It became apparent in the 1960s that re-afforestation, both private and public, was obscuring the last evidence of the native forest.[17] Recognition of the importance of Caledonian pinewoods increased from the mid-1970s. The subsequent shift towards multi-purpose forestry arrested the decline in favour of sustainable management.[18]

The NCMS interpretation of coniferous woodland was irregular tree cover where conifer crowns dominated the canopy and there was less than 25%

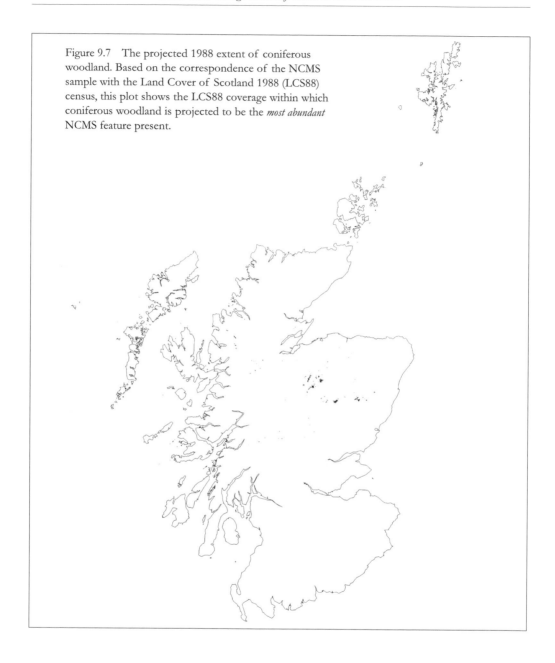

Figure 9.7 The projected 1988 extent of coniferous woodland. Based on the correspondence of the NCMS sample with the Land Cover of Scotland 1988 (LCS88) census, this plot shows the LCS88 coverage within which coniferous woodland is projected to be the *most abundant* NCMS feature present.

broadleaved cover. It included self-sown exotics (notably occurring south of the Highland boundary) as well as native Caledonian pinewood in the Highlands.

From the projected NCMS distribution, the late 1980s extent of coniferous woodland in Scotland was highly restricted (Figure 9.7). Its extent was halved from the 1940s to the 1970s, mainly by afforestation (Table 9.6, Figure 9.8), but the reduction was halted thereafter. Geographically it was reduced throughout its range (Figure 9.9).

Table 9.6   Coniferous woodland: regional estimates.

Region	Regional area (km²)	1940s (km²)	(%)	1970s (km²)	(%)	1980s (km²)	(%)	Net change 1940s–1980s (km²)	(% of 40s)	Sig.
Borders	4695	0	0	0	0	1	0	1	1700	
Central	2716	0	0	0	0	0	0	0	−50	
Dumfries & Galloway	6342	10	0	3	0	2	0	−8	−79	*
Fife	1377	0	0	0	0	0	0	0	11	
Grampian	8686	6	0	3	0	9	0	3	44	
Highland	24611	133	1	75	0	71	0	−62	−47	
Lothian	1814	1	0	1	0	1	0	0	81	
Strathclyde	14430	52	0	20	0	19	0	−33	−63	
Tayside	7394	4	0	5	0	5	0	1	31	
Orkney Islands	1115	0	0	0	0	0	0	0	0	
Shetland Islands	1810	0	0	0	0	0	0	0	0	
Western Isles	2847	0	0	0	0	0	0	0	0	
Scotland	77837	206	0	107	0	108	0	−97	−47	

Notes   • See Table 5.2 for explanation.
   • Planted conifers with an irregular appearance may have been interpreted as coniferous woodland.

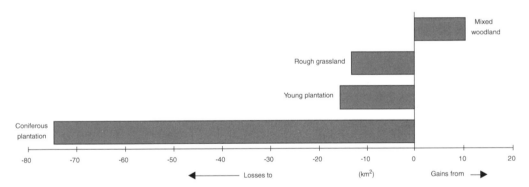

Figure 9.8   Coniferous woodland net gains and losses, 1940s–1980s (from matrices of interchange). See Figure 5.4 for explanation.

9.2.3 Coniferous plantation

'The most striking change in rural land use and landscape in Britain in the 20th century has been the expansion of forests'.[19] Scientific and technological advances since the Second World War revolutionised commercial forestry, with a threefold expansion in planting and a doubling of timber production. In the 1960s the axe and the cross-cut saw were replaced by the chainsaw, and in turn by the mechanised harvester; the horse by the mechanical winch and caterpillar tractor. Improved knowledge of land suitability, combined with an ability to modify its physical and chemical state, extended opportunities for planting. More powerful traction and new plough design allowed cultivation of deep peat. Technical advances thus 'transformed a largely rural craft into a highly organised and efficient industrial operation'.[20]

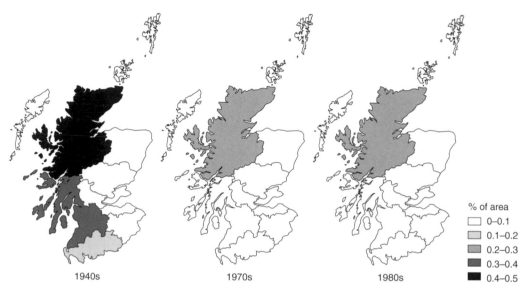

Figure 9.9   The pattern of geographical change for coniferous woodland.

Coniferous woodland summary *(see Table 9.6, Figure 9.8)*

1940s baseline

- less than 0.3% of Scotland

- only substantial amounts in Highland and Strathclyde

1940s–1980s change

- apparent reduction by nearly half

- apparent declines in Highland (47%) and Strathclyde (63%)

Dynamics of change

- reduction mainly due to afforestation, as well as clearance

- apparent small gains from other types of woodland

1980s outcome

- less than 0.2% of Scotland was coniferous woodland

- only found in substantial amounts in Highland

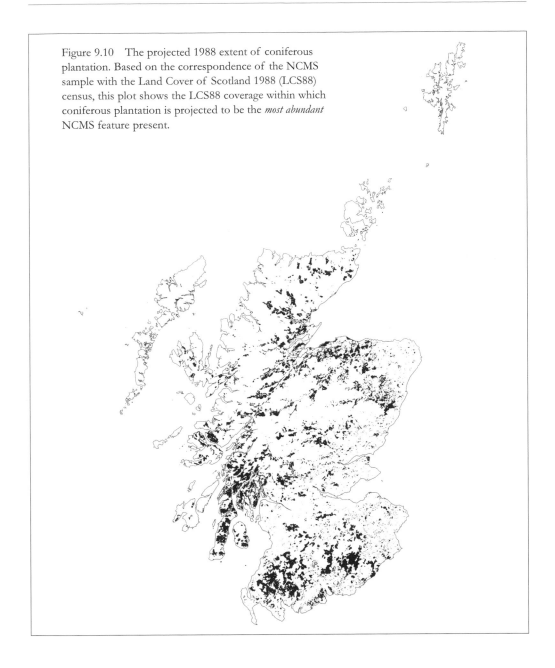

Figure 9.10   The projected 1988 extent of coniferous plantation. Based on the correspondence of the NCMS sample with the Land Cover of Scotland 1988 (LCS88) census, this plot shows the LCS88 coverage within which coniferous plantation is projected to be the *most abundant* NCMS feature present.

From a greatly depleted woodland cover at the start of the study period, the projected NCMS distribution illustrates the dominance of coniferous plantation by the late 1980s (Figure 9.10). The NCMS classification distinguished between young plantation, coniferous plantation and felled woodland.

Young plantation was defined as regularly planted trees of up to 3 m in height. Although the NCMS definition of young plantation included broadleaved plantation, it was negligible in extent during the study period. From a small initial extent in the 1940s, young plantation expanded by an order of magnitude during the study period, to cover 6% of Scotland in the late 1980s (Table 9.7). New planting took place mainly on mire, rough grassland and heather moorland (Figure 9.11).

Coniferous plantation was defined in the NCMS classification as regularly planted coniferous trees exceeding 3 m in height. By the late 1980s it had extended

Table 9.7   Young plantation: regional estimates (see Table 5.2 for explanation).

Region	Regional area (km²)	1940s (km²)	(%)	Area estimates 1970s (km²)	(%)	1980s (km²)	(%)	Net change 1940s–1980s (km²)	(% of 40s)	Sig.
Borders	4695	7	0	305	6	300	6	292	4048	***
Central	2716	13	0	33	1	118	4	105	781	
Dumfries & Galloway	6342	8	0	574	9	365	6	357	4400	***
Fife	1377	13	1	10	1	17	1	5	36	
Grampian	8686	79	1	122	1	342	4	263	334	**
Highland	24611	175	1	705	3	1636	7	1461	834	***
Lothian	1814	2	0	37	2	31	2	29	1210	
Strathclyde	14430	83	1	987	7	1494	10	1410	1694	***
Tayside	7394	49	1	106	1	124	2	75	152	
Orkney Islands	1115	0	0	0	0	0	0	0	0	
Shetland Islands	1810	0	0	0	0	0	0	0	0	
Western Isles	2847	0	0	0	0	0	0	0	−100	
Scotland	77837	430	1	2877	4	4426	6	3996	929	***

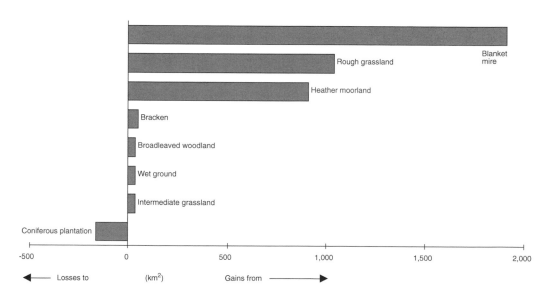

Figure 9.11   Young plantation net gains and losses, 1940s–1980s (from matrices of interchange). See Figure 5.4 for explanation.

Young plantation summary *(see Table 9.7, Figure 9.11)*

1940s baseline

- about 0.6% of the area of Scotland
- little in the Orkney Islands, the Shetland Islands or the Western Isles

1940s–1980s change

- increase in overall area of 929%
- substantial increases in Highland (834%), Strathclyde (1,694%), Dumfries & Galloway (4,400%), Borders (4,048%), and Grampian (334%)

Dynamics of change

- planting mostly on to blanket mire, rough grassland and heather moorland
- some matured as coniferous plantation

1980s outcome

- 6% of the area of Scotland
- notable in Highland (7%) and Strathclyde (10%)
- little in the Orkney Islands, the Shetland Islands or the Western Isles

Table 9.8   Coniferous plantation: regional estimates (see Table 5.2 for explanation).

Region	Regional area (km²)	1940s (km²)	(%)	1970s (km²)	(%)	1980s (km²)	(%)	1940s–1980s (km²)	(% of 40s)	Sig.
Borders	4695	66	1	269	6	418	9	353	535	***
Central	2716	17	1	70	3	92	3	74	436	
Dumfries & Galloway	6342	48	1	506	8	966	15	919	1934	***
Fife	1377	54	4	79	6	66	5	12	21	
Grampian	8686	228	3	816	9	858	10	630	276	***
Highland	24611	100	0	507	2	876	4	777	780	***
Lothian	1814	21	1	21	1	62	3	40	191	*
Strathclyde	14430	161	1	391	3	1051	7	890	552	***
Tayside	7394	142	2	312	4	316	4	174	123	*
Orkney Islands	1115	0	0	0	0	0	0	0	0	
Shetland Islands	1810	0	0	0	0	0	0	0	0	
Western Isles	2847	0	0	0	0	0	0	0	0	
Scotland	77837	837	1	2972	4	4705	6	3868	462	***

to more than five times its 1940s area (Table 9.8), mainly from planting on heather moorland, rough grassland and blanket mire (Figure 9.12). Established woodland was also converted to coniferous plantation.

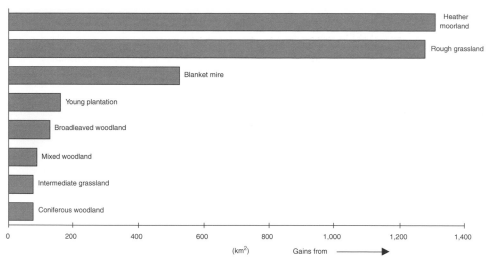

Figure 9.12   Coniferous plantation net gains and losses, 1940s–1980s (from matrices of interchange). See Figure 5.4 for explanation.

Coniferous plantation summary *(see Table 9.8, Figure 9.12)*

1940s baseline

- about 1% of the area of Scotland
- 4% of Fife and 3% of Grampian
- not found in the Orkney Islands, the Shetland Islands or the Western Isles

1940s–1980s change

- increase in area overall of 462%
- notable increases in Dumfries & Galloway (1,934%), Strathclyde (552%), Highland (780%) , Grampian (276%) and Borders (535%)

Dynamics of change

- main planting on heather moorland, rough grassland and blanket mire
- underplanting also in semi-natural or long-established woodlands

1980s outcome

- about 6% of the area of Scotland
- 15% of Dumfries & Galloway and 10% of Grampian
- little in the Orkney Islands, the Shetland Islands or the Western Isles

---

Felled woodland was defined as areas which had been clear-felled. 'For economic reasons management by patch clear-felling predominates in most extensive conifer forests, and rotation lengths are limited by wind-throw hazard.'[21] Except

Table 9.9   Felled woodland: regional estimates (see Table 5.2 for explanation).

Region	Regional area (km²)	1940s (km²)	(%)	1970s (km²)	(%)	1980s (km²)	(%)	Net change 1940s–1980s (km²)	(% of 40s)	Sig.
Borders	4695	9	0	5	0	31	1	22	255	
Central	2716	0	0	0	0	3	0	3	2445	
Dumf. & Gall.	6342	9	0	5	0	5	0	−4	−44	
Fife	1377	2	0	2	0	13	1	11	577	
Grampian	8686	1	0	3	0	19	0	17	1194	*
Highland	24611	2	0	5	0	1	0	−1	−61	
Lothian	1814	0	0	1	0	1	0	0	79	
Strathclyde	14430	4	0	45	0	19	0	15	423	*
Tayside	7394	3	0	9	0	18	0	15	606	
Orkney Islands	1115	0	0	0	0	0	0	0	0	
Shetland Islands	1810	0	0	0	0	0	0	0	0	
Western Isles	2847	0	0	0	0	0	0	0	−100	
Scotland	77837	29	0	75	0	108	0	79	267	**

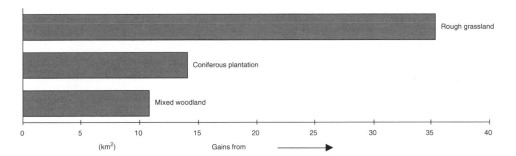

Figure 9.13   Felled woodland net gains and losses, 1940s–1980s (from matrices of interchange). See Figure 5.4 for explanation.

in special circumstances, the Forestry Commission requires felled woodland to be replanted. Although felling expanded, it was a relatively minor and short-lived feature throughout the study period (Table 9.9, Figure 9.13).

In geographical terms, except in the Western and Northern Isles, coniferous plantation expanded throughout Scotland, and became especially dominant in Strathclyde and Dumfries & Galloway (Figure 9.14).

9.2.4 Summary of woodland changes

Broadleaved woodland and mixed woodland, both small in extent, were reduced in area. Only very small areas of broadleaved plantation and parkland were detected. Small-scale interchanges, which tended to cancel out, were at the limit

Felled woodland summary *(see Table 9.9, Figure 9.13)*

1940s baseline

- less than 0.1% of the area of Scotland

- most in Borders and Dumfries & Galloway

1940s–1980s change

- increase in overall area of 267%

- notable increases in Grampian (1,194%) and Strathclyde (423%)

Dynamics of change

- felling included 'first generation' forest

1980s outcome

- about 0.1% of the area of Scotland

- about 1% of Borders and Fife

- little found in the Orkney Islands, the Shetland Islands or the Western Isles

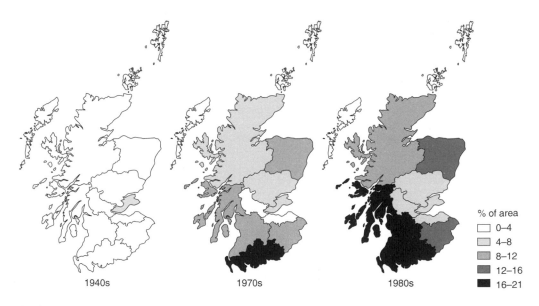

1940s   1970s   1980s

% of area
☐ 0–4
◻ 4–8
▨ 8–12
▩ 12–16
■ 16–21

Figure 9.14   The pattern of geographical change for coniferous plantation.

of the NCMS mapping resolution. Conversion to coniferous plantation was the main reason for a reduction in the extent of broadleaved woodland from the 1940s through to the 1980s (Table 9.10, Figure 9.15).

Table 9.10 Broadleaved woodland compositional changes, 1940s–1980s (see Table 5.5 for explanation).

	Broadleaved		Mixed		Plantation		Parkland	
	1940s went to (km²)	1980s came from (km²)	1940s went to (km²)	1980s came from (km²)	1940s went to (km²)	1980s came from (km²)	1940s went to (km²)	1980s came from (km²)
Rough grassland	135	94	53					
Smooth grassland	47	44					28	
Heather moorland	75	59						
Scrub	66	45	23	21				
Broadleaved woodland			52	61				
Mixed woodland	61	52						
Young + con. plantation	186		130					
Built + transp. corridor	44							
Bracken	40							
Others	149	162	115	90	24	29	43	66
(Unchanged area)	(707)	(707)	(168)	(168)	(10)	(10)	(7)	(7)
Total area	1510	1164	542	341	33	38	79	73

Note • Gains and losses less than 20 km² (40 km² for broadleaved woodland) have been grouped into 'Others'.

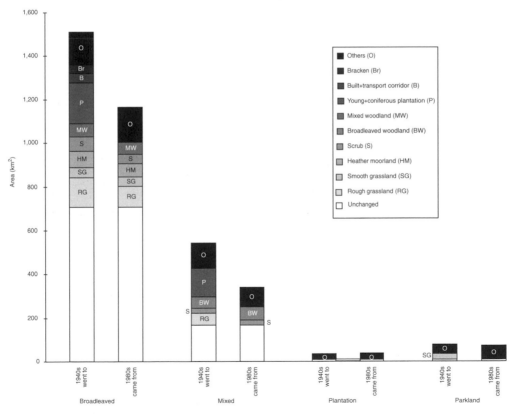

Figure 9.15 Broadleaved woodland compositional changes, 1940s–1980s. Note that gains and losses less than 20 km² (40 km² for broadleaved) have been grouped into 'Others'. See Figure 5.12 for full explanation.

Although the extent of coniferous woodland was already very restricted in the late 1940s it was reduced by half between then and the early 1970s, due largely to conversion to coniferous plantation (Table 9.11, Figure 9.16). The reduction was halted from the 1970s onwards.

The greatest change, however, was the continuous expansion of conifer planting. Taking young and coniferous plantation together, it increased from less than 2% of Scotland's land area in the 1940s to nearly 12% in the late 1980s. The expansion was predominantly on to rough grassland, blanket mire or heather moorland (Table 9.12, Figure 9.17).

Table 9.11   Coniferous woodland compositional changes, 1940s–1980s (see Table 5.5 for explanation).

	Coniferous woodland	
	1940s went to (km²)	1980s came from (km²)
Rough grassland	23	
Young + coniferous plantation	100	
Others	41	66
(Unchanged area)	(42)	(42)
Total area	206	108

Notes   • Gains and losses of less than 20 km² have been grouped into 'Others'.
   • Many of the apparent gains in coniferous woodland are probably due to inaccuracies inherent in the method. See Chapter 3 for details.

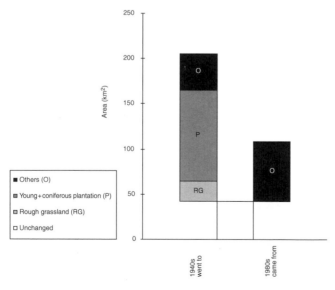

Figure 9.16   Coniferous woodland compositional changes, 1940s–1980s. Note that gains and losses less than 20 km² have been grouped into 'Others', and that many of the apparent gains in coniferous woodland are probably due to inaccuracies inherent in the method (see chapter 3). See Figure 5.12 for full explanation.

Table 9.12   Coniferous plantation compositional changes, 1940s–1980s.

	Young		Mature		Felled	
	1940s went to (km²)	1980s came from (km²)	1940s went to (km²)	1980s came from (km²)	1940s went to (km²)	1980s came from (km²)
Rough grassland		1096	130	1409		
Blanket mire		1912		526		
Heather moorland		918		1327		
Scrub				104		
Broadleaved woodland				142		
Mixed woodland				102		
Young plantation			99	259		
Coniferous plantation	259	99				
Others	113	344	207	436	29	108
(Unchanged area)	(58)	(58)	(401)	(401)	(0)	(0)
Total area	430	4426	837	4705	30	108

Notes
- Gains and losses less than 90 km² have been grouped into 'Others'.
- See Table 5.5 for explanation.

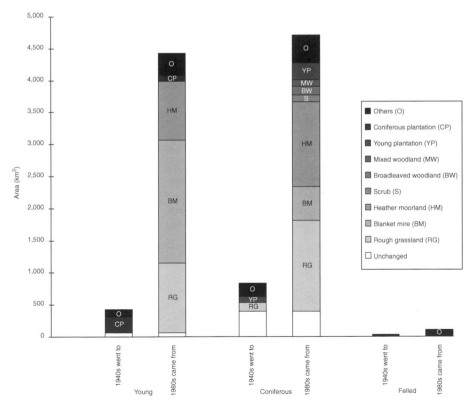

Figure 9.17   Coniferous plantation compositional changes, 1940s–1980s. Note that gains and losses less than 90 km² have been grouped into 'Others'. See Figure 5.12 for full explanation.

Case study in woodland changes

An NCMS sample square from the Borders in southern Scotland provides an example of afforestation of an area of rough grassland. Enclosed farmland occurs to the north of the views shown here.

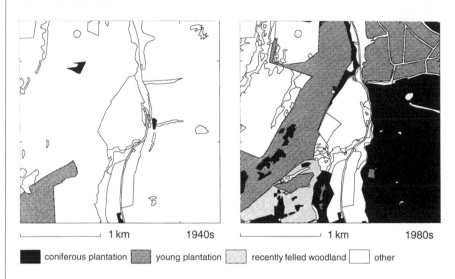

coniferous plantation   young plantation   recently felled woodland   other

The 1940s setting was an open landscape of mainly rough grassland. Other than three small isolated stands of conifers, a block of young plantation (lower left) presages more extensive afforestation to come.

The 1980s blanket forest was differentiated by blocks of mature, young and felled trees. The area which had been young plantation in the 1940s was extended so that in the 1980s view it was partly felled and partly replanted. Patches of mature trees within the young plantation are 'first generation' trees, and betray the fact that the young plantation in the 1980s scene is the result of replanting.

References

1   Ratcliffe, D.A. (ed.) (1977). *A Nature Conservation Review.* Cambridge: Cambridge University Press.

2   Gauld, J.H. and Bell, J.S. (1997). *Soils and Nature Conservation in Scotland.* Scottish Natural Heritage Review No. 62. Perth: Scottish Natural Heritage.

3   Nature Conservation Council (1986). *Nature Conservation and Afforestation in Britain.* Peterborough: NCC.

4   McVean, D.N. and Ratcliffe, D.A. (1962). *Monographs of the Nature Conservancy Number One: Plant Communities of the Scottish Highlands.* London: HMSO.

5   Smout, T.C. (1997). Highland land use before 1800. In Smout, T.C. (ed.). *Scottish Woodland History.* Edinburgh: Scottish Cultural Press.

6   Edlin, H.L. (1972). *The New Naturalist: Trees, Woods and Man*. London: Collins.

7   Pringle, D. (1994). *The First 75 Years: A Brief Account of the History of the Forestry Commission 1919–1994*. Edinburgh: The Forestry Commission.

8   Tompkins, S. (1989). *Forestry in Crisis: The Battle for the Hills*. London: Christopher Helm.

9   Pringle, D. (1994). *The First 75 Years: A Brief Account of the History of the Forestry Commission 1919–1994*. Edinburgh: The Forestry Commission.

10   Forestry Commission (1990). *Forest Nature Conservation Guidelines*. London: HMSO.

11   Nature Conservation Council (1986). *Nature Conservation and Afforestation in Britain*. Peterborough: NCC.

12   Stroud, D.A., Reed, T.M., Pienkowski, M.W. and Lindsay, R.A. (1987). *Birds, Bogs and Forestry: The Peatlands of Caithness and Sutherland*. Edited by Ratcliffe, D.A. and Oswald, P.H. Peterborough: Nature Conservation Council.

13   Hodge, S.J., Patterson, G. and McIntosh, R. (1996). *The Approach of the British Forestry Commission to the Conservation of Forestry Biodiversity*. Monte Verita Conference on Assessment of Biodiversity for Improved Forest Planning.

14   Evans, J. (1984). *Silviculture of Broadleaved Woodland*. Forestry Commission Bulletin 62. London: HMSO.

15   Critchfield, W.B. and Little, E.L. (1996). *Geographic Distribution of Pines of the World*. Washington D.C.: United States Department of Agriculture Miscellaneous Publication 991.

16   Rodwell, J.S. and Cooper, E.A. (1995). Scottish pinewoods in a European context. In Aldhous, J.R. (ed.). *Our Pinewood Heritage*. Forestry Commission, The Royal Society for the Protection of Birds and Scottish Natural Heritage, Conference Proceedings.

17   McVean, D.N. and Ratcliffe, D.A. (1962). *Monographs of the Nature Conservancy Number One: Plant Communities of the Scottish Highlands*. London: HMSO.

18   Callander, R.F. (1995). Native pinewoods: the last twenty years (1975–94). In Aldhous, J.R. (ed.). *Our Pinewood Heritage*. Forestry Commission, The Royal Society for the Protection of Birds and Scottish Natural Heritage, Conference Proceedings.

19   Mather, A. (ed.) (1993). *Afforestation Policies, Planning and Progress*. London: Belhaven Press.

20   Pringle, D. (1994). *The First 75 Years: A Brief Account of the History of the Forestry Commission 1919–1994*. Edinburgh: The Forestry Commission.

21   Hodge, S.J., Patterson, G. and McIntosh, R. (1996). *The Approach of the British Forestry Commission to the Conservation of Forestry Biodiversity*. Monte Verita Conference on Assessment of Biodiversity for Improved Forest Planning.

10   FRESH WATER ENVIRONMENTS

Nine-tenths of the standing fresh water volume of Great Britain lies within Scotland. The 30,000-or-more lochs and lochans include the largest by area (Lomond) and volume (Ness), the longest (Awe) and the deepest (Morar), while the 10,000-plus burns and rivers include the river of greatest discharge (Tay). For their purity and attractiveness, the fresh waters of Scotland are renowned internationally for sport, recreation, tourism and nature conservation.[1]

Due to the abundance of small lochans, the Western Isles have the highest number of standing waters on a comparative regional basis in Scotland. There is a decline in number towards the eastern side of the country. By virtue of topography and climate, the west and northeast highlands contain nine of Scotland's 13 largest lochs and the highest number of running waters (Figure 10.1). In these areas the water courses tend to be small and steep, and respond rapidly to precipitation and snow melt. Most of the larger rivers flow to the east coast, with lower gradients and more delayed response to precipitation.[2]

10.1 Historical background

From earliest times to the present day, Scotland's fresh waters have been vital for meeting a range of domestic and industrial demands. The technology of water power for milling grain, brought to Scotland by the Vikings, became widespread and large mill complexes were created in Glasgow, Edinburgh and Perth. The Industrial Revolution was founded on water for powering industrial machines, preceding and continuing after the advent of steam.[3]

Under pressure from urban growth and associated public health problems, local authorities from the mid nineteenth century onwards were given powers to develop public water supplies. During the Second World War security of supply became a major issue, leading to the Water (Scotland) Act 1946 which laid the foundations for existing arrangements. During the next 20 years, water supplies were improved and expanded.[4]

While the availability of fresh water in Great Britain far exceeds requirements, seasonal and regional differences in supply and demand mean that water needs to be stored in areas of surplus and piped to areas of deficit. Topography, geology and climate provide very favourable conditions for power generation, especially in the highlands. The power available from water increased dramatically with the advent of hydro-electricity, and in the 20 years following the Second World War a range of schemes was constructed.[5]

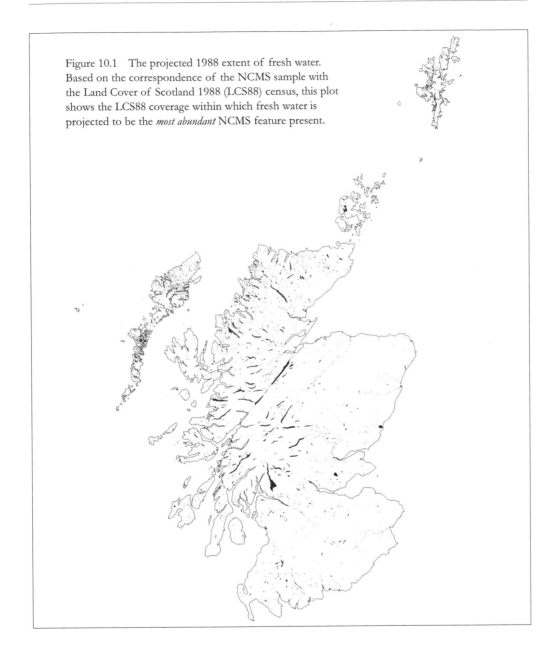

Figure 10.1   The projected 1988 extent of fresh water. Based on the correspondence of the NCMS sample with the Land Cover of Scotland 1988 (LCS88) census, this plot shows the LCS88 coverage within which fresh water is projected to be the *most abundant* NCMS feature present.

In addition to their nature conservation and aesthetic value, fresh waters are essential to a modern society for the supply of drinking water, irrigation and energy, and as a medium for the disposal of wastes. Activities which affect Scotland's fresh waters include river engineering and flood abatement measures, power generation, land drainage, abstraction for agriculture and industry, and fish farming. Recreational demand for such activities as angling, wildfowling, sailing, swimming, boating and water skiing continues to increase.[6]

River pollution control, first enacted in the early 1950s, has resulted in steady improvements in water quality. Nevertheless, the weakness of statutory powers to control diffuse pollution (e.g. atmospheric acid deposition, spillages and unconsented discharges, fertiliser run-off, and the legacy of nutrient enrichment and toxic leachates from Scotland's industrial past) poses a threat to Scotland's fresh waters. Good forestry and agricultural practice, combined with bankside habitat protection and restoration, can offer effective solutions in acid- or nitrogen-sensitive catchments, reduce levels of diffuse pollution through run-off, and improve conditions for fresh water life.[7]

10.2 NCMS findings

Surface fresh water habitats have traditionally been divided into wetlands (including peatlands) and open waters. They are highly variable in character, including running and standing waters, marshlands and acidic peat bogs, mountain streams and major rivers, small ponds and lochs. The NCMS classification of open water bodies is partly dependent upon the minimum mapping resolution, which is 0.1 ha for features mapped by area and 30 m for features mapped as lines. Open water bodies which were mapped by NCMS were as follows:

- fresh water *lochs*, as irregularly shaped expanses of water without evidence of impounding;

- *reservoirs*, where there was evidence of impounding;

- *rivers*, without evidence of canalisation and greater than 10 m in width, were mapped as areal features;

- narrower *streams* were mapped as linear features;

- *canals*, artificially confined to flow in a certain direction, were mapped as areal features where they were greater than 10 m in width; and

- narrower *ditches* were mapped as linear features.

In addition, NCMS mapped:

- *marginal inundation*, including swamp and fen margins typical of open water transition, the banks of ponds and ditches subject to periodic inundation, and the draw-down zones of reservoirs; and

- *wet ground*, such as wet areas in pasture or flushes in upland areas, often denoted by the presence of the rush *Juncus*, but lacking evidence of peat formation.

Overall, the area of open water increased, mainly due to reservoir construction from the 1940s to the 1970s (Table 10.1, Figure 10.2). The relative abundance of open water, which is greatest to the west and north (Figure 10.3), remained essentially unaltered during the study period.

Table 10.1   Fresh water group: area and length estimates.

Feature	Area estimates 1940s (km²)	(%)	1970s (km²)	(%)	1980s (km²)	(%)	Net change 1940s–1980s (km²)	(% of 40s)	Sig.
Lochs	1193	2	1102	1	1078	1	−115	−10	*
Reservoirs	150	0	288	0	323	0	172	115	**
Rivers	229	0	224	0	224	0	−5	−2	
Canals	7	0	8	0	7	0	0	−5	
Marginal inundation	46	0	51	0	56	0	11	23	
Wet ground	572	1	525	1	680	1	109	19	
Total area	2196	3	2199	3	2368	3	171	8	na

Feature	Length estimates 1940s (km)	(km/km²)	1970s (km)	(km/km²)	1980s (km)	(km/km²)	Net change 1940s–1980s (km)	(% of 40s)	Sig.
Streams	129579	1.7	127937	1.6	131058	1.7	1480	1	
Ditches	49478	0.6	62432	0.8	99621	1.3	50143	101	***

Notes   • See Table 5.1 for explanation.
• The km/km² column shows the average length of the feature per square kilometre of Scotland.

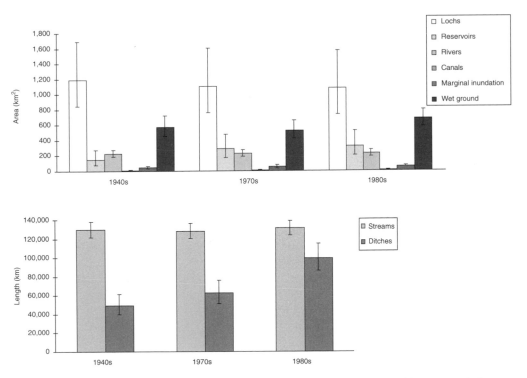

Figure 10.2   Fresh water composition (estimate and 95% confidence interval). Note: confidence intervals for area estimates cannot be used to assess the significance of net changes – refer to the relevant tables for net change.

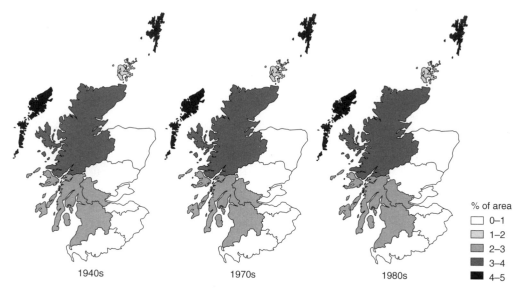

Figure 10.3   The pattern of geographical change for fresh water.

Fresh water summary *(see Table 10.1, Figure 10.2)*

1940s baseline

- comprised about 3% of the area of Scotland

- about half of the fresh water area was lochs, a quarter wet ground, with the remainder largely rivers and reservoirs

- on average about 1.7 km/km^2 of streams and 0.6 km/km^2 of ditches

1940s–1980s change

- slight increase in area, mainly 1970s to 1980s

- a reduction in loch area was related to a doubling of the reservoir area

- ditches doubled in overall length

1980s outcome

- about 3% of the total land area of Scotland

- just under half was lochs, nearly 30% wet ground, with the remainder largely rivers and reservoirs

- on average about 1.7 km/km^2 of streams and 1.3 km/km^2 of ditches

Table 10.2   Lochs: regional estimates (see Table 5.2 for explanation).

Region	Regional area (km²)	1940s (km²)	1940s (%)	1970s (km²)	1970s (%)	1980s (km²)	1980s (%)	Net change 1940s–1980s (km²)	Net change 1940s–1980s (% of 40s)	Sig.
Borders	4695	5	0	4	0	5	0	0	−1	
Central	2716	14	1	14	1	14	1	0	−2	***
Dumf. & Gall.	6342	41	1	40	1	40	1	−1	−3	
Fife	1377	1	0	1	0	1	0	0	−12	
Grampian	8686	20	0	20	0	20	0	0	1	
Highland	24611	613	2	550	2	525	2	−88	−14	
Lothian	1814	0	0	0	0	1	0	0	24	
Strathclyde	14430	252	2	241	2	243	2	−9	−4	
Tayside	7394	18	0	4	0	5	0	−13	−70	
Orkney Islands	1115	18	2	17	1	16	1	−2	−13	*
Shetland Islands	1810	74	4	74	4	75	4	0	1	
Western Isles	2847	136	5	136	5	134	5	−2	−1	
Scotland	77837	1193	2	1102	1	1078	1	−115	−10	*

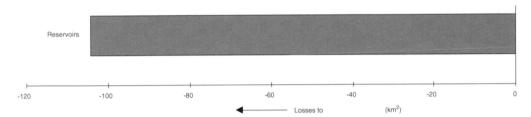

Figure 10.4   Lochs net gains and losses, 1940s–1980s (from matrices of interchange). See Figure 5.4 for explanation.

Table 10.3   Reservoirs: regional estimates (see Table 5.2 for explanation).

Region	Regional area (km²)	1940s (km²)	1940s (%)	1970s (km²)	1970s (%)	1980s (km²)	1980s (%)	Net change 1940s–1980s (km²)	Net change 1940s–1980s (% of 40s)	Sig.
Borders	4695	4	0	8	0	8	0	4	89	
Central	2716	50	2	51	2	49	2	−2	−3	
Dumf. & Gall.	6342	0	0	1	0	1	0	1	990	
Fife	1377	9	1	9	1	9	1	0	−1	
Grampian	8686	2	0	5	0	6	0	4	219	
Highland	24611	34	0	141	1	181	1	147	433	*
Lothian	1814	13	1	13	1	13	1	0	0	
Strathclyde	14430	33	0	37	0	37	0	3	10	
Tayside	7394	1	0	20	0	19	0	18	1438	
Orkney Islands	1115	0	0	0	0	0	0	0	100	
Shetland Islands	1810	3	0	3	0	0	0	−3	−98	
Western Isles	2847	0	0	0	0	0	0	0	2	
Scotland	77837	150	0	288	0	323	0	172	115	**

10.2.1 Lochs

Loch area was reduced by evidence of impoundment and thus conversion to reservoirs (Table 10.2, Figure 10.4). The greatest apparent reductions took place in Highland and Tayside but, because lochs are such a minor feature in terms of their overall extent, little statistical significance can be attributed to results.

Lochs summary *(see Table 10.2, Figure 10.4)*

1940s baseline

- about 1.5% of the area of Scotland
- relatively most abundant in the Western Isles (5% of region) and Shetland Islands (4%)

1940s–1980s change

- reduced in overall area by 10%
- declined by 13% in the Orkney Islands and 2% in Central
- suggested decline of 14% in Highland

Dynamics of change

- major cause of loss was through conversion to reservoirs

1980s outcome

- about 1.4% of the area of Scotland
- relatively most abundant in the Western Isles (5% of region) and the Shetland Islands (4%), with little found in Lothian or Fife

---

10.2.2 Reservoirs

Reservoirs expansion, which was greatest in Highland region (Table 10.3, Figure 10.5), inundated former lochs, heather moorland and rough grassland.

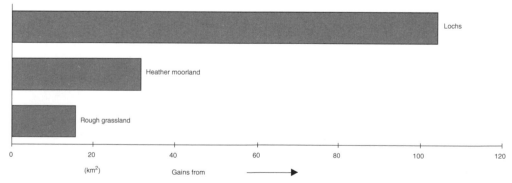

Figure 10.5   Reservoirs net gains and losses, 1940s–1980s (from matrices of interchange). See Figure 5.4 for explanation.

Reservoirs summary *(see Table 10.3, Figure 10.5)*

1940s baseline

- less than 0.2% of the area of Scotland

- relatively most abundant in Central (2%)

1940s–1980s change

- 115% increase in total area

- notable increase in Highland

Dynamics of change

- gains mainly from the conversion of lochs

1980s outcome

- less than 0.5% of the area of Scotland

- still relatively most abundant in Central (2%), but more than half of total area is in Highland

10.2.3 Rivers, streams and canals

Although of considerable natural heritage interest and interpreted in the study, the NCMS method did not produce meaningful regional estimates of change for rivers, streams and canals. An inherent problem in the estimation of rivers as a class of land cover was that, by measuring surface area, considerable variation could be experienced between low flow, bank-full and in-flood conditions. Canals were too scarce to be adequately represented in the study.

10.2.4 Ditches

The NCMS classification of a ditch was an artificially confined water course of less than 10 m in width. Although traditionally associated with field margins and roadside verges, ditches in the study were predominantly linked to mire drainage for afforestation. Consequently, the length of ditches doubled from the 1940s to the 1980s (Table 10.4).

10.2.5 Marginal inundation

Marginally inundated land included swamp and fen vegetation, representing plant communities of the transitional zone between open water and land. They frequently include plants whose roots lie under water but whose stems and leaves grow above the water surface. Plant communities tend to be dominated by sedges or reeds. These typically include common reed (*Phragmites australis*),

Table 10.4   Ditches: regional estimates.

Region	Regional area (km²)	1940s (km)	1940s (km/km²)	1970s (km)	1970s (km/km²)	1980s (km)	1980s (km/km²)	Net change 1940s–1980s (km)	Net change 1940s–1980s (% of 40s)	Sig.
Borders	4695	1735	0.4	1813	0.4	3537	0.8	1802	104	**
Central	2716	4161	1.5	3782	1.4	4573	1.7	412	10	
Dumfries & Galloway	6342	2429	0.4	4129	0.7	16982	2.7	14553	599	***
Fife	1377	1463	1.1	1435	1.0	1354	1.0	−109	−7	
Grampian	8686	2561	0.3	3424	0.4	8463	1.0	5903	231	***
Highland	24611	25946	1.1	34333	1.4	27615	1.1	1669	6	
Lothian	1814	904	0.5	798	0.4	1310	0.7	406	45	
Strathclyde	14430	5656	0.4	6598	0.5	25388	1.8	19732	349	***
Tayside	7394	2913	0.4	4084	0.6	7121	1.0	4208	144	***
Orkney Islands	1115	772	0.7	673	0.6	1166	1.0	394	51	**
Shetland Islands	1810	328	0.2	628	0.3	1018	0.6	690	210	***
Western Isles	2847	610	0.2	736	0.3	1095	0.4	485	79	***
Scotland	77837	49478	0.6	62432	0.8	99621	1.3	50143	101	***

Notes   • See Table 5.2 for explanation.
   • The km/km² column shows the average length of the feature per square kilometre of the region.

Ditches summary *(see Table 10.4)*

1940s baseline

- about 0.6 km of ditches per square km in Scotland

- greatest density in Central, Fife and Highland (all over 1 km/km²)

- least found in the Shetland Islands and the Western Isles (both 0.2 km/km²)

1940s–1980s change

- doubled in overall length

- notable increases in Strathclyde (349%), Dumfries & Galloway (599%), Grampian (231%) and Tayside (144%)

1980s outcome

- about 1.3 km/km² in Scotland

- greatest density in Dumfries & Galloway (2.7 km/km²), Strathclyde (1.8 km/km²) and Central (1.7 km/km²)

---

reed-grass (*Phalaris arundinacea*), bulrush (*Typha* spp.) and branched bur-reed (*Sparganium erectum*). Under-storey vegetation may include meadowsweet (*Filipendula ulmaria*), water mint (*Mentha aquatica*), common marsh bed-straw

Table 10.5   Marginal inundation: regional estimates (see Table 5.2 for explanation).

Region	Regional area (km²)	1940s (km²)	(%)	1970s (km²)	(%)	1980s (km²)	(%)	Net change 1940s–1980s (km²)	(% of 40s)	Sig.
Borders	4695	0	0	1	0	1	0	1	310	
Central	2716	0	0	0	0	2	0	2	1050	
Dumfries & Galloway	6342	1	0	1	0	5	0	3	284	***
Fife	1377	0	0	0	0	0	0	0	−20	
Grampian	8686	2	0	2	0	1	0	−2	−71	*
Highland	24611	28	0	31	0	25	0	−2	−9	
Lothian	1814	1	0	1	0	1	0	0	−31	
Strathclyde	14430	5	0	9	0	9	0	4	91	
Tayside	7394	3	0	2	0	4	0	2	56	
Orkney Islands	1115	2	0	2	0	2	0	0	−13	
Shetland Islands	1810	1	0	2	0	1	0	0	3	
Western Isles	2847	1	0	1	0	5	0	4	313	
Scotland	77837	46	0	51	0	56	0	11	23	

Marginal inundation summary *(see Table 10.5)*

1940s baseline

- less than 0.1% of the area of Scotland
- minor in all regions, with nearly 60% found in Highland

1940s–1980s change

- a small suggested increase in area
- small area changes in Dumfries & Galloway (increase) and in Grampian (decrease)

Dynamics of change

- no significant gains or losses

1980s outcome

- less than 0.1% of the area of Scotland
- 45% found in Highland and very small amounts in most other regions

---

(*Galium palustre*) and creeping bent (*Agrostis stolonifera*). Reed beds provide shade and shelter for young wildfowl, invertebrates and fish, as well as spawning sites for water snails and fish.

Among minor gains and losses, the area of marginal inundation showed no significant change (Table 10.5).

10.2.6 Wet ground

Wet ground was distinguished from mire in the NCMS classification by association with other habitats, such as inundated grassland or upland flushes in the absence of any evidence of peat. The occurrence of wet ground depends on such factors as underlying geology, local water table, rainfall and artificial drainage. Scotland has a relatively high proportion of wet ground compared to the rest of the UK, but sub-surface farmland drainage has substantially reduced the extent of waterlogged ground. In areas of impervious rocks, surface water may be channelled along small depressions to form a flush, which can add greatly to local species diversity.

Pasture tends to be less well-drained than arable land, especially in upland areas where conditions for farming are more marginal. The composition of plant communities depends upon such factors as degree of wetness, acidity of the soil and land use. Wet grasslands are often characterised by purple moor grass (*Molinia caerula*) and tufted hair-grass (*Deschampsia cespitosa*). Rushes tend to be abundant, especially soft rush (*Juncus effusus*), compact rush (*J. conglomeratus*) and, in upland heaths, heath rush (*J. squarrosus*). Tall herbs such as great willowherb (*Epilobium hirsutum*), are often present in lightly grazed lowland wet areas.

Wet areas can support a varied invertebrate fauna. Several species of bird are therefore associated with damp pastures and wet ground, such as lapwing (*Vanellus vanellus*), curlew (*Numenius arquata*), snipe (*Gallinago gallinago*) and redshank (*Tringa totanus*).

Among gains and losses there was no significant overall change in the extent of wet ground from the 1940s to the 1980s (Table 10.6, Figure 10.6). Wet ground expanded onto grassland and moorland, but was also lost to afforestation.

Table 10.6   Wet ground: regional estimates (see Table 5.2 for explanation).

Region	Regional area (km²)	1940s (km²)	1940s (%)	1970s (km²)	1970s (%)	1980s (km²)	1980s (%)	Net change 1940s–1980s (km²)	Net change 1940s–1980s (% of 40s)	Sig.
Borders	4695	41	1	30	1	32	1	−9	−22	
Central	2716	32	1	18	1	12	0	−19	−61	
Dumfries & Galloway	6342	37	1	34	1	151	2	114	310	**
Fife	1377	6	0	4	0	1	0	−5	−82	***
Grampian	8686	11	0	14	0	12	0	1	5	
Highland	24611	112	0	99	0	103	0	−9	−8	
Lothian	1814	5	0	7	0	6	0	1	33	
Strathclyde	14430	212	1	180	1	240	2	28	13	
Tayside	7394	81	1	96	1	76	1	−5	−7	
Orkney Islands	1115	5	0	5	0	5	0	0	−5	
Shetland Islands	1810	21	1	25	1	31	2	10	49	
Western Isles	2847	10	0	15	1	12	0	2	20	
Scotland	77837	572	1	525	1	680	1	109	19	

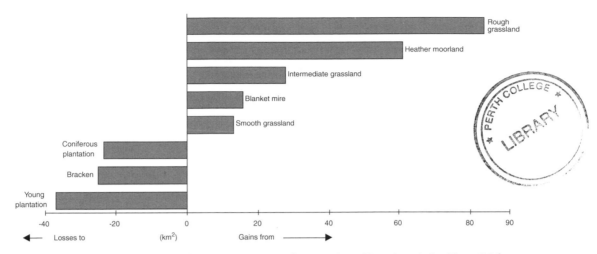

Figure 10.6   Wet ground net gains and losses, 1940s–1980s (from matrices of interchange). See Figure 5.4 for explanation.

Wet ground summary *(see Table 10.6, Figure 10.6)*

1940s baseline

- about 1% of the area of Scotland was wet ground

- relatively little found in Lothian, the Orkney Islands or Fife

1940s–1980s change

- apparent expansion in six regions, contraction in five regions

- suggested 19% increase in overall area

- 1980s photography shows increase in Dumfries & Galloway (310%)

- 82% reduction in Fife was small in area

Dynamics of change

- biggest gains from rough grassland and heather moorland

- biggest reductions through afforestation and spread of bracken

1980s outcome

- about 1% of the area of Scotland

- relatively most abundant in Dumfries & Galloway, Strathclyde and the Shetland Islands

10.2.7 Summary of changes in fresh waters

Lochs accounted for the greatest area of open water in Scotland (Table 10.7, Figure 10.7). Only gross changes arising from reservoir development were detectable in some areas. Other minor changes in open water features showed little or no statistical significance.

Table 10.7 Fresh water compositional changes, 1940s–1980s.

	Lochs		Reservoirs		Rivers		Canals		Marginal inundation		Wet ground	
	1940s went to (km²)	1980s came from (km²)	1940s went to (km²)	1980s came from (km²)	1940s went to (km²)	1980s came from (km²)	1940s went to (km²)	1980s came from (km²)	1940s went to (km²)	1980s came from (km²)	1940s went to (km²)	1980s came from (km²)
Rough grassland											146	230
Intermediate grassland												88
Blanket mire												82
Heather moorland												81
Lochs	114			114								
Reservoirs	73	73	24	82								
Others					83	78	3	3	33	44	339	113
(Unchanged area)	(1005)	(1005)	(126)	(126)	(146)	(146)	(4)	(4)	(12)	(12)	(85)	(85)
Total area	1193	1078	150	323	229	224	7	7	45	56	570	679

Notes • Gains and losses less than 70 km² have been grouped into 'Others'.
  • See Table 5.5 for explanation

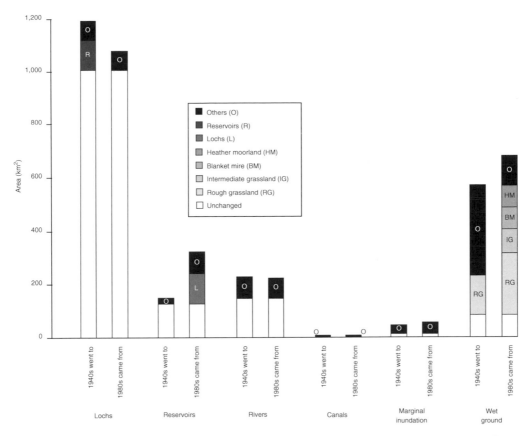

Figure 10.7 Fresh water compositional changes, 1940s–1980s. Note that gains and losses less than 70 km^2 have been grouped into 'Others'. See Figure 5.12 for full explanation.

References

1   Maitland, P.S., McLusky, D.S. and Boon, P.J. (1994). Integrating development and conservation. In Maitland, P.S., McLusky, D.S. and Boon, P.J. (eds). *The Fresh Waters of Scotland: A National Resource of International Significance*. Chichester: John Wiley & Sons.

2   Scottish Natural Heritage (1995). Fresh waters. In *The Natural Heritage of Scotland: An Overview*. Perth: Scottish Natural Heritage.

3   Butt, J. and Twidell, J. (1991). The power of Scotland. In: Magnusson, M. and White, G. (eds). *The Nature of Scotland: Landscape, Wildlife and People*. Edinburgh: Canongate Press plc.

4   MacDonald, T.D. (1994). Water supply. In Maitland, P.S., Boon, P.J. and McLusky, D.S. (eds) *The Fresh Waters of Scotland: A National Resource of International Significance*. Chichester: John Wiley & Sons.

5   Johnson, F.G. (1994). Hydro-electric generation. In Maitland, P.S., McLusky, D.S. and Boon, P.J. (eds). *The Fresh Waters of Scotland: A National Resource of International Significance*. Chichester: John Wiley & Sons.

6   Maitland, P.S. and Morgan, N.C. (1997). *Conservation Management of Freshwater Habitats: Lakes, Rivers and Wetlands*. London: Chapman & Hall Conservation Biology Series.

7   Howell, D.L. (1994). The role of environmental agencies. In Maitland, P.S., Boon, P.J. and McLusky, D.S. (eds). *The Fresh Waters of Scotland: A National Resource of International Significance*. Chichester: John Wiley & Sons.

11   BUILT AND BARE GROUND

The environment of towns and cities is now where most people in Scotland live, while advances in transport and communications have made once-remote parts of Scotland more accessible for development and recreation. The present-day Scottish population of 5.1 million people lives predominantly in the central lowlands (Figure 11.1), although growth rates have become especially rapid in the hinterlands of Aberdeen and Inverness. According to the 1988 land cover census, 97% of Scotland's land area is non-urban but about one-tenth of the population lives in rural areas.[1]

The NCMS classification of built and bare ground incorporated a range of features, from settlements and formal recreation ground in the countryside to naturally occurring scree and cliff.

11.1   Historical background

The cultural and natural heritage of Scotland has been radically altered by agricultural and industrial developments during the past 250 years. Broad tracts of wild, open land associated with remoteness today often would have supported farming communities in the past. A contracting agricultural labour force and a growing demand for industrial labour, especially around the coal and steel industries of the central belt, caused urban areas to expand and the rural population to fall from the 1850s onwards. At the beginning of the nineteenth century, one-fifth of the British population lived in towns. By the end of the century four-fifths were urban-based.[2]

Superimposed upon the landscape, the pattern of early towns and cities evolved in response to local circumstances. While the soils, vegetation, climate and hydrology of urban areas have been greatly modified,[3] relics of landscape features and wildlife habitats may survive as rivers and streams, fragments of ancient woods, moors and wetlands.[4] Vitally important to the quality of people's lives for leisure, health and environmental education, green spaces within urban settings may include remnants of ancient natural systems, pre-industrial encapsulated rural landscapes, town parks and private gardens, and naturally seeded urban or industrial sites.[5]

The plant and animal communities of urban areas are especially disadvantaged by habitat reduction, fragmentation, isolation and disturbance. Intensively managed mown grass for recreation, often improved by reseeding, fertilisers and weedkillers, is of low ecological value. Where less disturbed semi-natural vegetation is allowed to develop, a diversity of plants and animals can flourish.[6] Gardens and landscaped areas have resulted in an increase in invasive and introduced species.[7] Sometimes the most unpromising of derelict sites can be favourable for

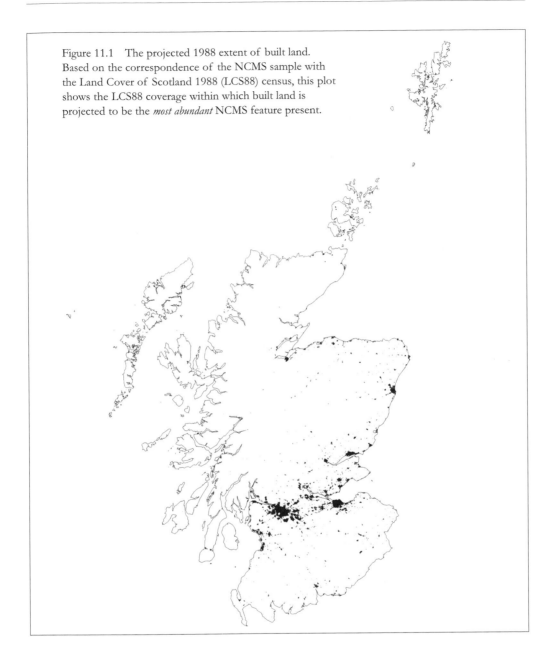

Figure 11.1   The projected 1988 extent of built land.
Based on the correspondence of the NCMS sample with
the Land Cover of Scotland 1988 (LCS88) census, this plot
shows the LCS88 coverage within which built land is
projected to be the *most abundant* NCMS feature present.

wildlife which is adapted to extreme environmental conditions of contamination and disturbance.[8]

The extent of road and railway is considerable. Where left relatively undisturbed, their verges can provide food plants for insects and refuges for mammals, reptiles and birds. Kestrels (*Falco tinnunculus*) commonly hunt over the broad verges of trunk roads and motorways, where dense herbage can support large numbers of small mammals. The plant communities and wild animals which they support are nevertheless vulnerable to numerous forms of disturbance, pollution and vegetation control. Roads and railways pose a barrier to the movement of species, and can fragment or isolate habitats through which they pass. 'Opportunities should therefore be explored for promoting a general policy of management of road verges in which the maximum wildlife interest is retained, consistent with the need to manage these habitats for other purposes.'[9]

Although frequently of earth science interest, active quarries tend to be highly disturbed, bare of vegetation, and therefore of low intrinsic ecological value. When redundant, however, quarry sites can provide a refuge for animals as they become partly flooded and colonised by plants, perhaps first by grasses and scrub, and subsequently by broadleaved woodland.

The extent to which naturally occurring or artificially created rock outcrops, cliffs and scree slopes become vegetated depends principally on the nature of the parent rock, altitude, climate, aspect and the stability of the substrate. In many cases the rock remains largely unvegetated, but cool, wet conditions in the western highlands favour colonisation by mosses, liverworts and lichens. Good air quality is vital to lichens and liverworts which are sensitive to air pollution, such as from sulphur dioxide emissions.

11.2 NCMS findings

Built and bare ground, as well as tracks, expanded over the study period (Table 11.1, Figure 11.2). The main growth took place in the Central Belt and Grampian region (Figure 11.3).

Table 11.1 Built and bare ground group: area and length estimates.

Feature	Area estimates 1940s (km²)	(%)	1970s (km²)	(%)	1980s (km²)	(%)	Net change 1940s–1980s (km²)	(% of 40s)	Sig.
Built	897	1	1214	2	1312	2	415	46	***
Recreation	71	0	140	0	168	0	98	138	***
Transport corridor	669	1	750	1	816	1	146	22	***
Quarry	45	0	71	0	92	0	47	104	
Rock	450	1	451	1	377	0	−73	−16	
Bare ground	42	0	70	0	219	0	177	418	**
Group total	2175	3	2696	3	2984	4	809	37	na

Feature	Length estimates 1940s (km)	(km/km²)	1970s (km)	(km/km²)	1980s (km)	(km/km²)	Net change 1940s–1980s (km)	(% of 40s)	Sig.
Tracks	29258	0.4	35952	0.5	37760	0.5	8501	29	***

Notes   • Only combined 1940s and 1970s results for built and transport corridor were available for Grampian and Lothian. The results include estimated areas for these regions.
• The km/km² column shows the average length of the feature per square kilometre of Scotland.
• See Table 5.1 for full explanation.

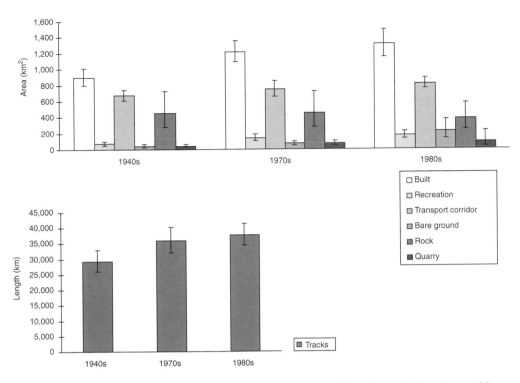

Figure 11.2   Built and bare ground composition (estimate and 95% confidence interval). Note that confidence intervals for area estimates cannot be used to assess the significance of net changes – refer to the relevant tables for net change.

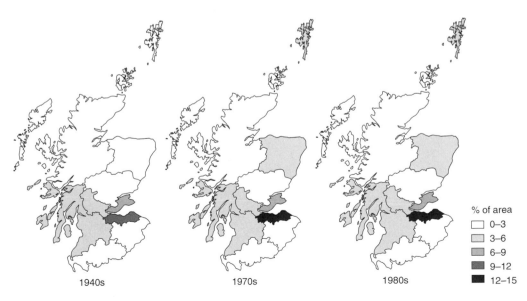

Figure 11.3   The pattern of geographical change for built land.

Built and bare ground summary *(see Table 11.1, Figure 11.2)*

1940s baseline

- about 3% of Scotland
- about 41% was built-up, 31% transport corridor and 21% rock
- 0.4 km/km² of tracks

1940s–1980s change

- increased in area by 37%
- expansion of built-up areas (46%), transport corridor (22%), recreation (138%) and bare ground (418%)
- tracks increased by 29% in overall length

1980s outcome

- about 4% of the area of Scotland
- 44% was built-up, 27% was transport corridor and 13% rock
- 0.5 km/km² of tracks

Table 11.2   Built-up areas: regional estimates (see Table 5.2 for explanation).

Region	Regional area (km²)	1940s (km²)	(%)	1970s (km²)	(%)	1980s (km²)	(%)	Net change 1940s–1980s (km²)	(% of 40s)	Sig.
Borders	4695	20	0	26	1	27	1	7	33	***
Central	2716	45	2	70	3	84	3	39	85	***
Dumfries & Galloway	6342	33	1	40	1	49	1	16	47	***
Fife	1377	60	4	85	6	92	7	32	54	***
Grampian	8686	(118)	1	(166)	2	169	2	(51)	43	(*)
Highland	24611	30	0	44	0	48	0	17	57	*
Lothian	1814	(152)	8	(196)	11	217	12	(65)	42	(***)
Strathclyde	14430	320	2	427	3	460	3	140	44	***
Tayside	7394	84	1	104	1	101	1	17	21	*
Orkney Islands	1115	12	1	12	1	11	1	−1	−7	
Shetland Islands	1810	18	1	40	2	47	3	29	163	
Western Isles	2847	5	0	5	0	8	0	3	59	*
Scotland	77837	(897)	1	(1214)	2	1312	2	(415)	46	***

Notes   • Only combined 1940s and 1970s results for built and transport corridor were available for Grampian and Lothian. The estimates in brackets assume the 1980s proportions of built and transport corridor.
• The significance of change shown for Grampian and Lothian is for built and transport corridor combined.

11.2.1 Built land

Built land in the NCMS classification referred to urban areas, including buildings, roads, gardens, parks and golf courses within the urban boundary, as well as isolated

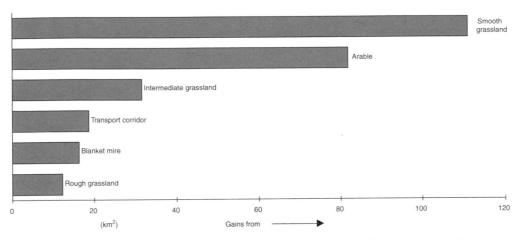

Figure 11.4   Built-up areas net gains and losses, 1940s–1980s (from matrices of interchange/excluding Grampian and Lothian). See Figure 5.4 for explanation.

Built land summary *(see Table 11.2, Figure 11.4)*

1940s baseline

- about 1.2% of Scotland
- relatively most abundant in Lothian (projected from 1980s estimate) and Fife (4%), least abundant in the Western Isles, Borders and Highland (all less than 0.5%)

1940s–1980s change

- increased in total area by 46%
- increases in most regions, most notably Central (85%)

Dynamics of change

- gains mostly from farmland but also from upland features

1980s outcome

- comprised about 1.7% of the area of Scotland
- relatively most abundant in Lothian (12%) and Fife (7%)
- less than 0.3% of the Western Isles and Highland

---

buildings outside urban areas. It increased by half of its 1940s extent (Table 11.2), mainly onto smooth or intermediate grassland and arable land (Figure 11.4).

11.2.2 Recreation land

Recreation land was taken to be land in the countryside, normally adjacent to urban areas, which was in formal recreation use. It included such features as playing fields, golf courses, camping and caravan sites, ski runs and motorcycle circuits.

Land Cover Change: Scotland from the 1940s to the 1980s

Recreation land doubled in area from the 1940s to the 1970s, and expanded by a further 20% to the 1980s (Table 11.3). Expansion was mainly onto former grassland or arable land (Figure 11.5).

Table 11.3   Recreation: regional estimates (see Table 5.2 for explanation).

Region	Regional area (km²)	1940s (km²)	(%)	1970s (km²)	(%)	1980s (km²)	(%)	Net change 1940s–1980s (km²)	(% of 40s)	Sig.
Borders	4695	4	0	6	0	7	0	3	80	
Central	2716	6	0	12	0	14	1	8	138	**
Dumf. & Gall.	6342	4	0	4	0	5	0	1	18	
Fife	1377	6	0	12	1	15	1	9	141	***
Grampian	8686	3	0	5	0	15	0	12	373	*
Highland	24611	1	0	4	0	4	0	3	625	
Lothian	1814	9	0	22	1	25	1	16	188	***
Strathclyde	14430	35	0	68	0	77	1	42	121	*
Tayside	7394	4	0	6	0	7	0	3	78	*
Orkney Islands	1115	0	0	0	0	0	0	0	0	
Shetland Islands	1810	0	0	0	0	1	0	1	764	
Western Isles	2847	0	0	0	0	0	0	0	88	
Scotland	77837	71	0	140	0	168	0	98	138	***

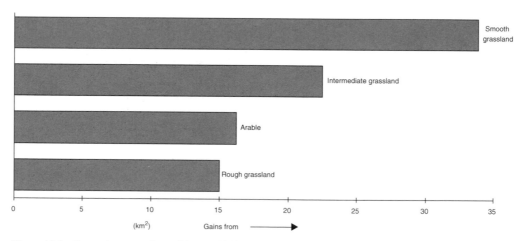

Figure 11.5   Recreation net gains and losses, 1940s–1980s (from matrices of interchange). See Figure 5.4 for explanation.

11.2.3 Transport corridor

Transport corridor referred mainly to roads, but included railways. Surfaced roads greater than 3 m in width which occurred outside built-up areas (greater than one

Recreation land summary *(see Table 11.3, Figure 11.5)*

1940s baseline

- less than 0.1% of the area of Scotland

- a minor feature in all regions, with about half found in Strathclyde

- very little in the Northern and Western Isles or Highland

1940s–1980s change

- increase in area of 138%

- increases in many regions, notably in Grampian (373%) and Lothian (188%)

Dynamics of change

- expanded onto grassland and arable land

1980s outcome

- about 0.2% of the area of Scotland

Transport corridor summary *(see Table 11.4, Figure 11.6)*

1940s baseline

- about 1% of the area of Scotland

- relatively most abundant in Central, Fife (both 2%) and Lothian (projected from 1980s estimate)

- least abundant in the Western Isles and Highland (both less than 0.5%)

1940s–1980s change

- increased in total area by 22%

- expanded on to farmland and open countryside

Dynamics of change

- expanded onto upland features and farmland

- reductions due to urban development

1980s outcome

- about 1% of the area of Scotland

- relatively most abundant in Central, Fife, Grampian, Lothian and the Orkney Islands (all about 2%)

building deep on either side of the road) were mapped as areal features. The land cover class included overbridges, carriageways, hard shoulders and other unvegetated roadway features. Where vegetated, roadside verges, cuttings and central reservations were classified according to their vegetation cover.

The area occupied by transport corridor increased by a fifth over the study period (Table 11.4), and some former transport corridor was incorporated within expanding settlements (Figure 11.6).

Table 11.4   Transport corridor: regional estimates.

Region	Regional area (km²)	1940s (km²)	(%)	Area estimates 1970s (km²)	(%)	1980s (km²)	(%)	Net change 1940s–1980s (km²)	(% of 40s)	Sig.
Borders	4695	39	1	40	1	41	1	3	8	
Central	2716	46	2	45	2	47	2	1	3	
Dumfries & Galloway	6342	60	1	63	1	81	1	22	36	***
Fife	1377	31	2	30	2	30	2	−2	−5	
Grampian	8686	(97)	1	(137)	2	139	2	(42)	43	(*)
Highland	24611	85	0	103	0	121	0	36	42	***
Lothian	1814	(31)	2	(40)	2	44	2	(13)	42	(***)
Strathclyde	14430	175	1	177	1	176	1	1	1	
Tayside	7394	65	1	68	1	82	1	17	26	*
Orkney Islands	1115	12	1	16	1	19	2	7	55	***
Shetland Islands	1810	15	1	16	1	18	1	3	18	
Western Isles	2847	14	0	16	1	18	1	4	28	
Scotland	77837	(669)	1	(750)	1	816	1	(146)	22	***

Notes
- See Table 5.2 for explanation.
- Only combined 1940s and 1970s results for built and transport corridor were available for Grampian and Lothian. The estimates in brackets assume the 1980s proportions of built and transport corridor.
- The significance of change shown for Grampian and Lothian is for built and transport corridor combined.

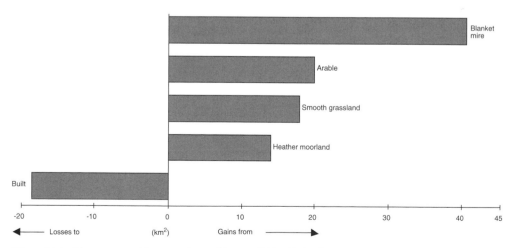

Figure 11.6   Transport corridor net gains and losses, 1940s–1980s (from matrices of interchange/excluding Grampian and Lothian). See Figure 5.4 for explanation.

Table 11.5   Tracks: regional estimates.

Region	Regional area (km²)	1940s (km)	1940s (km/km²)	1970s (km)	1970s (km/km²)	1980s (km)	1980s (km/km²)	Net change 1940s–1980s (km)	Net change 1940s–1980s (% of 40s)	Sig.
Borders	4695	1838	0.4	3476	0.7	4509	1.0	2671	145	***
Central	2716	1066	0.4	1607	0.6	1834	0.7	768	72	**
Dumfries & Galloway	6342	2009	0.3	3035	0.5	2698	0.4	689	34	*
Fife	1377	1525	1.1	1625	1.2	1367	1.0	−158	−10	
Grampian	8686	3610	0.4	3550	0.4	6532	0.8	2921	81	*
Highland	24611	6445	0.3	7899	0.3	5035	0.2	−1410	−22	
Lothian	1814	682	0.4	704	0.4	1106	0.6	423	62	***
Strathclyde	14430	6092	0.4	6898	0.5	8312	0.6	2220	36	***
Tayside	7394	3437	0.5	4743	0.6	3906	0.5	470	14	
Orkney Islands	1115	1264	1.1	1066	1.0	1051	0.9	−213	−17	***
Shetland Islands	1810	488	0.3	532	0.3	705	0.4	217	45	
Western Isles	2847	803	0.3	817	0.3	705	0.2	−98	−12	
Scotland	77837	29258	0.4	35952	0.5	37760	0.5	8501	29	***

Notes   • See Table 5.2 for explanation.
   • The km/km² column shows the average length of the feature per square kilometre of the region.

Tracks summary *(see Table 11.5)*

1940s baseline

- about 0.4 km of tracks per square km in Scotland
- especially dense in Fife and the Orkney Islands (both 1.1 km/km²), least so in Dumfries & Galloway, Highland, the Shetland Islands and the Western Isles (all 0.3 km/km²)

1940s–1980s change

- overall length increase of 29%
- increased in many regions, notably 145% in Borders and 81% in Grampian
- only notable decline in the Orkney Islands (17%)

1980s outcome

- about 0.5 km/km² on average in Scotland
- highest density in Borders and Fife (both 1 km/km²), least so in the Western Isles (0.2 km/km²)

11.2.4 Tracks

Unsurfaced tracks were mapped as linear features. Commonly associated with agricultural land, afforestation and upland areas, they were defined in the NCMS classification as (non-transient) routeways of up to 3 m width showing signs of use by wheeled vehicles. During the study period the length of track increased by nearly 30% (Table 11.5).

11.2.5 Quarry

Quarry included hard rock excavations, sand and gravel pits, open-cast mines and unvegetated spoil heaps. With minor expansion and contraction, an apparent overall increase was especially marked in Strathclyde (Table 11.6, Figure 11.7).

Table 11.6   Quarry: regional estimates (see Table 5.2 for explanation).

Region	Regional area (km²)	1940s (km²)	(%)	1970s (km²)	(%)	1980s (km²)	(%)	Net change 1940s–1980s (km²)	(% of 40s)	Sig.
Borders	4695	1	0	1	0	0	0	−1	−62	
Central	2716	3	0	4	0	3	0	−1	−16	
Dumf. & Gall.	6342	1	0	1	0	1	0	0	0	
Fife	1377	6	0	11	1	7	1	1	10	
Grampian	8686	2	0	4	0	3	0	1	32	
Highland	24611	2	0	7	0	1	0	−1	−56	
Lothian	1814	8	0	8	0	15	1	7	88	
Strathclyde	14430	18	0	27	0	59	0	41	219	
Tayside	7394	2	0	5	0	1	0	−1	−31	
Orkney Islands	1115	0	0	0	0	0	0	0	267	
Shetland Islands	1810	1	0	2	0	2	0	1	168	*
Western Isles	2847	0	0	1	0	0	0	0	−100	
Scotland	77837	45	0	71	0	92	0	47	104	

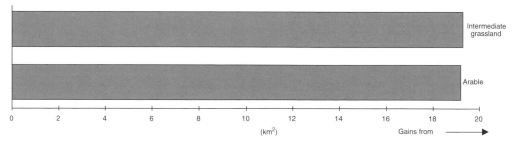

Figure 11.7   Quarry net gains and losses, 1940s–1980s (from matrices of interchange). See Figure 5.4 for explanation.

Quarry summary *(see Table 11.6, Figure 11.7)*

1940s baseline

- less than 0.1% of the area of Scotland
- a minor feature in all regions, with about 40% found in Strathclyde

1940s–1980s change

- a suggested increase in area of 104%
- increase in the Shetland Islands, based on small numbers, and suggested increase of 219% in Strathclyde

Dynamics of change

- some gains from farmland

1980s outcome

- about 0.1% of the area of Scotland
- nearly two-thirds was found in Strathclyde

Rock and cliff summary *(see Table 11.7, Figure 11.8)*

1940s baseline

- about 0.6% of the area of Scotland
- about 3% of the Western Isles and 1% of both Highland and Strathclyde; only small amounts found in the other regions

1940s–1980s change

- a suggested decline in area of 16%
- apart from a decline of 76% in Lothian, based on small numbers, there was a suggested decline of 40% in Strathclyde

Dynamics of change

- apparent losses to rough grassland and heather moorland

1980s outcome

- about 0.5% of the area of Scotland
- about 3% of the Western Isles and 1% of both Highland and Strathclyde; only small amounts found in the other regions

11.2.6 Rock and cliff

Rock and cliff were associated mostly with the uplands and included unquarried inland cliff, unvegetated rock and scree. Of very limited extent in Scotland, the definition also included limestone pavement. Due to the perspective of aerial photography, steeply inclined or vertical cliff faces, such as coastal cliff, were not represented. Results suggest only minor increases and decreases in rock and cliff (Table 11.7, Figure 11.8).

Table 11.7   Rock and cliff: regional estimates (see Table 5.2 for explanation).

Region	Regional area (km²)	1940s (km²)	(%)	1970s (km²)	(%)	1980s (km²)	(%)	Net change 1940s–1980s (km²)	(% of 40s)	Sig.
Borders	4695	0	0	0	0	0	0	0	−14	
Central	2716	1	0	1	0	1	0	0	−4	
Dumf. & Gall.	6342	4	0	4	0	1	0	−3	−72	
Fife	1377	0	0	0	0	0	0	0	−67	
Grampian	8686	8	0	7	0	7	0	−1	−12	
Highland	24611	160	1	160	1	162	1	2	1	
Lothian	1814	1	0	1	0	0	0	0	−76	*
Strathclyde	14430	176	1	176	1	106	1	−70	−40	
Tayside	7394	5	0	5	0	10	0	5	90	
Orkney Islands	1115	0	0	0	0	0	0	0	93	
Shetland Islands	1810	5	0	5	0	5	0	0	8	
Western Isles	2847	90	3	91	3	84	3	−6	−6	
Scotland	77837	450	1	451	1	377	0	−73	−16	

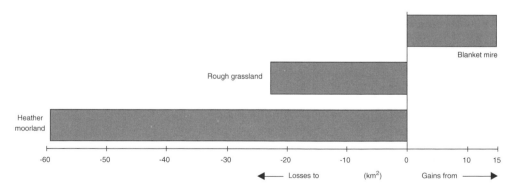

Figure 11.8   Rock and cliff net gains and losses, 1940s–1980s (from matrices of interchange). See Figure 5.4 for explanation.

11.2.7 Bare ground

Bare ground was land not covered by vegetation which did not fall into any other category. It represented a transition phase and included erosional features such as exposed gravel or soil in upland areas, but not temporarily bare arable land.

Although small in magnitude, bare ground expanded in every region, with a four-fold increase for Scotland as a whole. An increase from the 1970s to the 1980s was most distinct (Table 11.8, Figure 11.9). As bare ground often appeared

Table 11.8   Bare ground: regional estimates (see Table 5.2 for explanation).

Region	Regional area (km²)	1940s (km²)	(%)	1970s (km²)	(%)	1980s (km²)	(%)	Net change 1940s–1980s (km²)	(% of 40s)	Sig.
Borders	4695	0	0	2	0	5	0	4	1151	**
Central	2716	2	0	5	0	5	0	4	248	***
Dumfries & Galloway	6342	3	0	4	0	13	0	11	373	***
Fife	1377	2	0	3	0	7	0	5	329	**
Grampian	8686	1	0	4	0	11	0	11	1652	***
Highland	24611	18	0	16	0	95	0	76	416	
Lothian	1814	1	0	4	0	17	1	16	1276	***
Strathclyde	14430	7	0	20	0	35	0	28	405	***
Tayside	7394	1	0	2	0	11	0	10	1493	***
Orkney Islands	1115	0	0	1	0	1	0	1	285	***
Shetland Islands	1810	1	0	2	0	2	0	1	171	
Western Isles	2847	7	0	9	0	17	1	10	135	*
Scotland	77837	42	0	70	0	219	0	177	418	**

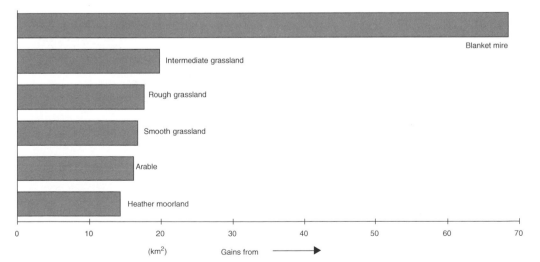

Figure 11.9   Bare ground net gains and losses, 1940s–1980s (from matrices of interchange). See Figure 5.4 for explanation.

Bare ground summary *(see Table 11.8, Figure 11.9)*

1940s baseline

• less than 0.1% of the area of Scotland

• a minor feature in all regions, with about 43% found in Highland

1940s–1980s change

• increase in area of 418%

• increases in most regions – notably in Grampian (1,652%), Tayside (1,493%) and Lothian (1,276%)

Dynamics of change

• biggest gains from mire and grassland

1980s outcome

• less than 0.3% of the area of Scotland

---

as small polygons, it may have shown up more clearly in the 1980s photography. Nevertheless, there were two identifiable reasons for the expansion of bare ground between the 1970s and the 1980s:

• in some locations, large areas of blanket mire or lowland mire were stripped of vegetation, possibly for peat extraction; and

• in many locations, especially on the periphery of urban areas or alongside new roads, bare ground appeared to be associated with construction activity.

11.2.8 Summary of changes in built and bare ground

The greatest change from the 1940s to the 1980s was an increase of 36% of the built land and transport corridor area (Table 11.9, Figure 11.10). This expansion was mainly from grassland and arable land. The area of recreational ground also expanded, as did quarry and bare ground.

Table 11.9   Built and bare ground compositional changes, 1940s–1980s.

	Built + transport corridor		Recreation		Quarry		Rock		Bare ground	
	1940s went to (km²)	1980s came from (km²)	1940s went to (km²)	1980s came from (km²)	1940s went to (km²)	1980s came from (km²)	1940s went to (km²)	1980s came from (km²)	1940s went to (km²)	1980s came from (km²)
Rough grassland		104								
Smooth grassland		302								
Heather moorland								112		
Arable		262								
Others	440	333	12	110	33	79	68	107	34	211
(Unchanged area)	(1127)	(1127)	(59)	(59)	(12)	(12)	(270)	(270)	(9)	(9)
Total area	1567	2128	71	168	45	92	450	377	42	219

Notes   • Gains and losses less than 100 km² have been grouped into 'Others'.
   • See Table 5.5 for explanation.

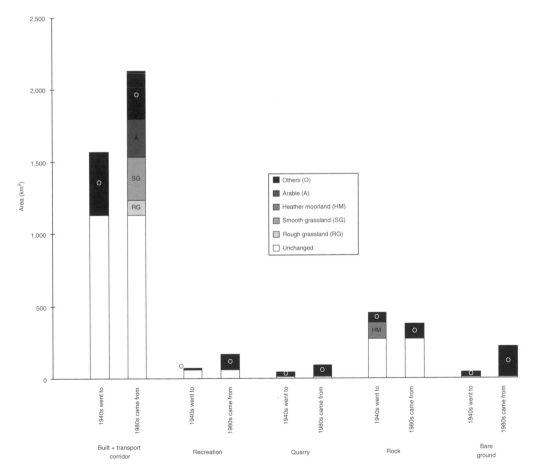

Figure 11.10   Built and bare ground compositional changes, 1940s–1980s. Note that gains and losses less than 100 km² have been grouped into 'Others'. See Figure 5.12 for full explanation.

A case study in urban growth

An example from a Central region square shows settlement and recreational ground expansion together with motorway development in an arable/grassland setting.

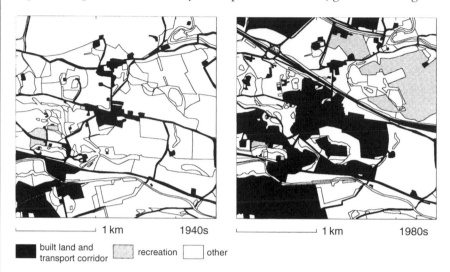

├────────┤ 1 km   1940s   ├────────┤ 1 km   1980s

■ built land and transport corridor   ▒ recreation   □ other

In this example a formerly farmland setting has been changed into one which became predominantly urban in character.

References

1   Government Statistical Service (1996). *The Scottish Environment Statistics, No.5*. Edinburgh: HMSO.

2   Marsden, T., Murdoch, J., Lowe, P., Munton, R. and Flynn, A. (1993). *Constructing the Countryside*. Restructuring Rural Areas 1. London: UCL Press Limited.

3   Gilbert, O.C. (1989). *The Ecology of Urban Habitats*. London: Chapman & Hall.

4   White, G. (1991). The greening of the cities. In: Magnusson, M. and White, G. (eds). *The Nature of Scotland: Landscape, Wildlife and People*. Edinburgh: Canongate.

5   McCall, A. and Doar, N. (1997). *The State of Scottish Greenspace*. Scottish Natural Heritage Review No. 88. Perth: Scottish Natural Heritage.

6   Johnston, J. (1990). *Nature Areas for City People*. Ecology Handbook 14. London: London Ecology Unit.

7   Spellerberg, I.F. (1991). *Monitoring Ecological Change*. Cambridge: Cambridge University Press.

8   Hough, M. (1984). *City Form and Natural Process*. London: Croom Helm.

9   Ratcliffe, D.A. (1977). *A Nature Conservation Review*. Cambridge: Cambridge University Press.

12 BRACKEN AND SCRUB

Bracken and scrub were both relatively minor features in the study. From the 1940s to the 1980s the extent of bracken increased appreciably, while there was a smaller increase in the extent of scrub (Table 12.1, Figure 12.1).

12.1 Bracken

In areas with a relatively mild climate, abundant rainfall and free-draining soils, bracken (*Pteridium aquilinum*) is a highly resilient invasive plant of rough grassland

Table 12.1 Bracken and scrub group (see Table 5.1 for explanation).

Feature	1940s (km²)	1940s (%)	1970s (km²)	1970s (%)	1980s (km²)	1980s (%)	Net change 1940s–1980s (km²)	Net change (% of 40s)	Sig.
Bracken	710	1	776	1	1268	2	558	79	***
Low scrub	442	1	441	1	446	1	4	1	
Tall scrub	192	0	220	0	240	0	48	25	*
Group total	1343	2	1437	2	1954	3	611	45	na

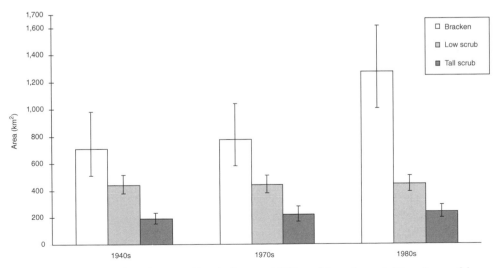

Figure 12.1 Bracken and scrub composition (estimate and 95% confidence interval). Note that confidence intervals for area estimates cannot be used to assess the significance of net changes – refer to the relevant tables for net changes.

Bracken and scrub group summary *(see Table 12.1, Figure 12.1)*

1940s baseline

- 2% of the area of Scotland was bracken or scrub
- of the total bracken and scrub area, just over half was bracken

1940s–1980s change

- increased in overall area by 45%
- bracken expanded by 80% and tall scrub by a quarter

1980s outcome

- 3% of the area of Scotland was bracken or scrub
- of the total bracken and scrub area, nearly two-thirds was bracken

and heather moorland.[1] It can form a dense canopy which is capable of suppressing other plant species. The spread of bracken across upland pastures has been favoured where wet fields have been drained or where a change from cattle to sheep production has reduced trampling and grazing pressure.

Bracken contains chemicals which are poisonous or carcinogenic. Large stands of bracken in a pasture reduce the grazing area of more palatable species. Ticks, often found in bracken litter, can carry sheep and grouse diseases, as well as Lyme's disease, which is debilitating to humans. Bracken has nectaries on its fronds which attract ants, which in turn protect it against leaf-eating insects. Coupled with the production of a variety of anti-herbivore chemicals, this results in bracken having a restricted invertebrate fauna.[2]

Land was classified as bracken where it dominated the ground cover. With its changing growth form through the year, the ability to identify bracken from air photographs is seasonally dependent. Bracken cannot be mapped under scrub or woodland, and can also be difficult to identify among grassland.

The study indicates that the extent of bracken in Scotland increased somewhat from the 1940s to the 1970s, but then expanded by 63% from the 1970s to the 1980s (Table 12.2, Figure 12.2), mainly on to rough grassland and heather moorland. Bracken expansion took place mainly in Strathclyde, Highland, Tayside and Dumfries & Galloway (Figure 12.3). The assessment of interpretational accuracy suggests that the extent of bracken was under-estimated throughout the study period and the increase in its area was over-estimated.

12.2 Scrub

Scrub was mapped by NCMS where woody plants, not exceeding 5 m in height, exceeded grassland cover. Grassland, scrub and woodland interchange during seral changes and nearly all unmanaged scrub communities will revert to wood-

Table 12.2   Bracken: regional estimates (see Table 5.2 for explanation).

Region	Regional area (km²)	1940s (km²)	(%)	1970s (km²)	(%)	1980s (km²)	(%)	Net change 1940s–1980s (km²)	(% of 40s)	Sig.
Borders	4695	12	0	13	0	63	1	50	404	**
Central	2716	40	1	62	2	58	2	18	45	
Dumfries & Galloway	6342	20	0	43	1	120	2	100	499	***
Fife	1377	1	0	3	0	2	0	1	127	
Grampian	8686	51	1	31	0	25	0	−26	−51	
Highland	24611	136	1	134	1	256	1	119	87	*
Lothian	1814	6	0	9	1	16	1	11	195	
Strathclyde	14430	337	2	368	3	506	4	168	50	*
Tayside	7394	104	1	113	2	222	3	118	114	
Orkney Islands	1115	2	0	0	0	2	0	−1	−32	
Shetland Islands	1810	1	0	0	0	0	0	−1	−100	
Western Isles	2847							(none found)		
Scotland	77837	710	1	776	1	1268	2	558	79	***

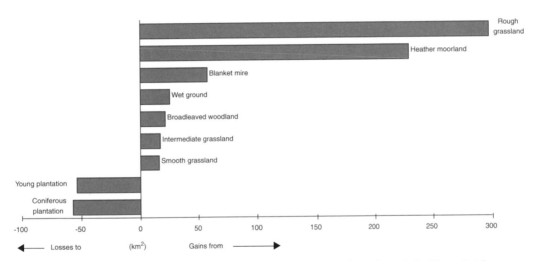

Figure 12.2   Bracken net gains and losses, 1940s–1980s (from matrices of interchange). See Figure 5.4 for explanation.

land. A climax scrub community occurs only where severe exposure retards tree growth, such as beyond the northern and altitudinal limits for tree survival, or in rocky or exposed maritime areas.[3]

Species forming scrub in the Scottish uplands include, most commonly, birch (*Betula* spp.), Scots pine (*Pinus sylvestris*), willows (*Salix* spp.), rowan (*Sorbus aucuparia*) and juniper (*Juniperus communis*). Less frequent are hazel (*Corylus avellana*), gorse (*Ulex europaeus*) and hawthorn (*Crataegus monogyna*). Through a long history of woodland clearance, burning and grazing, scrub in Scotland has become scarce and highly fragmented.[4]

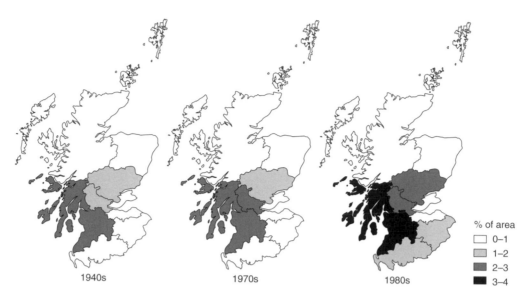

Figure 12.3   The pattern of geographical change for bracken.

Bracken summary *(see Table 12.2, Figure 12.2)*

1940s baseline

- about 1% of Scotland was bracken (probably under-estimated)
- relatively most abundant in Strathclyde (2%), with little found in the Western Isles, the Shetland Islands or Fife

1940s–1980s change

- 79% area expansion (probably over-estimated)
- notable increases in Dumfries & Galloway (499%), Borders (404%), Highland (87%) and Strathclyde (50%)

Dynamics of change

- biggest gains from rough grassland and heather moorland
- biggest reductions to afforestation

1980s outcome

- about 2% of the area of Scotland was bracken (probably under-estimated)
- relatively most abundant in Strathclyde (4%) and Tayside (3%), with little found in the Western Isles or the Shetland Islands

12.2.1 Low scrub

The NCMS interpretation of low scrub was an irregular canopy of trees or shrubs not exceeding 3 m in height. Characteristic species are bramble (*Rubus* spp.), juniper (*Juniperus* spp.), gorse (*Ulex* spp.) and broom (*Cytisus scoparius*). The overall extent of low scrub changed little (Table 12.3), with some encroachment onto heather moorland and grassland, but reduced by coniferous plantation (Figure 12.4).

Table 12.3   Low scrub: regional estimates (see Table 5.2 for explanation).

Region	Regional area (km²)	1940s (km²)	1940s (%)	1970s (km²)	1970s (%)	1980s (km²)	1980s (%)	Net change 1940s–1980s (km²)	Net change 1940s–1980s (% of 40s)	Sig.
Borders	4695	29	1	28	1	24	1	−6	−20	
Central	2716	15	1	16	1	17	1	2	13	
Dumf. & Gall.	6342	41	1	32	1	52	1	11	26	
Fife	1377	27	2	16	1	14	1	−12	−47	
Grampian	8686	128	1	156	2	113	1	−15	−12	
Highland	24611	41	0	51	0	39	0	−2	−4	
Lothian	1814	17	1	16	1	16	1	−1	−6	
Strathclyde	14430	66	0	64	0	127	1	61	92	**
Tayside	7394	76	1	62	1	42	1	−34	−45	
Orkney Islands	1115	1	0	0	0	0	0	−1	−94	
Shetland Islands	1810	0	0	0	0	0	0	0	−33	
Western Isles	2847	0	0	0	0	0	0	0	−100	
Scotland	77837	442	1	441	1	446	1	4	1	

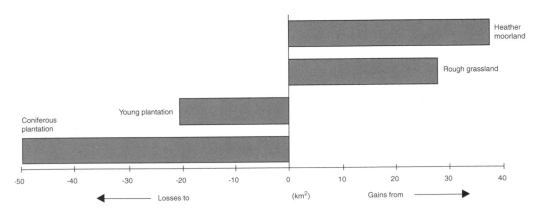

Figure 12.4   Low scrub net gains and losses, 1940s–1980s (from matrices of interchange). See Figure 5.4 for explanation.

Low scrub summary *(see Table 12.3, Figure 12.4)*

1940s baseline

- 0.6% of Scotland
- found in small amounts in all regions except the Orkney Islands, the Shetland Islands and the Western Isles

1940s–1980s change

- gains and losses with little overall change in area
- only statistically significant change was an increase in Strathclyde

Dynamics of change

- reduction to afforestation
- gains from heather moorland and rough grassland

1980s outcome

- little change since the 1940s

12.2.2 Tall scrub

The NCMS definition of tall scrub was a dense canopy of trees or shrubs of 3–5 m in height. Characteristic species are hawthorn (*Crataegus monogyna*), birch (*Betula* spp.), hazel (*Corylus avellana*), rhododendron (*Rhododendron ponticum*), elder (*Sambucus* spp.) and alder (*Alnus glutinosa*). Although afforestation replaced tall scrub in some areas, it expanded slightly in overall extent (Table 12.4, Figure 12.5).

In keeping with the low levels of change for this minor feature, the geographical distribution of scrub changed little over the study period (Figure 12.6).

12.3 Summary of changes in bracken and scrub

Bracken expanded appreciably (note interpretation difficulty), especially on to rough grassland and heather moorland. Scrub was a minor feature which changed little in overall extent. It was transitional in character with interchange evident among grassland, moorland and woodland features (Table 12.5, Figure 12.7).

Table 12.4   Tall scrub: regional estimates (see Table 5.2 for explanation).

Region	Regional area (km²)	1940s (km²)	(%)	1970s (km²)	(%)	1980s (km²)	(%)	Net change 1940s–1980s (km²)	(% of 40s)	Sig.
Borders	4695	21	0	12	0	10	0	−11	−52	
Central	2716	20	1	30	1	30	1	10	52	
Dumf. & Gall.	6342	19	0	20	0	15	0	−4	−19	
Fife	1377	6	0	6	0	7	0	1	12	
Grampian	8686	40	0	44	1	32	0	−7	−18	
Highland	24611	16	0	37	0	34	0	18	113	**
Lothian	1814	8	0	12	1	9	0	1	7	
Strathclyde	14430	39	0	36	0	81	1	42	109	***
Tayside	7394	24	0	24	0	22	0	−2	−8	
Orkney Islands	1115	0	0	0	0	0	0	0	0	
Shetland Islands	1810	0	0	0	0	0	0	0	100	
Western Isles	2847	0	0	0	0	0	0	0	−100	
Scotland	77837	192	0	220	0	240	0	48	25	*

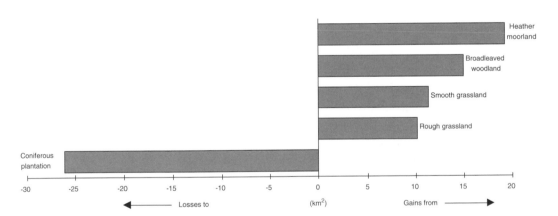

Figure 12.5   Tall scrub net gains and losses, 1940s–1980s (from matrices of interchange). See Figure 5.4 for explanation.

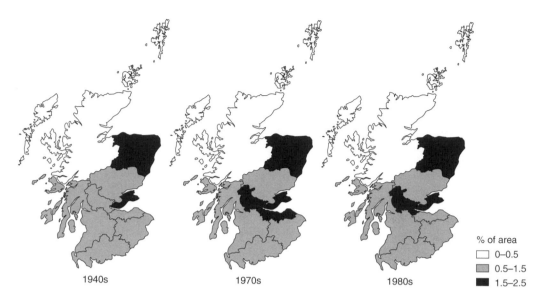

Figure 12.6   The pattern of geographical change for scrub.

Tall scrub summary *(see Table 12.4, Figure 12.5)*

1940s baseline

- less than 0.3% of Scotland
- found in small amounts in all regions except the Orkney Islands, the Shetland Islands and the Western Isles

1940s–1980s change

- 25% increase in area
- notable increases in Highland (113%) and Strathclyde (109%)

Dynamics of change

- biggest reduction to afforestation
- biggest gains from heather moorland, grassland and broadleaved woodland

1980s outcome

- small net expansion since the 1940s

Table 12.5   Bracken and scrub compositional changes, 1940s–1980s.

	Bracken		Low scrub		Tall scrub	
	1940s went to (km²)	1980s came from (km²)	1940s went to (km²)	1980s came from (km²)	1940s went to (km²)	1980s came from (km²)
Rough grassland	204	501	76	104		
Intermediate grassland		57	41	48		
Smooth grassland			46	52		
Blanket mire		71				
Heather moorland	44	273		49		
Broadleaved woodland		40				
Young + coniferous plantation	145		91		44	
Others	145	153	142	148	125	217
(Unchanged area)	(172)	(172)	(46)	(46)	(23)	(23)
Total area	710	1268	442	446	192	240

Notes   • Gains and losses less than 40 km² have been grouped into 'Others'.
• See Table 5.5 for explanation.

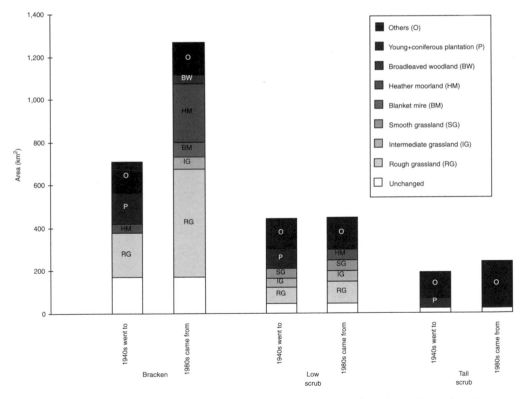

Figure 12.7   Bracken and scrub compositional changes, 1940s–1980s. Note that gains and losses less than 40 km² have been grouped into 'Others'. See Figure 5.12 for full explanation.

References

1   Marrs, R.H. and Pakeman, R.J. (1995). Bracken invasion: lessons from the past and prospects for the future. In Thompson, D.B.A., Hester, A.J. and Usher, M.B. (eds). *Heaths and Moorland: Cultural Landscapes*. Edinburgh: HMSO.

2   Birnie, R.V., Horne, P.L., Miller, D.R. and MacDonald, A. (1996). *Potential Impacts of Bracken Spread on Natural Heritage Features in Scotland*. Scottish Natural Heritage and Scottish Office Agriculture, Environment and Fisheries Department contract report.

3   Duffey, E., Morris, M.G., Sheail, J., Ward, L.K., Wells, D.A. and Wells, T.C.E. (1974). *Grassland Ecology and Wildlife Management*. London: Chapman & Hall.

4   Hester, A.J. (1995). *Scrub in the Scottish Uplands*. Scottish Natural Heritage Review, No. 24. Perth: Scottish Natural Heritage.

PLATE 1 THE NCMS METHOD

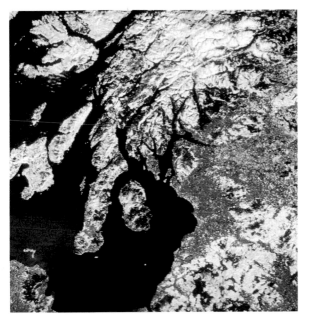

*Landsat multi-spectral scanner images were classified
into broad strata for random sampling.
(Strathclyde and Central regions. Photo: E. Hume).*

*Air photography, mainly panchromatic (black and white)
and at a scale of 1:24,000, provided land cover information
for dates around 1947, 1973 and 1988. (Caithness 1980s,
Highland region. Photo: Planning & Mapping Ltd).*

*Interpreted maps were drawn at
a scale of 1:10,000 before being
digitised for GIS processing.
(Gavin Tudor, NCMS Project
Manager. Photo: P. Shaw).*

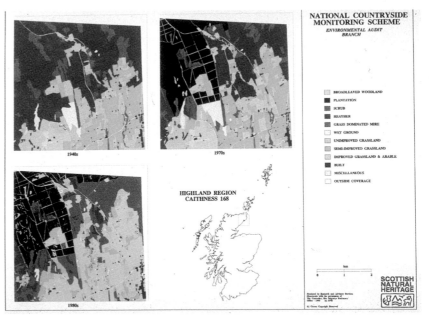

*Each of the 467 sample squares was mapped from 1940s, 1970s and 1980s
photography in order to estimate land cover stock and change. (Land cover change in a
Caithness square. Photo: P. Shaw).*

PLATE 2 FARMLAND

*Rough grassland decreased by around 10%,
mainly due to afforestation and grassland improvement.
(Rest and be Thankful, Strathclyde region. Photo: L. Gill).*

*Intermediate grassland increased by 15%, mainly from
rough grassland, heather moorland and drained mire.
(Mengaster Vow, Shetland Islands. Photo: L. Gill).*

*While grassland improvement took place, smooth grassland
nevertheless decreased by 11% mainly due to its conversion
to arable use or urban development.
(Galashiels, Borders region. Photo: L. Gill).*

*An 11% increase in the arable area, especially in
the east, was mainly at the expense of smooth grassland.
(Bankfoot, Tayside region. Photo: L. Gill).*

PLATE 3 MIRE AND MOORLAND

Blanket mire was interpreted as heather-dominated or grass-dominated. Overall it decreased by around 21%, mainly due to afforestation and drainage. (Rannoch Moor, Highland region. Photo: L. Gill).

Lowland mire decreased by around 44%, mainly due to afforestation and drainage. (Garnwath Moss, Strathclyde region. Photo: L. Gill).

A reduction of 23% in the area of heather moorland was due mainly to afforestation and conversion to rough grassland. (Tomintoul, Grampian region. Photo: L. Gill).

Regenerating the heather after 'muirburn', an essential element of heathland management, is included in the NCMS definition of heather moorland. (Glen Gairn, Grampian region. Photo: J. Macpherson).

PLATE 4 WOODLAND

Young coniferous plantation increased nine-fold and mature coniferous plantation increased more than four-fold, mainly on blanket mire, rough grassland and heather moorland. (Coniferous plantation at Glenshee, Tayside region. Photo: L. Gill).

Coniferous woodland decreased by 47%, mainly being replaced by coniferous plantation. (Cairngorms, Grampian region. Photo: L. Gill).

Broadleaved woodland decreased by 23%, mainly being replaced by coniferous plantations. (Strathspey, Grampian region. Photo: L. Gill).

As plantations reached maturity, felled woodland more than tripled in area. (Near Moneydie, Tayside region. Photo: L. Gill).

PLATE 5 BUILT LAND

*Built land increased by 46%, mainly on smooth grassland
and arable farmland. (Glasgow, Strathclyde region.
Photo: L. Gill).*

*The area of transport corridor increased by 22%, mainly
on mire, arable, smooth grassland and heather moorland.
(Edinburgh, Lothian region. Photo: L. Gill).*

*Recreational land increased by around 138%,
mainly on grassland and arable land.
(Gleneagles, Central region. Photo: L. Gill).*

*Bare ground increased four-fold, mainly related to peat
extraction on mire or urban and road development.
(Leatham Moss, Central region. Photo: L. Gill).*

PLATE 6 FRESH WATERS

Fresh water covered 3% of Scotland in both the 1940s and the 1980s. (Sutherland, Highland region. Photo: L. Gill).

The expansion of reservoirs by 115% replaced former lochs and moorland. (Loch Lyon, Strathclyde/Highland region. Photo: L. Gill).

BRACKEN AND SCRUB

(Above) A 79% increase (probably over-estimated) in bracken cover was mainly on rough grassland and heather moorland. (Creag Meagaidh, Highland region. Photo: L. Gill).

(Right) Tall scrub increased by 25% but the area of low scrub remained essentially unchanged. (Muir of Dinnet, Grampian region. Photo: F. MacPherson).

PLATE 7 LINEAR FEATURES

Hedgerow length was reduced by half, from over 40,000 km in the 1940s to under 20,000 km in the 1980s. (Moneydie, Tayside region. Photo: L. Gill).

The length of unsurfaced tracks increased by 29%. (Glen Bruar, Tayside region. Photo: L. Gill).

Lines of trees, associated with field boundaries, showed no significant change. (Near Bankfoot, Tayside region. Photo: L. Gill).

The length of ditches doubled, largely associated with mire drainage. (Plough lines in Caithness, Highland region. Photo: S. Moore).

PLATE 8 ENVIRONMENTAL EDUCATION

The lessons from the NCMS have been made available as curriculum support materials for schools in Scotland. (Land cover change poster. Photo: L. Gill).

13 HEDGEROWS AND TREES

13.1 Hedgerow

Enclosure was the most obvious aspect of agricultural change in the latter half of the eighteenth century and early years of the nineteenth. Whereas in England the enclosure of open-field arable land required a separate Act of Parliament for each parish, in Scotland the process of amalgamating the fragmented and intermixed strips and blocks of land was for the most part accomplished by landowners on their own estates.[1] Enclosures were bounded by open ditches in low-lying areas and elsewhere by hedges, commonly using quick-growing hawthorn (*Crataegus monogyna*). In many lowland areas walls were made of field stones thrown up by cultivation, but upland boundary dykes might be from stone quarried specifically for that purpose. Throughout the uplands, drystone dykes provided effective barriers and a means of using up large quantities of stones from the glacial tills. In some areas, such as Buchan, there was little enclosure until the second half of the nineteenth century, when they went often straight to barbed wire.

Small-scale field systems were incompatible with mechanisation. By occupying potentially productive land, hedges came to be viewed as an obstruction to agricultural efficiency. In the mid twentieth century grants became available for hedgerow removal.[2]

Countryside change brought about by hedgerow clearance stimulated concern for the broader value of hedges, in historical, landscape and wildlife terms. Hedge-species richness is related to the age of the hedge, climate, soil, management and other geographical factors. According to their structure and diversity, hedges can be important for food and shelter to invertebrates, birds, mammals, amphibians and reptiles.[3] The sunny edge of woodland is an especially favourable habitat for insects, and thus insectivorous birds. It is also important nesting habitat for many species of bird which feed on open ground. Hedges can serve as woodland edges, and may contain an abundance of fruit-bearing woodland-edge shrubs. Common woodland birds can become dependent on hedges for song-posts, and as structures in which to feed, roost, hide and nest.

The conservation of hedgerows for wildlife has most urgency in areas where deciduous woodland is absent or nearly so. Hedges can also be of landscape and archaeological value.[4]

The NCMS definition of hedgerow was a line of shrubs and trees less than 4 m in height and 5 m in width. It was classified as continuous if gaps were less than 10 m wide.

The survey indicates that the length of hedgerow in the 1980s was less than half of that in the 1940s (Table 13.1). Hedgerow clearance took place throughout Scotland, except in the Western and Northern Isles where hedges were rarely

Table 13.1   Hedgerows: regional estimates.

Region	Regional area (km²)	1940s (km)	1940s (km/km²)	1970s (km)	1970s (km/km²)	1980s (km)	1980s (km/km²)	Net change 1940s–1980s (km)	Net change 1940s–1980s (% of 40s)	Sig.
Borders	4695	4661	1.0	2138	0.5	1781	0.4	−2880	−62	***
Central	2716	4269	1.6	1879	0.7	1224	0.5	−3045	−71	
Dumfries & Galloway	6342	6156	1.0	4229	0.7	3104	0.5	−3051	−50	***
Fife	1377	3115	2.3	2113	1.5	1061	0.8	−2054	−66	***
Grampian	8686	8237	0.9	4761	0.5	2812	0.3	−5426	−66	***
Highland	24611	721	0.0	588	0.0	374	0.0	−348	−48	*
Lothian	1814	2860	1.6	1836	1.0	1570	0.9	−1290	−45	***
Strathclyde	14430	8585	0.6	5010	0.3	6054	0.4	−2531	−29	***
Tayside	7394	3944	0.5	2722	0.4	1444	0.2	−2500	−63	
Orkney Islands	1115	2	0.0	2	0.0	27	0.0	26	1683	
Shetland Islands	1810	5	0.0	4	0.0	11	0.0	5	99	
Western Isles	2847									
Scotland	77837	42556	0.5	25282	0.3	19463	0.3	−23093	−54	***

Notes   • The km/km² column shows the average length of the feature per square kilometre of the region.
• See Table 5.2 for full explanation.

Hedgerow summary *(see Table 13.1)*

1940s baseline

- total length exceeded 42,000 km

- on average there was about 0.5 km of hedgerow per square km in Scotland

- highest density in Fife (2.3 km/km²), Central and Lothian (both 1.6 km/km²)

- little found in the Western Isles, Orkney Islands or the Shetland Islands

1940s–1980s change

- overall length reduced by half

- Fife, Grampian and Borders lost about two-thirds of their hedgerow

1980s outcome

- average of about 0.3 km/km² in Scotland

- highest densities in Lothian (0.9 km/km²) and Fife (0.8 km/km²)

---

encountered. An exception to this is seen in results for Strathclyde, which showed an apparent increase in hedgerow length between the 1970s and the 1980s. That result, however, was due to better-quality 1980s photography and suggests that hedgerow length in the earlier periods (and certainly for Strathclyde in the 1970s) may have been underestimated.

Case study in hedgerow removal

A Borders square illustrates the way in which the small-scale intricacy of fields and hedgerows was changed when fields were enlarged:

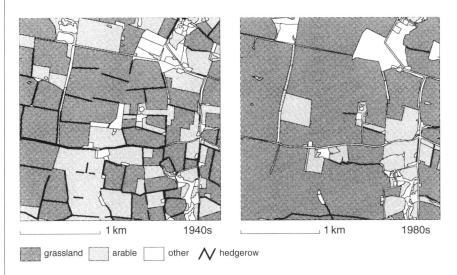

| | 1 km | 1940s | | 1 km | 1980s |

☐ grassland ☐ arable ☐ other ⋀ hedgerow

In a mixed grassland–arable setting, the square contained 80 km of hedgerow in the 1940s. The grassland area expanded, and field enlargement reduced the hedgerow length to 48 km in the 1970s and 30 km in the 1980s.

13.2 Lines of trees

As remnants of former woodland or amenity planting, or as relics of unkempt, gappy hedges, lines of trees are often encountered along field margins. The NCMS interpretation of lines of trees required a minimum of three trees, greater than 4 m in height and less than two canopy widths apart.

With notable regional differences, there was no significant change in the overall length of lines of trees from the 1940s to the 1980s (Table 13.2). Unusually in Highland, the length of lines of trees increased from the 1970s to the 1980s. This was due to the widespread appearance of many small lines of trees in the 1980s.

References

1   Whyte, I. and Whyte, K. (1991). *The Changing Scottish Landscape 1500–1800*. London: Routledge.
2   Pollard, E., Hooper, M.D. and Moore, N.W. (1974). *The New Naturalist: Hedges*. London: Collins.
3   Dowdeswell, W.H. (1983). *Hedgerows and Verges*. London: Allen & Unwin.
4   Ratcliffe, D.A. (ed.) (1977). A *Nature Conservation Review*. Cambridge: Cambridge University Press.

Table 13.2   Lines of trees: regional estimates.

Region	Regional area (km²)	1940s (km)	1940s (km/km²)	1970s (km)	1970s (km/km²)	1980s (km)	1980s (km/km²)	Net change 1940s–1980s (km)	Net change 1940s–1980s (% of 40s)	Sig.
Borders	4695	1796	0.4	1156	0.2	1406	0.3	−390	−22	
Central	2716	1311	0.5	1138	0.4	1033	0.4	−277	−21	
Dumf. & Gall.	6342	2089	0.3	1749	0.3	1971	0.3	−118	−6	
Fife	1377	1325	1.0	1063	0.8	992	0.7	−333	−25	**
Grampian	8686	2106	0.2	1988	0.2	2230	0.3	124	6	
Highland	24611	1128	0.0	978	0.0	1775	0.1	647	57	**
Lothian	1814	1288	0.7	1034	0.6	1192	0.7	−96	−7	
Strathclyde	14430	4280	0.3	4166	0.3	4741	0.3	461	11	
Tayside	7394	2278	0.3	2667	0.4	2118	0.3	−159	−7	
Orkney Islands	1115	1	0.0	1	0.0	8	0.0	7	772	**
Shetland Islands	1810	10	0.0	5	0.0	1	0.0	−9	−91	
Western Isles	2847					3	0.0	3		
Scotland	77837	17611	0.2	15946	0.2	17471	0.2	−140	−1	

Notes   • The km/km² column shows the average length of the feature per square kilometre of the region.
• See Table 5.2 for full explanation.

Lines of trees summary *(see Table 13.2)*

1940s baseline

- about 0.2 km of treeline per square km in Scotland

- highest density in Fife (1.0 km/km²) and Lothian (0.7 km/km²)

1940s–1980s change

- little change in overall length

- reduced in Fife (25%) but increased in Highland (57%) and the Orkney Islands (772%)

1980s outcome

- about 0.2 km/km² in Scotland

- highest density in Lothian and Fife (0.7 km/km²)

PART FOUR

GEOGRAPHICAL ANALYSIS OF REGIONAL VARIATION

Prior to local government reorganisation in April 1996, Scotland was administered as nine regions and three island councils, which were sub-divided into 53 districts. Thus during the life of the NCMS the regions defined by the Local Government (Scotland) Act 1973 served as administrative units for strategic planning and environmental reporting in Scotland.[1] They were also the divisions upon which statistics were systematically collected for and by the member states of the European Community.[2] Administrative regions were therefore adopted in the NCMS statistical design as the principal geographical unit for analysis and reporting.

Problems encountered in agreeing regional boundaries had testified to 'the great difficulty involved in creating a rational pattern of local government areas, especially in an area so diverse in terms of landscape, population distribution, economic character and historical heritage as Scotland'.[3] Regional differences in both land cover and rates of land cover change might therefore be expected in the results. For instance, land cover change (estimated for each region to be the proportional area which changed from the 1940s to the 1980s) took place throughout Scotland but the degree of change was greatest to the south and east, and least to the north and west (Part 4: Figure 1).

Another way of looking at this is to consider the persistence of long-established or semi-natural land cover. If rough grassland, mire, heather moorland, woodland and scrub are considered to be semi-natural in character then there was a reduction in semi-natural land cover throughout Scotland. The geographical pattern of change from the 1940s to the 1980s illustrates that semi-natural vegetation tended to be most preserved in regions which experienced relatively low levels of change (Part 4: Table 1, Figure 2).

In view of such geographical differences, a summary analysis of land cover change is presented in turn for each of the nine regions and the three islands councils.

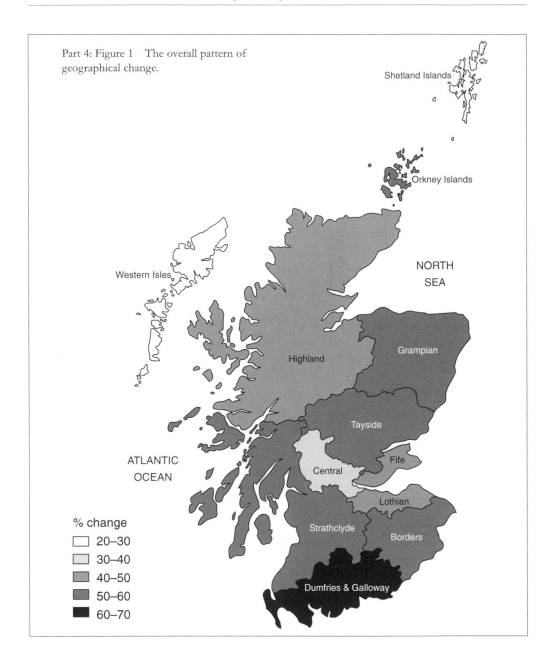

Part 4: Figure 1   The overall pattern of geographical change.

References

1   Government Statistical Service (1996). *The Scottish Environment Statistics*. Edinburgh: HMSO.
2   Commission of the European Communities (1991). *CORINE Biotopes Manual*: Data Specifications Part 1. Luxembourg: CEC.
3   Lea, K.J. (1977). *A Geography of Scotland*. Newton Abbot: David & Charles.

Part 4: Table 1   Semi-natural features: extent and change across Scotland.

Region	Regional area (km²)	1940s (km²)	1940s (%)	1970s (km²)	1970s (%)	1980s (km²)	1980s (%)	Net change 1940s–1980s (km²)	Net change 1940s–1980s (% of 40s)
Borders	4695	2573	55	1869	40	1494	32	−1079	−42
Central	2716	1690	62	1600	59	1437	53	−253	−15
Dumf. & Gall.	6342	3517	55	2405	38	2006	32	−1511	−43
Fife	1377	168	12	125	9	98	7	−69	−41
Grampian	8686	3912	45	3150	36	2959	34	−953	−24
Highland	24611	21979	89	20890	85	19426	79	−2553	−12
Lothian	1814	631	35	576	32	526	29	−105	−17
Strathclyde	14430	8754	61	7428	51	6417	44	−2338	−27
Tayside	7394	4531	61	4115	56	3872	52	−659	−15
Orkney Islands	1115	484	43	432	39	346	31	−138	−29
Shetland Islands	1810	1578	87	1500	83	1460	81	−118	−7
Western Isles	2847	2423	85	2393	84	2398	84	−25	−1
Scotland	77837	52240	67	46484	60	42439	55	−9800	−19

Notes • Semi-natural features have been defined as: rough grassland, blanket and lowland mire, heather moorland, broadleaved and coniferous woodland, low and tall scrub.
 • All areas are rounded to the nearest square kilometre.
 • Area percentages show the percentage of the region that is occupied by semi-natural features.
 • Net change percentages show the increase or reduction in semi-natural features as a percentage of their 1940s extent.

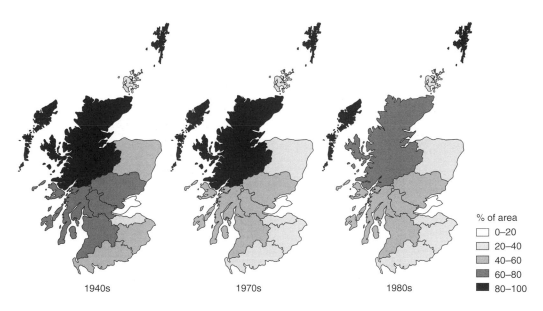

% of area
☐ 0–20
▨ 20–40
▨ 40–60
▨ 60–80
■ 80–100

1940s   1970s   1980s

Part 4: Figure 2   The pattern of geographical change for semi-natural land cover.

14 BORDERS

Borders region (Figure 14.1) is dominated by the Southern Uplands, except for the north-west of Tweeddale which crosses the Southern Upland fault and therefore falls within the Midland Valley. Broadly encompassing the catchment of the River Tweed to the southeast of Scotland, the districts of Berwickshire, Ettrick & Lauderdale, Roxburgh and Tweeddale had an estimated area of 4,695 km^2, representing 6% of the land area of Scotland. The 1994 population density in Borders region was about a third of the average for Scotland. Land capability for both agriculture and forestry was relatively favourable.[1]

Figure 14.1   Borders.

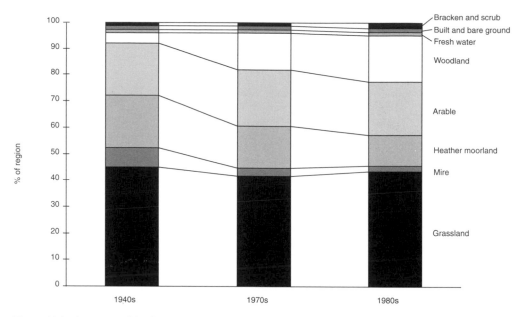

Figure 14.2   Summary of land cover change in Borders region.

Results from the study (Figure 14.2) indicate that the area of woodland expanded while the extents of mire and of heather moorland were reduced.

14.1   Increases

Detail is provided in Tables 14.1 and 14.2, from which it can be seen that coniferous plantation, intermediate grassland, bracken, built land, bare ground and broadleaved plantation all expanded in area. The length of tracks and ditches also increased.

14.2   Decreases

Rough grassland, heather moorland, blanket mire and lowland mire all contracted. The length of hedgerow was reduced.

Table 14.1   Land cover stock estimates for Borders region (total area: 4695 km^2).
See Table 4.1 for explanation.

Areal features

Feature group	Feature type	1940s (km^2)	(%)	1970s (km^2)	(%)	1980s (km^2)	(%)
Grassland	Rough grassland	1174	25	879	19	760	16
	Intermediate grassland	351	7	393	8	524	11
	Smooth grassland	581	12	676	14	755	16
	Group total	2105	45	1948	41	2039	43

continued

Table 14.1 — *continued*

Feature group	Feature type	1940s (km²)	(%)	1970s (km²)	(%)	1980s (km²)	(%)
Mire	Blanket mire	332	7	145	3	96	2
	Lowland mire	13	0	10	0	8	0
	Group total	345	7	155	3	104	2
Heather moorland	Heather moorland	939	20	742	16	546	12
	Group total	939	20	742	16	546	12
Arable	Arable	933	20	1010	22	946	20
	Group total	933	20	1010	22	946	20
Woodland	Broadleaved woodland	64	1	54	1	51	1
	Mixed woodland	33	1	26	1	24	1
	Broadleaved plantation	0	0	1	0	1	0
	Parkland	5	0	2	0	3	0
	Coniferous woodland	0	0	0	0	1	0
	Young plantation	7	0	305	6	300	6
	Coniferous plantation	66	1	269	6	418	9
	Felled woodland	9	0	5	0	31	1
	Group total	185	4	661	14	828	18
Fresh water	Lochs	5	0	4	0	5	0
	Reservoirs	4	0	8	0	8	0
	Rivers	10	0	10	0	10	0
	Canals	0	0	0	0	0	0
	Wet ground	41	1	30	1	32	1
	Marginal inundation	0	0	1	0	1	0
	Group total	61	1	53	1	56	1
Built and bare ground	Built	20	0	26	1	27	1
	Recreation	4	0	6	0	7	0
	Transport corridor	39	1	40	1	41	1
	Quarry	1	0	1	0	0	0
	Rock	0	0	0	0	0	0
	Bare ground	0	0	2	0	5	0
	Group total	64	1	74	2	81	2
Bracken and scrub	Bracken	12	0	13	0	63	1
	Low scrub	29	1	28	1	24	1
	Tall scrub	21	0	12	0	10	0
	Group total	62	1	52	1	96	2

Linear features

Feature type	1940s (km)	(km/km²)	1970s (km)	(km/km²)	1980s (km)	(km/km²)
Hedgerows	4661	1.0	2138	0.5	1781	0.4
Treeline	1796	0.4	1156	0.2	1406	0.3
Streams	6107	1.3	5825	1.2	6402	1.4
Ditches	1735	0.4	1813	0.4	3537	0.8
Tracks	1838	0.4	3476	0.7	4509	1.0

Table 14.2   Borders region land cover change, 1940s–1980s. Features ordered by magnitude of change (with statistically significant change judged at the 5% level). See Table 4.4 for explanation.

Areal features

Feature type	Lower (km²)	Change (km²)	Upper (km²)	(%)
Significant increases				
Coniferous plantation	173	353	532	535
Young plantation	152	292	432	4048
Intermediate grassland	57	173	289	49
Bracken	14	50	86	404
Built	3	7	10	33
Bare ground	2	4	7	1151
Broadleaved plantation	0	1	2	1463
Non-significant increases				
Smooth grassland	−48	174	396	30
Felled woodland	−16	22	60	255
Arable	−165	13	191	1
Reservoirs	−2	4	10	89
Transport corridor	−4	3	9	8
Recreation	−2	3	7	80
Marginal inundation	0	1	2	310
Coniferous woodland	*	1	*	1700
Canals	*	0	*	*
Non-significant decreases				
Rock	*	0	*	−14
Lochs	*	0	*	−1
Rivers	*	0	*	−5
Quarry	−1	−1	0	−62
Parkland	−8	−3	3	−50
Low scrub	−15	−6	3	−20
Mixed woodland	−25	−9	7	−27
Wet ground	−22	−9	4	−22
Tall scrub	−24	−11	2	−52
Broadleaved woodland	−28	−14	0	−21
Significant decreases				
Lowland mire	−9	−5	0	−37
Blanket mire	−427	−236	−46	−71
Heather moorland	−639	−394	−149	−42
Rough grassland	−711	−414	−117	−35

Linear features

Feature type	Lower (km)	Change (km)	Upper (km)	(%)
Significant increases				
Tracks	1383	2671	3960	145
Ditches	679	1802	2925	104
Non-significant increases				
Streams	−266	295	857	5

continued

Table 14.2 – *continued*

Feature type	Lower (km)	Change (km)	Upper (km)	(%)
Non-significant decreases				
Treeline	−813	−390	33	−22
Significant decreases				
Hedgerows	−4251	−2880	−1509	−62

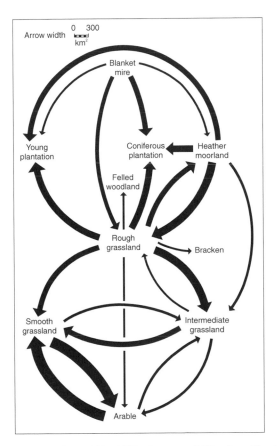

Figure 14.3   Borders: 1940s–1980s changes >0.5% of total land area.

14.3 Interchange

The interchange of gains and losses (Figure 14.3) shows that blanket mire, heather moorland and rough grassland were all reduced by afforestation. Blanket mire was further reduced by drainage, thereby being reclassified as heather moorland or rough grassland according to its dominant vegetation cover. There was interchange

Borders summary

1940s baseline

- 45% of Borders was grassland of which over half was rough

- 20% arable

- 20% heather moorland

- 7% was mire, almost all blanket mire

- 4% was woodland, 39% of which was young or mature plantation

- average of 1 km/km² of hedgerow and 0.4 km/km² of ditches and tracks

1940s–1980s change

- expansion in coniferous and young plantation (535% and 4,048%), intermediate grassland (49%) and bracken (404%)

- contraction in rough grassland (35%), heather moorland (42%) and blanket mire (71%)

- the length of tracks increased by 145% and ditches by 104%

- nearly two-thirds of hedgerow lost

Dynamics of change

- expansion of plantation mainly on to heather moorland, rough grassland and blanket mire

- heather moorland also lost out to rough and intermediate grassland

- trend towards grassland improvement

- rotation between arable and smooth grassland

- increase in bracken largely at the expense of rough grassland

1980s outcome

- Borders 43% grassland of which 37% was rough

- 20% was arable and 12% heather moorland

- 18% was woodland, 87% of which was young or mature plantation

- average of 0.4 km/km² of hedgerow, 1 km/km² of tracks and 0.8 km/km² of ditches

between heather moorland and rough grassland, with a tendency to grassland expansion at the expense of heather. Among the grassland transitions, there was a net tendency to grassland improvement.

References

1   Government Statistical Service (1996). *The Scottish Environment Statistics*. Edinburgh: HMSO.

15 CENTRAL

Central region (Figure 15.1) straddles the Highland boundary fault, one of the major cross-cutting faults of Scotland. To the south lies the Midland Valley, to the north the highlands. Central region comprised Stirling district, and the upper-Forth estuary bounded by Clackmannan and Falkirk. With an estimated area of 2,716 km², it represented 3.5% of the land area of Scotland. The 1994 population density was about 1.5 times the average for Scotland. Agricultural land capability was about average for Scotland as a whole, while land capability for forestry was relatively favourable.[1]

Results from the study (Figure 15.2) indicate that the area of woodland and scrub expanded while the grassland area was reduced.

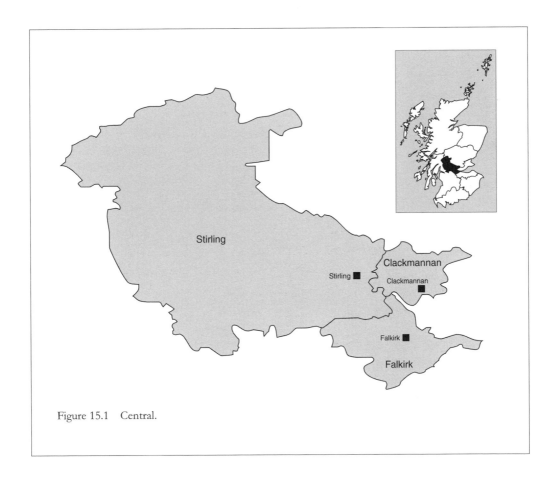

Figure 15.1   Central.

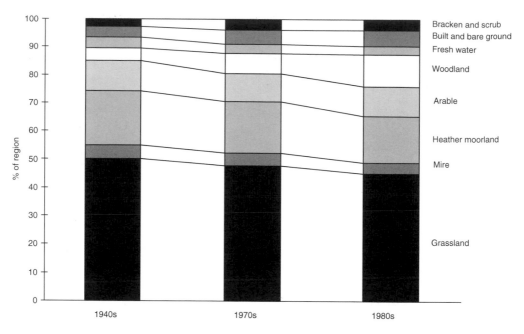

Figure 15.2   Summary of land cover change in Central region.

15.1 Increases

In Tables 15.1 and 15.2, it can be seen that features associated with urban development increased significantly and afforestation was substantial. The length of tracks increased.

15.2 Decreases

Rough grassland and heather moorland contracted. Results for hedgerow, lines of trees and streams suggest reductions.

Table 15.1 Land cover stock estimates for Central region (total area: 2716 km^2).
See Table 4.1 for explanation.

Areal features

Feature group	Feature type	1940s (km^2)	(%)	1970s (km^2)	(%)	1980s (km^2)	(%)
Grassland	Rough grassland	944	35	877	32	770	28
	Intermediate grassland	90	3	84	3	110	4
	Smooth grassland	332	12	338	12	340	13
	Group total	1365	50	1299	48	1220	45

continued

Table 15.1 – *continued*

Feature group	Feature type	1940s (km²)	(%)	1970s (km²)	(%)	1980s (km²)	(%)
Mire	Blanket mire – heather-dominated	69	3	68	3	68	2
	Blanket mire – grass-dominated	11	0	7	0	8	0
	Lowland mire	51	2	42	2	31	1
	Group total	131	5	118	4	107	4
Heather moorland	Heather moorland	519	19	498	18	449	17
	Group total	519	19	498	18	449	17
Arable	Arable	294	11	270	10	286	11
	Group total	294	11	270	10	286	11
Woodland	Broadleaved woodland	60	2	62	2	64	2
	Mixed woodland	23	1	20	1	22	1
	Broadleaved plantation	4	0	8	0	8	0
	Parkland	5	0	1	0	2	0
	Coniferous woodland	0	0	0	0	0	0
	Young plantation	13	0	33	1	118	4
	Coniferous plantation	17	1	70	3	92	3
	Felled woodland	0	0	0	0	3	0
	Group total	123	5	194	7	309	11
Fresh water	Lochs	14	1	14	1	14	1
	Reservoirs	50	2	51	2	49	2
	Rivers	8	0	8	0	8	0
	Canals	1	0	1	0	1	0
	Marginal inundation	0	0	0	0	2	0
	Wet ground	32	1	18	1	12	0
	Group total	105	4	92	3	86	3
Built and bare ground	Built	45	2	70	3	84	3
	Recreation	6	0	12	0	14	1
	Transport corridor	46	2	45	2	47	2
	Quarry	3	0	4	0	3	0
	Rock	1	0	1	0	1	0
	Bare ground	2	0	5	0	5	0
	Group total	104	4	137	5	154	6
Bracken and scrub	Bracken	40	1	62	2	58	2
	Low scrub	15	1	16	1	17	1
	Tall scrub	20	1	30	1	30	1
	Group total	75	3	108	4	105	4

Linear features

Feature type	1940s (km)	(km/km²)	1970s (km)	(km/km²)	1980s (km)	(km/km²)
Hedgerows	4269	1.6	1879	0.7	1224	0.5
Treeline	1311	0.5	1138	0.4	1033	0.4
Streams	6229	2.3	6123	2.3	6025	2.2
Ditches	4161	1.5	3782	1.4	4573	1.7
Tracks	1066	0.4	1607	0.6	1834	0.7

Table 15.2   Central region land cover change, 1940s–1980s. Features ordered by magnitude of change (with statistically significant change judged at the 5% level). See Table 4.4 for explanation.

Areal features

Feature type	Lower (km²)	Change (km²)	Upper (km²)	(%)
Significant increases				
Built	31	39	46	85
Recreation	3	8	13	138
Broadleaved plantation	2	4	6	108
Bare ground	2	4	6	248
Non-significant increases				
Young plantation	−5	105	215	781
Coniferous plantation	−11	74	160	436
Intermediate grassland	−51	20	92	23
Bracken	−27	18	63	45
Tall scrub	−3	10	23	52
Smooth grassland	−53	8	69	2
Broadleaved woodland	−18	4	26	7
Felled woodland	−2	3	7	2445
Low scrub	−9	2	13	13
Marginal inundation	−2	2	6	1050
Transport corridor	−18	1	21	3
Canals	0	0	0	13
Non-significant decreases				
Rock	*	0	*	−4
Rivers	−1	0	0	−2
Coniferous woodland	*	0	*	−50
Quarry	−5	−1	4	−16
Mixed woodland	−9	−1	7	−5
Blanket mire – heather-dominated	−6	−1	3	−2
Reservoirs	−6	−2	2	−3
Parkland	−5	−3	0	−53
Blanket mire – grass-dominated	−10	−3	3	−30
Arable	−40	−8	25	−3
Wet ground	−38	−19	0	−61
Lowland mire	−60	−20	20	−39
Significant decreases				
Lochs	0	0	0	−2
Heather moorland	−135	−71	−6	−14
Rough grassland	−324	−174	−23	−18

Linear features

Feature type	Lower (km)	Change (km)	Upper (km)	(%)
Significant increases				
Tracks	251	768	1285	72
Non-significant increases				
Ditches	−3422	412	4245	10

continued

Table 15.2 – *continued*

Feature type	Lower (km)	Change (km)	Upper (km)	(%)
Non-significant decreases				
Streams	−417	−204	9	−3
Treeline	−561	−277	7	−21
Hedgerows	−6512	−3045	423	−71

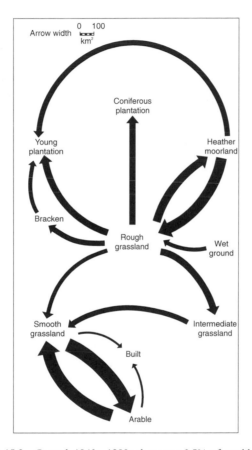

Figure 15.3   Central: 1940s–1980s changes >0.5% of total land area.

15.3 Interchange

Heather moorland and rough grassland were both reduced by afforestation (Figure 15.3). There was interchange between heather moorland and rough grassland, with a tendency to grassland expansion at the expense of heather. Wet ground was converted to rough grassland and bracken expanded on rough grassland. There was a tendency towards grassland improvement. Built land expanded onto smooth grassland and arable.

Central summary

1940s baseline

- half of Central was grassland of which about 70% was rough
- 19% heather moorland
- 11% arable
- 5% mire, of which 39% was lowland mire
- 5% woodland, 24% of which was plantation
- remainder consisted of built and bare ground (4%), water (4%) and bracken and scrub (3%)
- average of 1.6 km/km² of hedgerow, 1.5 km/km² of ditches and 0.4 km/km² of tracks

1940s–1980s change

- expansion in built (85%), recreational land (138%), broadleaved plantation (108%) and bare ground (248%)
- likely increases in coniferous and young plantation (436% and 781%)
- contraction in rough grassland (18%) and heather moorland (14%)
- likely decline in wet ground (61%)
- the length of tracks increased by 72%
- likely declines in hedgerows (71%) and lines of trees (21%)

Dynamics of change

- expansion of coniferous plantation, mainly on to rough grassland and heather moorland
- interchange between heather moorland and rough grassland
- grassland improvement as smooth gained from rough and intermediate, and intermediate gained from rough
- rotation between arable and smooth grassland
- bracken expanded on to rough grassland but some lost to plantation
- built land encroached on to arable and smooth grassland

1980s outcome

- 45% of Central was grassland, of which 63% was rough
- 17% was heather moorland
- 11% arable
- mire comprised 4%, of which 29% was lowland mire
- 11% was woodland, 68% of which was plantation
- the remainder consisted of built and bare ground (6%), bracken and scrub (4%) and water (3%)
- average of 0.5 km/km² of hedgerow, 1.7 km/km² of ditches and 0.7 km/km² of tracks

References

1   Government Statistical Service (1996). *The Scottish Environment Statistics*. Edinburgh: HMSO.

16 DUMFRIES & GALLOWAY

To the southwest of Scotland, Dumfries & Galloway (Figure 16.1) abuts the coast of the Solway Firth. The rivers Cree, Dee, Nith and Annan sub-divide the uplands of its northern regional boundary. Reflecting the northwest–southeast orientation of the river valleys, Dumfries & Galloway comprised the four districts of Wigtown, Stewartry, Nithsdale and Annandale & Eskdale. With an estimated area of 6,342 km^2, it represented 8% of the land area of Scotland. The 1994 population density was about a third of the average for Scotland. Land capability for both agriculture and forestry was relatively favourable.[1]

Results from the study (Figure 16.2) indicate that the areas of arable, woodland, and bracken and scrub all expanded. Heather moorland, mire and grassland were reduced.

Figure 16.1   Dumfries & Galloway.

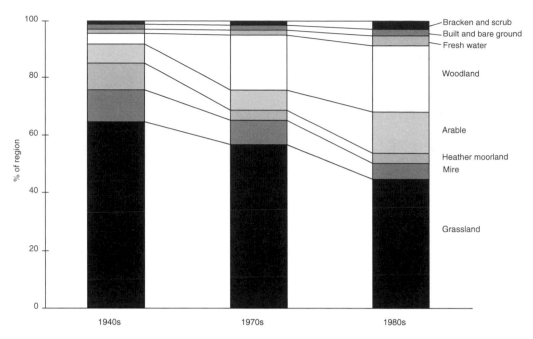

Figure 16.2   Summary of land cover change in Dumfries & Galloway region.

16.1   Increases

Tables 16.1 and 16.2 show that coniferous afforestation resulted in a five-fold expansion of the woodland area from the 1940s to the 1970s, and a lesser rate of expansion thereafter. The arable area doubled from the 1970s to the 1980s. Bracken doubled in area from the 1940s to the 1970s, with a further three-fold expansion from the 1970s to the 1980s. Features associated with urbanisation expanded. The length of ditches and tracks increased.

Table 16.1 Land cover stock estimates for Dumfries & Galloway region (total area: 6342 km^2).
See Table 4.1 for explanation.

Areal features

Feature group	Feature type	1940s (km^2)	(%)	1970s (km^2)	(%)	1980s (km^2)	(%)
Grassland	Rough grassland	2047	32	1526	24	1264	20
	Intermediate grassland	685	11	702	11	555	9
	Smooth grassland	1363	21	1372	22	1019	16
	Group total	4095	65	3600	57	2839	45
Mire	Blanket mire	660	10	523	8	333	5
	Lowland mire	48	1	20	0	9	0
	Group total	708	11	543	9	342	5

continued

Table 16.1 – *continued*

Feature group	Feature type	1940s (km²)	(%)	1970s (km²)	(%)	1980s (km²)	(%)
Heather moorland	Heather moorland	601	9	208	3	240	4
	Group total	601	9	208	3	240	4
Arable	Arable	414	7	456	7	900	14
	Group total	414	7	456	7	900	14
Woodland	Broadleaved woodland	91	1	72	1	91	1
	Mixed woodland	52	1	49	1	29	0
	Broadleaved plantation	1	0	4	0	6	0
	Parkland	19	0	12	0	2	0
	Coniferous woodland	10	0	3	0	2	0
	Young plantation	8	0	574	9	365	6
	Coniferous plantation	48	1	506	8	966	15
	Felled woodland	9	0	5	0	5	0
	Group total	238	4	1225	19	1466	23
Fresh water	Lochs	41	1	40	1	40	1
	Reservoirs	0	0	1	0	1	0
	Rivers	22	0	22	0	22	0
	Canals	0	0	0	0	0	0
	Marginal inundation	1	0	1	0	5	0
	Wet ground	37	1	34	1	151	2
	Group total	101	2	98	2	218	3
Built and bare ground	Built	33	1	40	1	49	1
	Recreation	4	0	4	0	5	0
	Transport corridor	60	1	63	1	81	1
	Quarry	1	0	1	0	1	0
	Rock	4	0	4	0	1	0
	Bare ground	3	0	4	0	13	0
	Group total	105	2	117	2	150	2
Bracken and scrub	Bracken	20	0	43	1	120	2
	Low scrub	41	1	32	1	52	1
	Tall scrub	19	0	20	0	15	0
	Group total	80	1	96	2	187	3

Linear features

Feature type	1940s (km)	(km/km²)	1970s (km)	(km/km²)	1980s (km)	(km/km²)
Hedgerows	6156	1.0	4229	0.7	3104	0.5
Treeline	2089	0.3	1749	0.3	1971	0.3
Streams	6994	1.1	7105	1.1	8672	1.4
Ditches	2429	0.4	4129	0.7	16982	2.7
Tracks	2009	0.3	3035	0.5	2698	0.4

Notes • Planted or self-sown conifers with an irregular appearance may have been interpreted as coniferous woodland.

Table 16.2   Dumfries & Galloway region land cover change, 1940s–1980s. Features ordered by magnitude of change (with statistically significant change judged at the 5% level). See Table 4.4 for explanation.

Areal features

Feature type	Lower (km²)	Change (km²)	Upper (km²)	(%)
Significant increases				
Coniferous plantation	709	919	1129	1934
Arable	321	486	651	118
Young plantation	184	357	530	4400
Wet ground	38	114	190	310
Bracken	41	100	158	499
Transport corridor	12	22	32	36
Built	9	16	22	47
Bare ground	7	11	14	373
Broadleaved plantation	0	5	10	511
Marginal inundation	2	3	5	284
Non-significant increases				
Low scrub	−4	11	26	26
Reservoirs	0	1	2	990
Recreation	0	1	2	18
Canals	*	0	*	*
Broadleaved woodland	−20	0	20	0
Non-significant decreases				
Rivers	−4	−1	3	−3
Lochs	−4	−1	1	−3
Rock	−8	−3	2	−72
Tall scrub	−10	−4	3	−19
Felled woodland	−14	−4	6	−44
Intermediate grassland	−426	−130	166	−19
Blanket mire	−706	−328	50	−50
Significant decreases				
Coniferous woodland	−15	−8	0	−79
Parkland	−30	−17	−5	−89
Mixed woodland	−37	−23	−10	−45
Lowland mire	−72	−39	−5	−81
Smooth grassland	−612	−343	−75	−25
Heather moorland	−700	−361	−23	−60
Rough grassland	−1203	−783	−363	−38

Linear features

Feature type	Lower (km)	Change (km)	Upper (km)	(%)
Significant increases				
Ditches	9680	14553	19426	599
Streams	547	1678	2809	24
Tracks	18	689	1360	34
Non-significant decreases				
Treeline	−429	−118	193	−6
Significant decreases				
Hedgerows	−4642	−3051	−1460	−50

Dumfries & Galloway summary

1940s baseline

- nearly two-thirds of Dumfries & Galloway was grassland of which half was rough
- 11% mire – over 90% was blanket mire
- 9% heather moorland
- 7% arable
- 4% woodland, of which 24% was plantation
- built and bare ground, fresh water and bracken and scrub made up the remaining 5%
- average of 1 km/km² of hedgerow and 0.4 km/km² of ditches

1940s–1980s change

- expansion in coniferous and young plantation (1,934% and 4,400%), arable (118%), wet ground (310%), bracken (499%) and built and transport corridor (47% and 36%)
- contraction in rough grassland (38%), heather moorland (60%), smooth grassland (25%) and lowland mire (81%) with a likely 50% reduction in blanket mire
- six-fold increase in the length of ditches
- hedgerows reduced by half

Dynamics of change

- expansion of coniferous plantation mainly on to rough grassland, heather moorland and blanket mire
- gains in rough grassland and heather moorland from blanket mire
- interchange between heather moorland and rough grassland
- tendency to grassland improvement as smooth gained from intermediate and intermediate gained from rough
- expansion in arable from smooth and intermediate grassland
- bracken and wet ground expanded on rough grassland

1980s outcome

- 45% of Dumfries & Galloway was grassland, of which almost half was rough
- 5% mire
- 4% heather moorland
- 14% arable
- 23% woodland, about 91% of which was coniferous plantation
- the remainder consisted of fresh water (3%), bracken and scrub (3%) and built and bare ground (2%)
- average of 0.5 km/km² of hedgerow and 2.7 km/km² of ditches

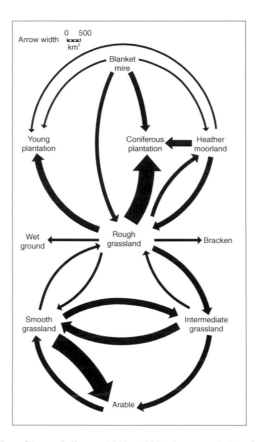

Figure 16.3   Dumfries & Galloway: 1940s–1980s changes >0.5% of total land area.

16.2   Decreases

Rough grassland, heather moorland, lowland mire and semi-natural or long-established woodland were reduced in area. Smooth grassland was also reduced. Results suggest that blanket mire was reduced by half. The hedgerow length was halved.

16.3   Interchange

The interchange of gains and losses (Figure 16.3) shows that blanket mire, heather moorland and rough grassland were all reduced by afforestation. Blanket mire was also converted to heather moorland or rough grassland through drainage. There was a degree of interchange between heather moorland and rough grassland, with a slight tendency to grassland expansion at the expense of heather. Bracken expanded on rough grassland. There was a net tendency to grassland improvement, with a substantial conversion of grassland to arable.

References

1   Government Statistical Service (1996). *The Scottish Environment Statistics*. Edinburgh: HMSO.

17 Fife

In eastern Scotland, the peninsula of Fife (Figure 17.1) is bordered to the north by the Firth of Tay and to the south by the Firth of Forth. The Ochil hills rise to the west, marked by the eastern extension of the Ochil fault. The gently rolling Fife countryside is punctuated by a series of basaltic 'laws'. Fife region was made up of the three districts of Dunfermline and Kirkcaldy on the north bank of the Firth of Forth, and North East Fife. With an estimated area of 1,377 km^2, it represented 2% of the land area of Scotland. The 1994 population density was about four times the average for Scotland. Land capability for both agriculture and forestry in Fife was highly favourable.[1]

Figure 17.1   Fife.

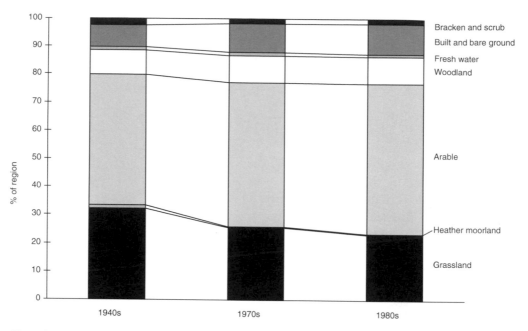

Figure 17.2   Summary of land cover change in Fife region.

Results from the study (Figure 17.2) indicate that the arable and built areas expanded, while the grassland and heather moorland areas contracted.

17.1   Increases

From Tables 17.1 and 17.2 it can be seen that the arable area increased by 15%. The built area expanded by 54%, with increases also in recreational and bare ground.

Table 17.1 Land cover stock estimates for Fife region (total area: 1377 km²).
See Table 4.1 for explanation.

Areal features

Feature group	Feature type	1940s (km²)	1940s (%)	1970s (km²)	1970s (%)	1980s (km²)	1980s (%)
Grassland	Rough grassland	88	6	73	5	51	4
	Intermediate grassland	87	6	60	4	117	9
	Smooth grassland	269	20	219	16	151	11
	Group total	444	32	352	26	319	23

continued

Table 17.1 – *continued*

Feature group	Feature type	1940s (km²)	(%)	1970s (km²)	(%)	1980s (km²)	(%)
Mire	Blanket mire – heather-dominated	0	0	0	0	0	0
	Blanket mire – grass-dominated	0	0	0	0	0	0
	Lowland mire	2	0	1	0	0	0
	Group total	2	0	1	0	1	0
Heather moorland	Heather moorland	15	1	5	0	5	0
	Group total	15	1	5	0	5	0
Arable	Arable	637	46	706	51	732	53
	Group total	637	46	706	51	732	53
Woodland	Broadleaved woodland	30	2	25	2	21	2
	Mixed woodland	16	1	11	1	12	1
	Broadleaved plantation	4	0	5	0	4	0
	Parkland	4	0	1	0	1	0
	Coniferous woodland	0	0	0	0	0	0
	Young plantation	13	1	10	1	17	1
	Coniferous plantation	54	4	79	6	66	5
	Felled woodland	2	0	2	0	13	1
	Group total	123	9	133	10	135	10
Fresh water	Lochs	1	0	1	0	1	0
	Reservoirs	9	1	9	1	9	1
	Rivers	1	0	1	0	0	0
	Canals	0	0	0	0	0	0
	Marginal inundation	0	0	0	0	0	0
	Wet ground	6	0	4	0	1	0
	Group total	17	1	15	1	12	1
Built and bare ground	Built	60	4	85	6	92	7
	Recreation	6	0	12	1	15	1
	Transport corridor	31	2	30	2	30	2
	Quarry	6	0	11	1	7	1
	Rock	0	0	0	0	0	0
	Bare ground	2	0	3	0	7	0
	Group total	106	8	142	10	151	11
Bracken and scrub	Bracken	1	0	3	0	2	0
	Low scrub	27	2	16	1	14	1
	Tall scrub	6	0	6	0	7	0
	Group total	34	2	24	2	23	2

Linear features

Feature type	1940s (km)	(km/km²)	1970s (km)	(km/km²)	1980s (km)	(km/km²)
Hedgerows	3115	2.3	2113	1.5	1061	0.8
Treeline	1325	1.0	1063	0.8	992	0.7
Streams	566	0.4	534	0.4	594	0.4
Ditches	1463	1.1	1435	1.0	1354	1.0
Tracks	1525	1.1	1625	1.2	1367	1.0

Table 17.2   Fife region land cover change, 1940s–1980s. Features ordered by magnitude of change (with statistically significant change judged at the 5% level). See Table 4.4 for explanation.

Areal features

Feature type	Lower (km²)	Change (km²)	Upper (km²)	(%)
Significant increases				
Arable	37	95	153	15
Built	22	32	43	54
Intermediate grassland	9	30	52	35
Recreation	5	9	13	141
Bare ground	2	5	8	329
Non-significant increases				
Coniferous plantation	−19	12	42	21
Felled woodland	−3	11	25	577
Young plantation	−7	5	16	36
Bracken	−1	1	3	127
Tall scrub	−2	1	3	12
Quarry	−5	1	7	10
Broadleaved plantation	−2	0	2	12
Blanket mire – grass-dominated	0	0	1	*
Coniferous woodland	*	0	*	11
Blanket mire – heather-dominated	*	0	*	*
Canals	*	0	*	*
Non-significant decreases				
Rock	*	0	*	−67
Marginal inundation	0	0	0	−20
Reservoirs	−1	0	1	−1
Lochs	0	0	0	−12
Rivers	−2	−1	0	−57
Transport corridor	−5	−2	1	−5
Mixed woodland	−8	−3	2	−22
Low scrub	−27	−12	2	−47
Significant decreases				
Lowland mire	−3	−2	0	−85
Parkland	−5	−3	0	−64
Wet ground	−7	−5	−2	−82
Broadleaved woodland	−15	−10	−4	−32
Heather moorland	−18	−10	−1	−66
Rough grassland	−55	−37	−18	−42
Smooth grassland	−180	−118	−57	−44

Linear features

Feature type	Lower (km)	Change (km)	Upper (km)	(%)
Non -significant increases				
Streams	−166	28	222	5
Non-significant decreases				
Ditches	−286	−109	68	−7
Tracks	−346	−158	29	−10
Significant decreases				
Treeline	−559	−333	−106	−25
Hedgerows	−2640	−2054	−1468	−66

Fife summary

1940s baseline

- 46% of Fife was arable
- 32% was grassland, of which 60% was smooth
- 9% was woodland, 54% of which was plantation
- 8% was built and bare ground, about 86% of which was built land or transport corridor
- the remainder was largely made up of heather moorland, fresh water (both 1%) and bracken and scrub (2%)
- average of 2.3 km/km^2 of hedgerows and 1 km/km^2 of treeline

1940s–1980s change

- expansion in arable (15%) and intermediate grassland (35%)
- expansion of features associated with urban development: built (54%), recreation (141%) and bare ground (329%)
- contraction in smooth grassland (44%) and semi-natural features: rough grassland (42%), heather moorland (66%) and broadleaved woodland (32%)
- hedgerows reduced by two-thirds and lines of trees by a quarter

Dynamics of change

- interchange between smooth grassland and arable with a net shift towards arable
- gains in intermediate grassland from smooth and rough grassland
- rough grassland lost to coniferous plantation and grassland improvement
- expansion in built land at the expense of arable and smooth grassland

1980s outcome

- over half of Fife was arable
- 23% was grassland, of which 47% was smooth
- 10% was woodland, about 61% of which was plantation
- 11% was built or bare ground, about 81% of which was built land or transport corridor
- the remainder was largely made up of bracken and scrub (2%) and fresh water (1%)
- average of 0.8 km/km^2 of hedgerows and 0.7 km/km^2 of treeline

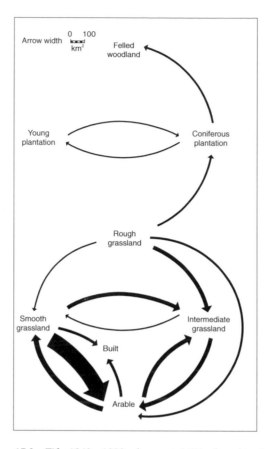

Figure 17.3 Fife: 1940s–1980s changes >0.5% of total land area.

17.2 Decreases

Smooth and rough grassland, heather moorland, broadleaved woodland, wet ground and lowland mire were reduced in area. The lengths of hedgerow and lines of trees decreased.

17.3 Interchange

The interchange of gains and losses (Figure 17.3) shows that rough grassland was afforested or converted to intermediate grassland, smooth grassland or arable. There was a substantial shift from grassland to arable. Built land expanded on to smooth grassland and arable land.

References

1   Government Statistical Service (1996). *The Scottish Environment Statistics*. Edinburgh: HMSO.

18   GRAMPIAN

Bounded by the Moray Firth to the north, and the North Sea to the east, Grampian region (Figure 18.1) embraced the headwaters of the rivers Dee and Don flowing to the east, and the lower Spey flowing to the north. The low-lying eastern plains contrast with the Grampian Mountains to the west, rising to Ben Macdui (1,038 m) in the Cairngorm Mountains. With an estimated area of 8,686 km[2], it represented 11% of the land area of Scotland. The 1994 population density was about 10% below the average for Scotland. Land capability for both agriculture and forestry in Grampian was moderately favourable.[1]

Figure 18.1   Grampian.

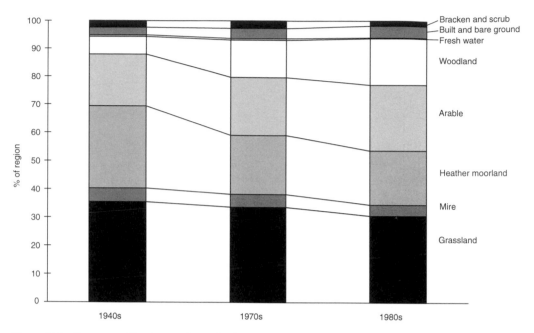

Figure 18.2   Summary of land cover change in Grampian region.

Results from the study (Figure 18.2) show a 1940s scene of mainly grassland, heather moorland, arable and woodland. The areas of arable and woodland expanded. Heather moorland and grassland were reduced.

18.1   Increases

Tables 18.1 and 18.2 indicate that coniferous plantation expanded considerably from the 1940s to the 1970s, and by a lesser extent thereafter. The arable area expanded by more than a quarter. Intermediate grassland increased in extent. Features associated with urbanisation expanded. The length of ditches and tracks increased.

Table 18.1 Land cover stock estimates for Grampian region (total area: 8686 km^2).
See Table 4.1 for explanation.

Areal features

Feature group	Feature type	1940s (km^2)	(%)	1970s (km^2)	(%)	1980s (km^2)	(%)
Grassland	Rough grassland	608	7	607	7	688	8
	Intermediate grassland	237	3	263	3	639	7
	Smooth grassland	2231	26	2045	24	1323	15
	Group total	3076	35	2916	34	2650	31

continued

Table 18.1 – *continued*

Feature group	Feature type	1940s (km²)	(%)	1970s (km²)	(%)	1980s (km²)	(%)
Mire	Blanket mire	406	5	397	5	355	4
	Lowland mire	7	0	5	0	2	0
	Group total	414	5	402	5	357	4
Heather moorland	Heather moorland	2536	29	1809	21	1647	19
	Group total	2536	29	1809	21	1647	19
Arable	Arable	1595	18	1803	21	2036	23
	Group total	1595	18	1803	21	2036	23
Woodland	Broadleaved woodland	180	2	129	1	113	1
	Mixed woodland	66	1	49	1	67	1
	Broadleaved plantation	1	0	1	0	3	0
	Parkland	9	0	25	0	22	0
	Coniferous woodland	6	0	3	0	9	0
	Young plantation	79	1	122	1	342	4
	Coniferous plantation	228	3	816	9	858	10
	Felled woodland	1	0	3	0	19	0
	Group total	571	7	1149	13	1433	16
Fresh water	Lochs	20	0	20	0	20	0
	Reservoirs	2	0	5	0	6	0
	Rivers	12	0	12	0	13	0
	Canals	0	0	0	0	0	0
	Marginal inundation	2	0	2	0	1	0
	Wet ground	11	0	14	0	12	0
	Group total	47	1	53	1	50	1
Built and bare ground	Built	(118)	1	(166)	2	169	2
	Recreation	3	0	5	0	15	0
	Transport corridor	(97)	1	(137)	2	139	2
	Quarry	2	0	4	0	3	0
	Rock	8	0	7	0	7	0
	Bare ground	1	0	4	0	11	0
	Group total	229	3	324	4	343	4
Bracken and scrub	Bracken	51	1	31	0	25	0
	Low scrub	128	1	156	2	113	1
	Tall scrub	40	0	44	1	32	0
	Group total	219	3	231	3	171	2

Linear features

	Feature type	1940s (km)	(km/km²)	1970s (km)	(km/km²)	1980s (km)	(km/km²)
	Hedgerows	8237	0.9	4761	0.5	2812	0.3
	Treeline	2106	0.2	1988	0.2	2230	0.3
	Streams	5931	0.7	5533	0.6	5932	0.7
	Ditches	2561	0.3	3424	0.4	8463	1.0
	Tracks	3610	0.4	3550	0.4	6532	0.8

Notes   • Only combined results for built and transport corridor were available for the 1940s and 1970s. The estimates in brackets assume the 1980s proportions of these features.

Table 18.2   Grampian region land cover change, 1940s–1980s. Features ordered by magnitude of change (with statistically significant change judged at the 5% level). See Table 4.4 for explanation.

Areal features

Feature type	Lower (km²)	Change (km²)	Upper (km²)	(%)
Significant increases				
Coniferous plantation	412	630	848	276
Arable	68	441	814	28
Intermediate grassland	247	402	557	170
Young plantation	100	263	427	334
Built + transport corridor	16	92	169	43
Felled woodland	3	17	31	1194
Parkland	4	12	21	131
Recreation	1	12	22	373
Bare ground	6	11	16	1652
Non-significant increases				
Rough grassland	−77	79	236	13
Reservoirs	−3	4	11	219
Coniferous woodland	−7	3	13	44
Broadleaved plantation	−1	2	6	373
Rivers	−1	1	3	9
Mixed woodland	−16	1	18	1
Quarry	−1	1	2	32
Wet ground	−6	1	7	5
Lochs	*	0	*	1
Non-significant decreases				
Canals	*	0	*	−100
Rock	−3	−1	1	−12
Lowland mire	−12	−6	1	−77
Tall scrub	−19	−7	5	−18
Low scrub	−49	−15	19	−12
Bracken	−53	−26	1	−51
Blanket mire	−120	−51	18	−13
Significant decreases				
Marginal inundation	−3	−2	0	−71
Broadleaved woodland	−96	−67	−38	−37
Heather moorland	−1193	−889	−586	−35
Smooth grassland	−1199	−908	−617	−41

Linear features

Feature type	Lower (km)	Change (km)	Upper (km)	(%)
Significant increases				
Ditches	4507	5903	7299	231
Tracks	282	2921	5560	81
Non-significant increases				
Treeline	−268	124	515	6
Streams	−731	1	733	0
Significant decreases				
Hedgerows	−7196	−5426	−3655	−66

Grampian summary

1940s baseline

- 35% was grassland, of which nearly three-quarters was smooth
- 29% heather moorland
- 18% arable
- 7% woodland, 54% of which was plantation
- the remainder was largely made up of mire (5%), built and bare ground (3%) and bracken and scrub (3%)
- average of 0.9 km/km^2 of hedgerows, 0.3 km/km^2 of ditches and 0.4 km/km^2 of tracks

1940s–1980s change

- expansion in young, coniferous and felled plantation (334%, 276% and 1,194% respectively)
- expansion of arable (28%) and intermediate grassland (170%)
- expansion of features associated with urban development: built and transport corridor (43%), recreation (373%) and bare ground (1,652%)
- contraction in smooth grassland (41%), heather moorland (35%) and broadleaved woodland (37%)
- hedgerow length was reduced by two-thirds
- ditches and tracks were extended by 231% and 81% respectively

Dynamics of change

- expansion of coniferous plantation, largely at the expense of heather moorland and rough grassland
- interchange between smooth grassland and arable with a net shift towards arable
- gains to intermediate grassland largely from smooth grassland and arable
- rough grassland expanded at the expense of heather moorland, smooth and intermediate grassland
- some mire drainage apparent in the loss to heather moorland
- expansion of built land at the expense of smooth grassland

1980s outcome

- 31% was grassland, of which nearly half was smooth
- 23% arable
- 19% heather moorland
- 16% woodland, about 84% of which was plantation
- remainder was largely made up of mire (4%) and built and bare ground (4%)
- average of 0.3 km/km^2 of hedgerows, 1 km/km^2 of ditches and 0.8 km/km^2 of tracks

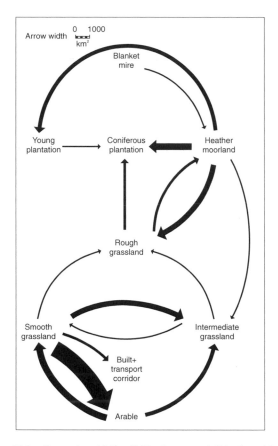

Figure 18.3   Grampian: 1940s–1980s changes >0.5% of total land area.

18.2 Decreases

Smooth grassland, heather moorland and broadleaved woodland each contracted by more than a third. The hedgerow length was reduced by two-thirds.

18.3 Interchange

The interchange of gains and losses (Figure 18.3) shows that blanket mire was partly converted to heather moorland (through drainage). Heather moorland and rough grassland were reduced by afforestation. There was interchange between heather moorland and rough grassland, with a tendency to grassland expansion at the expense of heather. Smooth grassland was lost to arable and to built land.

References

1   Government Statistical Service (1996). *The Scottish Environment Statistics*. Edinburgh: HMSO.

19 HIGHLAND

Extending from the Morvern peninsula on its southwest coast to the northern coast of mainland Scotland, Highland region (Figure 19.1) was characterised by mountains and coast. It comprised the eight districts of Badenoch & Strathspey, Caithness, Inverness, Lochaber, Nairn, Ross & Cromarty, Skye & Lochalsh, and Sutherland. With an estimated area of 24,611 km², it accounted for 32% of the land area of Scotland. The 1994 population density was about 12% of the

Figure 19.1   Highland.

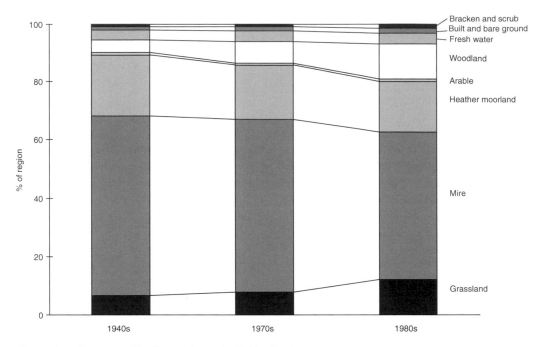

Figure 19.2 Summary of land cover change in Highland region.

average for Scotland. The land capability in Highland was mainly suited to rough grazing, with restricted potential for forestry.[1]

Results from the study (Figure 19.2) show a 1940s scene dominated by mire and heather moorland. Both were reduced, while the area of grassland and woodland expanded.

19.1 Increases

More detail is provided by Tables 19.1 and 19.2, from which it can be seen that coniferous plantation expanded considerably throughout the study period, as did rough grassland. The expansion of reservoirs was partly at the expense of former

Table 19.1 Land cover stock estimates for Highland region (total area: 24611 km^2).
See Table 4.1 for explanation.

Areal features

Feature group	Feature type	1940s (km^2)	(%)	1970s (km^2)	(%)	1980s (km^2)	(%)
Grassland	Rough grassland	925	4	1062	4	2222	9
	Intermediate grassland	365	1	446	2	337	1
	Smooth grassland	345	1	387	2	410	2
	Group total	1635	7	1896	8	2968	12

continued

Table 19.1 – *continued*

Feature group	Feature type	1940s (km²)	(%)	1970s (km²)	(%)	1980s (km²)	(%)
Mire	Blanket mire – heather-dominated	9113	37	8574	35	6859	28
	Blanket mire – grass-dominated	6006	24	6019	24	5587	23
	Lowland mire	17	0	12	0	9	0
	Group total	15136	61	14605	59	12455	51
Heather moorland	Heather moorland	5222	21	4603	19	4249	17
	Group total	5222	21	4603	19	4249	17
Arable	Arable	195	1	165	1	226	1
	Group total	195	1	165	1	226	1
Woodland	Broadleaved woodland	507	2	458	2	356	1
	Mixed woodland	120	0	108	0	48	0
	Broadleaved plantation	1	0	2	0	4	0
	Parkland	1	0	1	0	22	0
	Coniferous woodland	133	1	75	0	71	0
	Young plantation	175	1	705	3	1636	7
	Coniferous plantation	100	0	507	2	876	4
	Felled woodland	2	0	5	0	1	0
	Group total	1038	4	1861	8	3014	12
Fresh water	Lochs	613	2	550	2	525	2
	Reservoirs	34	0	141	1	181	1
	Rivers	103	0	98	0	100	0
	Canals	6	0	7	0	5	0
	Marginal inundation	28	0	31	0	25	0
	Wet ground	112	0	99	0	103	0
	Group total	896	4	926	4	940	4
Built and bare ground	Built	30	0	44	0	48	0
	Recreation	1	0	4	0	4	0
	Transport corridor	85	0	103	0	121	0
	Quarry	2	0	7	0	1	0
	Rock	160	1	160	1	162	1
	Bare ground	18	0	16	0	95	0
	Group total	296	1	333	1	430	2
Bracken and scrub	Bracken	136	1	134	1	256	1
	Low scrub	41	0	51	0	39	0
	Tall scrub	16	0	37	0	34	0
	Group total	193	1	222	1	329	1

Linear features

Feature type	1940s (km)	(km/km²)	1970s (km)	(km/km²)	1980s (km)	(km/km²)
Hedgerows	721	0.0	588	0.0	374	0.0
Treeline	1128	0.0	978	0.0	1775	0.1
Streams	51622	2.1	50737	2.1	50026	2.0
Ditches	25946	1.1	34333	1.4	27615	1.1
Tracks	6445	0.3	7899	0.3	5035	0.2

Table 19.2 Highland region land cover change, 1940s–1980s. Features ordered by magnitude of change (with statistically significant change judged at the 5% level). See Table 4.4 for explanation.

Areal features

Feature type	Lower (km²)	Change (km²)	Upper (km²)	(%)
Significant increases				
Young plantation	657	1461	2265	834
Rough grassland	890	1297	1704	140
Coniferous plantation	445	777	1109	780
Reservoirs	25	147	268	433
Bracken	26	119	212	87
Transport corridor	17	36	55	42
Parkland	6	21	36	1992
Tall Scrub	6	18	31	113
Built	3	17	31	57
Non-significant increases				
Bare ground	−40	76	193	416
Smooth grassland	−20	64	148	19
Arable	−11	31	73	16
Recreation	−1	3	8	625
Broadleaved plantation	−1	3	7	476
Rock	−24	2	27	1
Non-significant decreases				
Canals	−3	−1	2	−12
Felled woodland	−3	−1	1	−61
Quarry	−3	−1	0	−56
Low scrub	−20	−2	17	−4
Marginal inundation	−16	−2	11	−9
Rivers	−16	−3	10	−3
Lowland mire	−27	−9	10	−50
Wet ground	−62	−9	45	−8
Intermediate grassland	−116	−28	60	−8
Coniferous woodland	−161	−62	38	−47
Lochs	−184	−88	8	−14
Blanket mire – grass-dominated	−1922	−418	1085	−7
Significant decreases				
Mixed woodland	−137	−72	−6	−60
Broadleaved woodland	−225	−151	−76	−30
Heather moorland	−1610	−973	−336	−19
Blanket mire – heather-dominated	−3863	−2254	−645	−25

Linear features

Feature type	Lower (km)	Change (km)	Upper (km)	(%)
Significant increases				
Treeline	239	647	1055	57
Non-significant increases				
Ditches	−11286	1669	14623	6

continued

Table 19.2 – *continued*

Feature type	Lower (km)	Change (km)	Upper (km)	(%)
Non-significant decreases				
Tracks	−2864	−1410	44	−22
Streams	−6283	−1597	3090	−3
Significant decreases				
Hedgerows	−659	−348	−36	−48

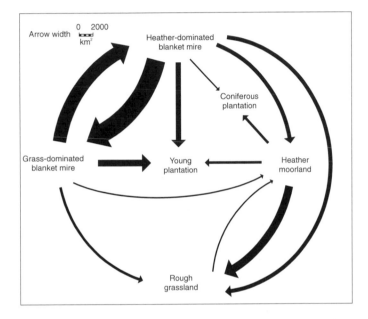

Figure 19.3   Highland: 1940s–1980s changes >0.5% of total land area.

lochs. Bracken, parkland and tall scrub all increased. The area of built land and transport corridor expanded. The length of lines of trees increased.

19.2 Decreases

Blanket mire and heather moorland were reduced in extent, as was broadleaved and mixed woodland. The length of hedgerow was reduced by almost half.

19.3 Interchange

There was appreciable interchange between heather-dominated and grass-dominated blanket mire, with a net tendency towards grass cover (Figure 19.3). Mire was partly converted to heather moorland or rough grassland (through drainage). Mire, heather moorland and rough grassland were all reduced by afforestation.

Highland summary

1940s baseline

- 61% was mire, almost all of which was blanket mire
- 21% heather moorland
- 7% grassland, of which 57% was rough
- 4% woodland, about a quarter of which was coniferous plantation
- remainder mainly fresh water (4%), of which two-thirds was lochs and 4% reservoirs
- less than 0.05 km/km^2 of hedgerows and treeline
- 1.1 km/km^2 of ditches and 0.3 km/km^2 of tracks

1940s–1980s change

- expansion in young and coniferous plantation (834% and 780%), rough grassland (140%), reservoirs (433%) and bracken (87%)
- contraction in heather-dominated blanket mire (25%), heather moorland (19%) and broadleaved and mixed woodland (30% and 60%)
- hedgerow length reduced by almost half, lines of trees extended by 57%

Dynamics of change

- substantial interchange between grass-dominated and heather-dominated blanket mire
- afforestation at the expense of blanket mire and heather moorland
- rough grassland expanded from heather moorland
- mire drainage also apparent

1980s outcome

- just over half was mire, almost all of which was blanket mire
- 17% heather moorland
- 12% grassland, of which three-quarters was rough
- 12% woodland, about 83% of which was plantation
- remainder mainly fresh water (4%), of which 56% was lochs and 19% reservoirs
- less than 0.05 km/km^2 of hedgerows and 0.1 km/km^2 treeline
- 1.1 km/km^2 of ditches and 0.2 km/km^2 of tracks

References

1   Government Statistical Service (1996). *The Scottish Environment Statistics*. Edinburgh: HMSO.

20 LOTHIAN

Flanking the coastal lowlands of the Firth of Forth and including the Edinburgh conurbation, Lothian region (Figure 20.1) extended from Lanark in the west to the North Sea coast in the east. To its southern boundary rise the Pentland, Moorfoot and Lammermuir Hills. It comprised the four districts of West Lothian, City of Edinburgh, Midlothian and East Lothian. With an estimated area of 1,814 km^2, it accounted for 2% of the land area of Scotland. The 1994 population density was about six times the average for Scotland. Land capability for both agriculture and forestry in Lothian region was highly favourable.[1]

Results from the study (Figure 20.2) show a 1940s scene which was predominantly grassland and arable, but with appreciable areas of heather moorland, built land and woodland. The area of built land expanded. Arable and grassland contracted. Unusually, the extent of heather moorland seemingly expanded from the 1970s to the 1980s.

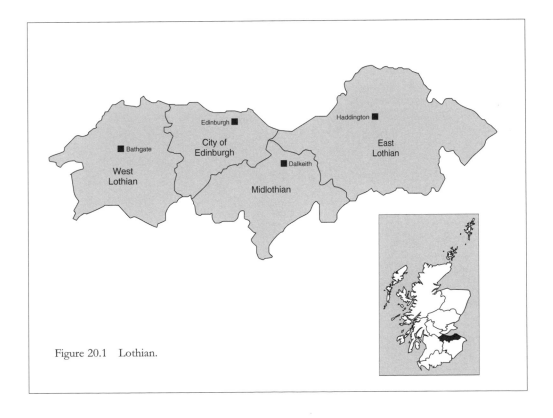

Figure 20.1   Lothian.

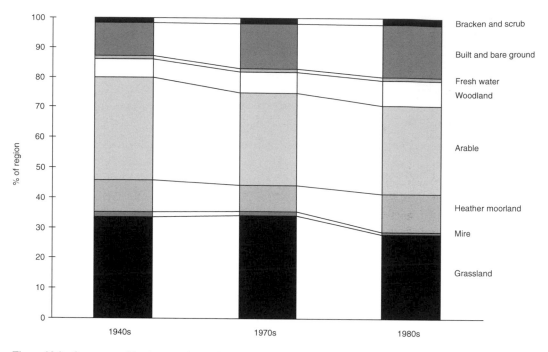

Figure 20.2   Summary of land cover change in Lothian region.

20.1   Increases

More detail is provided by Tables 20.1 and 20.2, from which it can be seen that features associated with urban development and disturbance expanded, as did coniferous plantation. The length of tracks increased.

Table 20.1   Land cover stock estimates for Lothian region (total area: 1814 km^2). See Table 4.1 for explanation.

Areal features

Feature group	Feature type	1940s (km^2)	(%)	1970s (km^2)	(%)	1980s (km^2)	(%)
Grassland	Rough grassland	317	17	320	18	209	12
	Intermediate grassland	128	7	125	7	133	7
	Smooth grassland	164	9	175	10	163	9
	Group total	610	34	620	34	505	28
Mire	Blanket mire	26	1	19	1	13	1
	Lowland mire	3	0	2	0	2	0
	Group total	28	2	22	1	14	1

continued

Table 20.1 – *continued*

Feature group	Feature type	1940s (km²)	(%)	1970s (km²)	(%)	1980s (km²)	(%)
Heather moorland	Heather moorland	194	11	158	9	231	13
	Group total	194	11	158	9	231	13
Arable	Arable	617	34	559	31	530	29
	Group total	617	34	559	31	530	29
Woodland	Broadleaved woodland	65	4	48	3	46	3
	Mixed woodland	9	1	8	0	8	0
	Broadleaved plantation	0	0	0	0	1	0
	Parkland	11	1	8	0	2	0
	Coniferous woodland	1	0	1	0	1	0
	Young plantation	2	0	37	2	31	2
	Coniferous plantation	21	1	21	1	62	3
	Felled woodland	0	0	1	0	1	0
	Group total	110	6	124	7	151	8
Fresh water	Lochs	0	0	0	0	1	0
	Reservoirs	13	1	13	1	13	1
	Rivers	3	0	3	0	3	0
	Canals	0	0	0	0	0	0
	Marginal inundation	1	0	1	0	1	0
	Wet ground	5	0	7	0	6	0
	Group total	22	1	24	1	24	1
Built and bare ground	Built	(152)	8	(196)	11	217	12
	Recreation	9	0	22	1	25	1
	Transport corridor	(31)	2	(40)	2	44	2
	Quarry	8	0	8	0	15	1
	Rock	1	0	1	0	0	0
	Bare ground	1	0	4	0	17	1
	Group total	201	11	271	15	318	18
Bracken and scrub	Bracken	6	0	9	1	16	1
	Low scrub	17	1	16	1	16	1
	Tall scrub	8	0	12	1	9	0
	Group total	31	2	37	2	41	2

Linear features

Feature type	1940s (km)	(km/km²)	1970s (km)	(km/km²)	1980s (km)	(km/km²)
Hedgerows	2860	1.6	1836	1.0	1570	0.9
Treeline	1288	0.7	1034	0.6	1192	0.7
Streams	1296	0.7	1280	0.7	1289	0.7
Ditches	904	0.5	798	0.4	1310	0.7
Tracks	682	0.4	704	0.4	1106	0.6

Notes   • Only combined results for built and transport corridor were available for the 1940s and 1970s. The estimates in brackets assume the 1980s proportions of these features.

Table 20.2   Lothian region land cover change, 1940s–1980s. Features ordered by magnitude of change (with statistically significant change judged at the 5% level). See Table 4.4 for explanation.

Areal features

Feature type	Lower (km²)	Change (km²)	Upper (km²)	(%)
Significant increases				
Built + transport corridor	49	78	107	42
Coniferous plantation	4	40	76	191
Recreation	8	16	25	188
Bare ground	7	16	24	1276
Non-significant increases				
Heather moorland	−51	36	123	19
Young plantation	−4	29	61	1210
Bracken	−5	11	26	195
Quarry	−6	7	20	88
Intermediate grassland	−41	5	50	4
Wet ground	−2	1	5	33
Tall scrub	−3	1	4	7
Broadleaved plantation	0	1	1	179
Coniferous woodland	−1	0	1	81
Felled woodland	0	0	1	79
Lochs	0	0	0	24
Canals	*	0	*	*
Non-significant decreases				
Reservoirs	−2	0	2	0
Rivers	−1	0	0	−6
Marginal inundation	−1	0	0	−31
Lowland mire	−2	−1	0	−24
Low scrub	−6	−1	4	−6
Mixed woodland	−4	−1	2	−12
Smooth grassland	−46	−1	43	−1
Blanket mire	−37	−13	10	−51
Significant decreases				
Rock	−1	0	0	−76
Parkland	−14	−9	−3	−80
Broadleaved woodland	−28	−20	−12	−30
Arable	−159	−87	−15	−14
Rough grassland	−193	−108	−22	−34

Linear features

Feature type	Lower (km)	Change (km)	Upper (km)	(%)
Significant increases				
Tracks	246	423	601	62
Non-significant increases				
Ditches	−64	406	875	45
Non-significant decreases				
Streams	−174	−7	160	−1
Treeline	−249	−96	57	−7
Significant decreases				
Hedgerows	−1863	−1290	−718	−45

21   STRATHCLYDE

Strathclyde region (Figure 21.1) was large and diverse, embracing the west coast and islands of Argyll, the Glasgow conurbation, and Ayrshire. It was divided into sampling districts of Ayrshire & Arran, Clyde Valley, Mid-Strathclyde, North Argyll, South Argyll, and Strathclyde islands (including Mull, Coll, Tiree and Islay). With an estimated area of 14,430 km^2, it accounted for 19% of the land area of Scotland. The 1994 population density was 2.5 times the average for Scotland. Land capability for agriculture and forestry in Strathclyde region was about average for Scotland as a whole.[1]

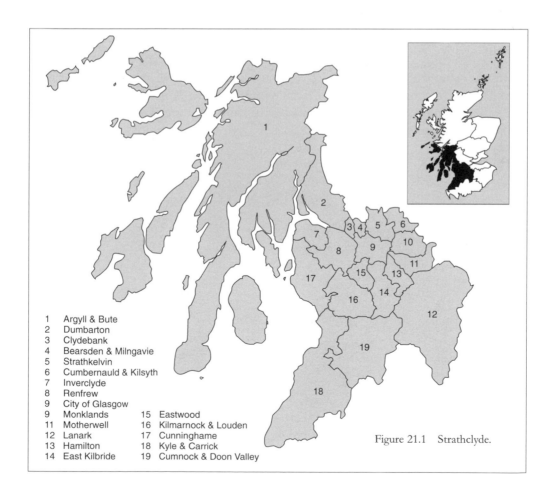

1   Argyll & Bute
2   Dumbarton
3   Clydebank
4   Bearsden & Milngavie
5   Strathkelvin
6   Cumbernauld & Kilsyth
7   Inverclyde
8   Renfrew
9   City of Glasgow
9   Monklands
11 Motherwell
12 Lanark
13 Hamilton
14 East Kilbride

15 Eastwood
16 Kilmarnock & Louden
17 Cunninghame
18 Kyle & Carrick
19 Cumnock & Doon Valley

Figure 21.1   Strathclyde.

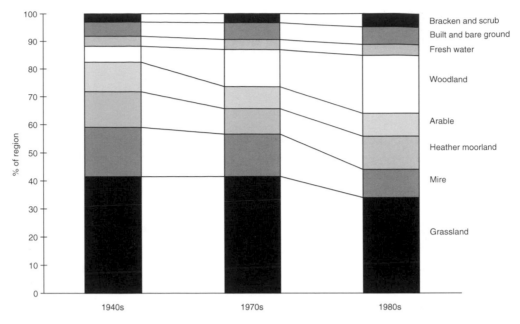

Figure 21.2 Summary of land cover change in Strathclyde region.

Results from the study (Figure 21.2) show a 1940s scene of extensive grassland, as well as mire, heather moorland, arable and woodland. The area of woodland expanded appreciably while the areas of grassland and mire contracted, especially from the 1970s to the 1980s.

21.1 Increases

Tables 21.1 and 21.2 show that features associated with afforestation and urban development expanded. The length of ditches and tracks also increased.

Table 21.1 Land cover stock estimates for Strathclyde region (total area: 14430 km²). See Table 4.1 for explanation.

Areal features

Feature group	Feature type	1940s (km²)	(%)	1970s (km²)	(%)	1980s (km²)	(%)
Grassland	Rough grassland	3811	26	3453	24	2705	19
	Intermediate grassland	729	5	838	6	749	5
	Smooth grassland	1441	10	1703	12	1445	10
	Group total	5981	41	5995	42	4898	34
Mire	Blanket mire – heather-dominated	905	6	701	5	551	4
	Blanket mire – grass-dominated	1555	11	1415	10	834	6
	Lowland mire	86	1	72	0	64	0
	Group total	2546	18	2188	15	1449	10

continued

Table 21.1 – *continued*

Feature group	Feature type	1940s (km²)	(%)	1970s (km²)	(%)	1980s (km²)	(%)
Heather moorland	Heather moorland	1832	13	1321	9	1697	12
	Group total	1832	13	1321	9	1697	12
Arable	Arable	1519	11	1140	8	1185	8
	Group total	1519	11	1140	8	1185	8
Woodland	Broadleaved woodland	409	3	346	2	339	2
	Mixed woodland	90	1	104	1	63	0
	Broadleaved plantation	11	0	8	0	7	0
	Parkland	23	0	12	0	8	0
	Coniferous woodland	52	0	20	0	19	0
	Young plantation	83	1	987	7	1494	10
	Coniferous plantation	161	1	391	3	1051	7
	Felled woodland	4	0	45	0	19	0
	Group total	831	6	1911	13	3000	21
Fresh water	Lochs	252	2	241	2	243	2
	Reservoirs	33	0	37	0	37	0
	Rivers	45	0	45	0	45	0
	Canals	0	0	0	0	0	0
	Marginal inundation	5	0	9	0	9	0
	Wet ground	212	1	180	1	240	2
	Group total	547	4	512	4	574	4
Built and bare ground	Built	320	2	427	3	460	3
	Recreation	35	0	68	0	77	1
	Transport corridor	175	1	177	1	176	1
	Quarry	18	0	27	0	59	0
	Rock	176	1	176	1	106	1
	Bare ground	7	0	20	0	35	0
	Group total	732	5	895	6	913	6
Bracken and scrub	Bracken	337	2	368	3	506	4
	Low scrub	66	0	64	0	127	1
	Tall scrub	39	0	36	0	81	1
	Group total	442	3	467	3	714	5

Linear features

Feature type	1940s (km)	(km/km²)	1970s (km)	(km/km²)	1980s (km)	(km/km²)
Hedgerows	8585	0.6	5010	0.3	6054	0.4
Treeline	4280	0.3	4166	0.3	4741	0.3
Streams	31352	2.2	31378	2.2	31719	2.2
Ditches	5656	0.4	6598	0.5	25388	1.8
Tracks	6092	0.4	6898	0.5	8312	0.6

Table 21.2   Strathclyde region land cover change, 1940s–1980s. Features ordered by magnitude of change (with statistically significant change judged at the 5% level). See Table 4.4 for explanation.

Areal features

Feature type	Lower (km²)	Change (km²)	Upper (km²)	(%)
Significant increases				
Young plantation	994	1410	1827	1694
Coniferous plantation	544	890	1236	552
Bracken	0	168	337	50
Built	70	140	210	44
Low scrub	21	61	100	92
Tall scrub	18	42	67	109
Recreation	5	42	79	121
Bare ground	13	28	44	405
Felled woodland	0	15	30	423
Non-significant increases				
Quarry	−39	41	120	219
Wet ground	−76	28	132	13
Intermediate grassland	−186	20	226	3
Marginal inundation	0	4	9	91
Smooth grassland	−349	4	357	0
Reservoirs	−8	3	14	10
Transport corridor	−10	1	12	1
Rivers	−2	1	4	2
Non-significant decreases				
Canals	−1	0	0	−53
Broadleaved plantation	−10	−4	3	−33
Lochs	−24	−9	5	−4
Parkland	−29	−14	0	−64
Lowland mire	−49	−22	4	−26
Mixed woodland	−59	−27	5	−30
Coniferous woodland	−88	−33	23	−63
Rock	−167	−70	27	−40
Heather moorland	−700	−135	430	−7
Arable	−677	−334	10	−22
Significant decreases				
Broadleaved woodland	−121	−70	−18	−17
Blanket mire – heather-dominated	−569	−354	−139	−39
Blanket mire – grass-dominated	−1061	−721	−381	−46
Rough grassland	−1659	−1107	−555	−29

Linear features

Feature type	Lower (km)	Change (km)	Upper (km)	(%)
Significant increases				
Ditches	15216	19732	24247	349
Tracks	1170	2220	3271	36
Non-significant increases				
Treeline	−267	461	1189	11
Streams	−1600	367	2333	1
Significant decreases				
Hedgerows	−3569	−2531	−1494	−29

Strathclyde summary

1940s baseline

- 41% was grassland, nearly two-thirds of which was rough
- 18% mire, almost all blanket mire
- 13% heather moorland
- 11% arable
- 6% woodland, 29% of which was plantation
- 5% built or bare ground, 44% of which was built land
- remainder comprised fresh water (4%) and bracken and scrub (3%)
- 0.6 km/km² of hedgerows and 0.3 km/km² treeline
- 0.4 km/km² of ditches and tracks

1940s–1980s change

- expansion in young, mature and felled plantation (1,694%, 552% and 423% respectively), features associated with urban development: built (44%), recreation (121%) and bare ground (405%) as well as low and tall scrub (92% and 109%) and bracken (50%)
- contraction in rough grassland (29%), heather- and grass-dominated blanket mire (39% and 46%) and broadleaved woodland (17%)
- hedgerow length reduced by 29%
- ditches and tracks extended by 349% and 36% respectively

dynamics of change

- afforestation at the expense of heather moorland, rough grassland and blanket mire
- blanket mire also lost to heather moorland and rough grassland through drainage
- substantial interchange between heather moorland and rough grassland
- rough grassland lost to bracken and wet ground
- substantial rotation between arable and smooth grassland
- expansion of built from smooth grassland

1980s outcome

- 34% was grassland, 55% of which was rough
- 10% mire
- 12% heather moorland
- 8% arable
- 21% woodland, 85% of which was plantation
- 6% built or bare ground, half of which was built land
- remainder comprised bracken and scrub (5%) and fresh water (4%)
- 0.4 km/km² of hedgerows and 0.3 km/km² treeline
- 1.8 km/km² of ditches and 0.6 km/km² tracks

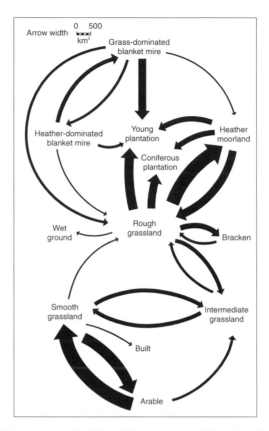

Figure 21.3   Strathclyde: 1940s–1980s changes >0.5% of total land area.

21.2 Decreases

Rough grassland, mire and semi-natural woodland were all reduced in extent. Results suggest that arable land and heather moorland were also reduced, although heather moorland recovered from the 1970s to the 1980s. The length of hedgerow was reduced by almost a third.

21.3 Interchange

The interchange of gains and losses (Figure 21.3) shows that mire was reduced mainly by afforestation, although some conversion to rough grassland or heather moorland also occurred (due to drainage). Heather moorland and rough grassland were reduced by afforestation. The interchange between rough grassland and heather moorland was in favour of heather moorland expansion at the expense of rough grassland. Bracken expanded on to rough grassland. Interchange between grassland and arable was in favour of grassland.

References

1   Government Statistical Service (1996). *The Scottish Environment Statistics*. Edinburgh: HMSO.

22   TAYSIDE

Tayside region (Figure 22.1) encompassed the catchment and river system of the River Tay, from the watershed in the Grampian Mountains to the northern coast of the Firth of Tay. It comprised the three districts of Perth & Kinross, the City of Dundee and Angus. With an estimated area of 7,394 km^2, it accounted for 9% of the land area of Scotland. The 1994 population density was about four-fifths of the average for Scotland. Land capability for agriculture and forestry in Tayside was highly favourable.[1]

Results from the study (Figure 22.2) show a 1940s scene of extensive grassland, heather moorland and arable, with lesser expanses of mire and woodland. Woodland expanded from the 1940s to 1970s, and the arable area expanded from the 1970s to the 1980s. The extent of heather moorland contracted appreciably.

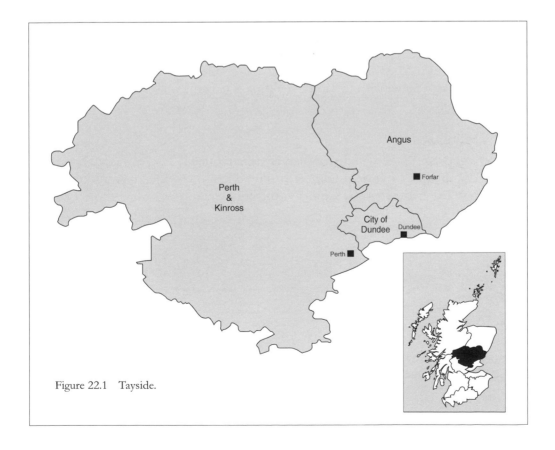

Figure 22.1   Tayside.

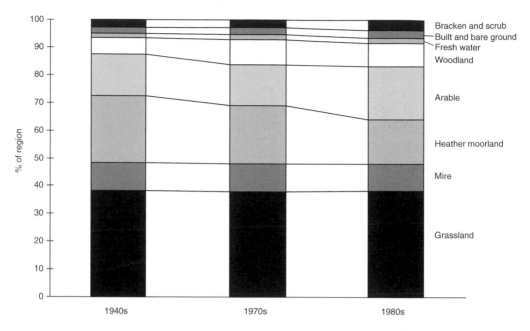

Figure 22.2   Summary of land cover change in Tayside region.

22.1   Increases

Detail in Tables 22.1 and 22.2 shows that the arable area, coniferous plantation and features associated with urban development expanded. The length of ditches increased.

22.2   Decreases

Heather moorland and mixed woodlands were reduced. There was a shift from heather-dominated to grass-dominated mire. There was an apparent reduction in the length of hedgerows by almost two-thirds.

Table 22.1   Land cover stock estimates for Tayside region (total area: 7394 km²).
See Table 4.1 for explanation.

Areal features

Feature group	Feature type	1940s (km²)	(%)	1970s (km²)	(%)	1980s (km²)	(%)
Grassland	Rough grassland	1799	24	1621	22	1819	25
	Intermediate grassland	375	5	474	6	284	4
	Smooth grassland	665	9	707	10	723	10
	Group total	2839	38	2802	38	2826	38

continued

Table 22.1 – *continued*

Feature group	Feature type	1940s (km²)	(%)	1970s (km²)	(%)	1980s (km²)	(%)
Mire	Blanket mire – heather-dominated	628	8	630	9	420	6
	Blanket mire – grass-dominated	101	1	107	1	311	4
	Lowland mire	0	0	0	0	0	0
	Group total	730	10	737	10	731	10
Heather moorland	Heather moorland	1796	24	1564	21	1170	16
	Group total	1796	24	1564	21	1170	16
Arable	Arable	1095	15	1080	15	1420	19
	Group total	1095	15	1080	15	1420	19
Woodland	Broadleaved woodland	103	1	103	1	83	1
	Mixed woodland	132	2	126	2	66	1
	Broadleaved plantation	12	0	9	0	3	0
	Parkland	1	0	8	0	10	0
	Coniferous woodland	4	0	5	0	5	0
	Young plantation	49	1	106	1	124	2
	Coniferous plantation	142	2	312	4	316	4
	Felled woodland	3	0	9	0	18	0
	Group total	445	6	678	9	626	8
Fresh water	Lochs	18	0	4	0	5	0
	Reservoirs	1	0	20	0	19	0
	Rivers	22	0	23	0	20	0
	Canals	0	0	0	0	0	0
	Marginal inundation	3	0	2	0	4	0
	Wet ground	81	1	96	1	76	1
	Group total	126	2	144	2	125	2
Built and bare ground	Built	84	1	104	1	101	1
	Recreation	4	0	6	0	7	0
	Transport corridor	65	1	68	1	82	1
	Quarry	2	0	5	0	1	0
	Rock	5	0	5	0	10	0
	Bare ground	1	0	2	0	11	0
	Group total	160	2	189	3	211	3
Bracken and scrub	Bracken	104	1	113	2	222	3
	Low scrub	76	1	62	1	42	1
	Tall scrub	24	0	24	0	22	0
	Group total	204	3	198	3	285	4

Linear features

Feature type	1940s (km)	(km/km²)	1970s (km)	(km/km²)	1980s (km)	(km/km²)
Hedgerows	3944	0.5	2722	0.4	1444	0.2
Treeline	2278	0.3	2667	0.4	2118	0.3
Streams	9556	1.3	9509	1.3	9717	1.3
Ditches	2913	0.4	4084	0.6	7121	1.0
Tracks	3437	0.5	4743	0.6	3906	0.5

Note   • Apparent increase in area of mire in Tayside due to anomalies in air-photo interpretation.

Table 22.2   Tayside region land cover change, 1940s–1980s. Features ordered by magnitude of change (with statistically significant change judged at the 5% level). See Table 4.4 for explanation.

Areal features

Feature type	Lower (km²)	Change (km²)	Upper (km²)	(%)
Significant increases				
Arable	62	325	588	30
Coniferous plantation	4	174	344	123
Built	4	17	31	21
Transport corridor	4	17	30	26
Bare ground	6	10	15	1493
Parkland	2	9	16	731
Recreation	0	3	6	78
Non-significant increases				
Blanket mire – grass-dominated	−155	210	574	207
Bracken	−98	118	334	114
Young plantation	−3	75	153	152
Smooth grassland	−271	58	388	9
Rough grassland	−285	20	324	1
Reservoirs	−11	18	46	1438
Felled woodland	−15	15	45	606
Rock	−2	5	11	90
Marginal inundation	−3	2	6	56
Coniferous woodland	−5	1	7	31
Canals	*	0	*	*
Lowland mire	−3	0	3	*
Non-significant decreases				
Quarry	−2	−1	1	−31
Rivers	−8	−2	4	−9
Tall scrub	−17	−2	13	−8
Wet ground	−69	−5	58	−7
Broadleaved plantation	−24	−8	8	−70
Lochs	−37	−13	12	−70
Broadleaved woodland	−47	−20	8	−19
Low scrub	−74	−34	5	−45
Intermediate grassland	−206	−92	23	−24
Blanket mire – heather-dominated	−569	−208	152	−33
Significant decreases				
Mixed woodland	−117	−66	−15	−50
Heather moorland	−1074	−626	−178	−35

Linear features

Feature type	Lower (km)	Change (km)	Upper (km)	(%)
Significant increases				
Ditches	2285	4208	6132	144
Non-significant increases				
Tracks	−931	470	1870	14
Streams	−1364	161	1686	2
Non-significant decreases				
Treeline	−708	−159	389	−7
Hedgerows	−6149	−2500	1149	−63

Tayside summary

1940s baseline

- 38% was grassland, nearly two-thirds of which was rough

- 24% heather moorland

- 15% arable

- 10% mire, almost all of which was blanket mire

- 6% woodland, 43% of which was plantation

- remainder comprised bracken and scrub (3%), built and bare ground (2%) and fresh water (2%)

- 0.5 km/km^2 of hedgerows and 0.4 km/km^2 of ditches

1940s–1980s change

- notable expansion in arable (30%) and coniferous plantation (123%)

- features associated with expanding urban development were built (21%) and transport corridor (26%)

- bare ground also increased

- contraction in heather moorland (35%) and mixed woodland (50%)

- ditches extended by 144%

Dynamics of change

- conversion of heather to grass-dominated blanket mire

- heather moorland converted to grassland, coniferous plantation and bracken

- trend towards grassland improvement

- expansion in arable largely from smooth and intermediate grassland

1980s outcome

- 38% was grassland, nearly two-thirds of which was rough

- 16% heather moorland

- 19% arable

- 10% mire

- 8% woodland and scrub, 70% of which was plantation

- remainder comprised bracken and scrub (4%), built and bare ground (3%) and fresh water (2%)

- 0.2 km/km^2 of hedgerows and 1 km/km^2 of ditches

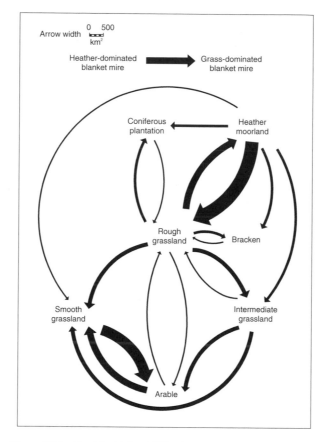

Figure 22.3 Tayside: 1940s–1980s changes >0.5% of total land area.

22.3 Interchange

The interchange of gains and losses (Figure 22.3) shows that, while the overall extent of mire was largely unchanged, a shift from heather to grass vegetation cover occurred from the 1970s to 1980s. Heather moorland was converted to grassland, and reduced by bracken expansion. Rough grassland and heather moorland were reduced by afforestation. There was a marked tendency to grassland improvement and arable expansion.

References

1   Government Statistical Service (1996). *The Scottish Environment Statistics*. Edinburgh: HMSO.

23 ORKNEY ISLANDS

Located off the northern coast of mainland Scotland, the Orkney Islands (Figure 23.1) are separated from the Scottish mainland by the Pentland Firth. With an estimated area of 1,115 km², they represented 1.5% of the land area of Scotland. The 1994 population density was about a third of the average for Scotland. Although suitable for only a narrow range of crops, land capability for agriculture in Orkney was relatively favourable. In contrast, prospects for forestry were highly restricted.[1]

Results from the study (Figure 23.2) show a 1940s scene of extensive arable, mire and grassland, with some heather moorland. The grassland area expanded

Figure 23.1   Orkney Islands.

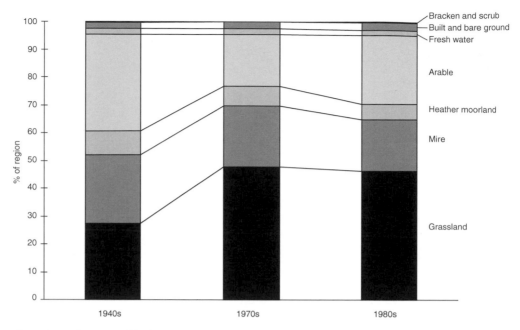

Figure 23.2   Summary of land cover change in Orkney Islands.

appreciably from the 1940s to the 1970s, while the arable area contracted. Some recovery of the arable area occurred from the 1970s to the 1980s.

23.1   Increases

More detail is provided by Tables 23.1 and 23.2, from which it can be seen that the area of smooth and intermediate grassland expanded. The area of transport corridor increased. The length of ditches also increased. Results suggest a small extension of the length of lines of trees.

Table 23.1   Land cover stock estimates for Orkney Islands (total area: 1115 km^2).
See Table 4.1 for explanation.

Areal features

Feature group	Feature type	1940s (km^2)	(%)	1970s (km^2)	(%)	1980s (km^2)	(%)
Grassland	Rough grassland	114	10	109	10	75	7
	Intermediate grassland	60	5	120	11	138	12
	Smooth grassland	131	12	302	27	301	27
	Group total	305	27	530	48	514	46
Mire	Blanket mire	272	24	240	22	202	18
	Lowland mire	3	0	3	0	3	0
	Group total	275	25	243	22	205	18

continued

Table 23.1 – *continued*

Feature group	Feature type	1940s (km²)	(%)	1970s (km²)	(%)	1980s (km²)	(%)
Heather moorland	Heather moorland	94	8	80	7	64	6
	Group total	94	8	80	7	64	6
Arable	Arable	388	35	209	19	276	25
	Group total	388	35	209	19	276	25
Woodland	Broadleaved woodland	0	0	0	0	0	0
	Mixed woodland	0	0	0	0	0	0
	Broadleaved plantation	0	0	0	0	0	0
	Parkland	0	0	0	0	0	0
	Coniferous woodland	0	0	0	0	0	0
	Young plantation	0	0	0	0	0	0
	Coniferous plantation	0	0	0	0	0	0
	Felled woodland	0	0	0	0	0	0
	Group total	0	0	0	0	0	0
Fresh water	Lochs	18	2	17	1	16	1
	Reservoirs	0	0	0	0	0	0
	Rivers	0	0	0	0	0	0
	Canals	0	0	0	0	0	0
	Marginal inundation	2	0	2	0	2	0
	Wet ground	5	0	5	0	5	0
	Group total	25	2	24	2	22	2
Built and bare ground	Built	12	1	12	1	11	1
	Recreation	0	0	0	0	0	0
	Transport corridor	12	1	16	1	19	2
	Quarry	0	0	0	0	0	0
	Rock	0	0	0	0	0	0
	Bare ground	0	0	1	0	1	0
	Group total	24	2	29	3	31	3
Bracken and scrub	Bracken	2	0	0	0	2	0
	Low scrub	1	0	0	0	1	0
	Tall scrub	0	0	0	0	0	0
	Group total	3	0	0	0	2	0

Linear features

Feature type	1940s (km)	(km/km²)	1970s (km)	(km/km²)	1980s (km)	(km/km²)
Hedgerows	2	0.0	2	0.0	27	0.0
Treeline	1	0.0	1	0.0	8	0.0
Streams	479	0.4	490	0.4	451	0.4
Ditches	772	0.7	673	0.6	1166	1.0
Tracks	1264	1.1	1066	1.0	1051	0.9

Table 23.2   Orkney Islands land cover change, 1940s–1980s. Features ordered by magnitude of change (with statistically significant change judged at the 5% level). See Table 4.4 for explanation.

Areal features

Feature type	Lower (km²)	Change (km²)	Upper (km²)	(%)
Significant increases				
Smooth grassland	3	170	337	130
Intermediate grassland	55	77	100	128
Transport corridor	5	7	8	55
Bare ground	1	1	1	285
Non-significant increases				
Low scrub	−1	0	2	37
Quarry	0	0	1	267
Lowland mire	0	0	1	9
Rock	*	0	*	93
Coniferous plantation	*	0	*	*
Recreation	0	0	0	*
Broadleaved plantation	*	0	*	*
Young plantation	*	0	*	*
Broadleaved woodland	*	0	*	*
Reservoirs	*	0	*	100
Rivers	*	0	*	*
Canals	*	0	*	*
Coniferous woodland	*	0	*	*
Felled woodland	*	0	*	*
Mixed woodland	*	0	*	*
Parkland	*	0	*	*
Tall scrub	*	0	*	*
Non-significant decreases				
Wet ground	−3	0	3	−5
Marginal inundation	−1	0	0	−13
Bracken	−2	−1	1	−32
Built	−2	−1	1	−7
Heather moorland	−85	−30	25	−32
Rough grassland	−86	−39	9	−34
Arable	−229	−113	4	−29
Significant decreases				
Lochs	−4	−2	0	−13
Blanket mire	−130	−70	−10	−26

Linear features

Feature type	Lower (km)	Change (km)	Upper (km)	(%)
Significant increases				
Ditches	156	394	632	51
Treeline	2	7	11	772
Non-significant increases				
Hedgerows	−24	26	76	1683
Non-significant decreases				
Streams	−81	−28	24	−6
Significant decreases				
Tracks	−336	−213	−91	−17

Orkney Islands summary

1940s baseline

- 35% was arable

- 27% was grassland, 37% of which was rough

- 25% mire, almost all of which was blanket mire

- 8% heather moorland

- almost all of the remainder comprised built and bare ground (2%) and fresh water (2%)

- less than 0.05 km/km² of hedgerows and treeline

- 0.7 km/km² of ditches and 1.1 km/km² of tracks

1940s–1980s change

- notable expansion in smooth and intermediate grassland (130% and 128%) and transport corridor (55%)

- contraction in blanket mire (26%) and likely reduction in arable (29%)

- ditches extended by 51% and treeline by 772%

- tracks reduced by 17%

Dynamics of change

- loss of blanket mire to heather moorland and to all grassland types

- similarly heather moorland lost out to all grassland types

- reduction in arable largely due to losses to smooth grassland

- transport corridor gained mainly from arable

- some evidence of grassland improvement

1980s outcome

- 25% was arable

- 46% was grassland, 15% of which was rough

- 18% mire

- 6% heather moorland

- almost all of the remainder comprised built and bare ground (3%) and fresh water (2%)

- less than 0.05 km/km² of hedgerows and treeline

- 1.0 km/km² of ditches and 0.9 km/km² of tracks

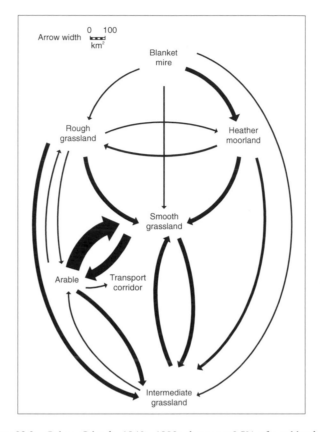

Figure 23.3   Orkney Islands: 1940s–1980s changes >0.5% of total land area.

23.2 Decreases

The extent of blanket mire and the area of loch were reduced. Results suggest reductions in the area of arable and rough grassland. Upgrading of the road network appears to have resulted in a reduction in the length of tracks.

23.3 Interchange

The interchange of gains and losses (Figure 23.3) shows that blanket mire was evidently drained and thus converted to heather moorland or grassland. Heather moorland was also converted to grassland. There was a tendency towards grassland improvement, and interchange between arable and smooth grassland was in favour of grassland at the expense of arable.

References

1   Government Statistical Service (1996). *The Scottish Environment Statistics*. Edinburgh: HMSO.

24 SHETLAND ISLANDS

The most northerly of the isles, the Shetland Islands (Figure 24.1) lie as far north of the mainland coast of Scotland as Aberdeen does to the south. With an estimated area of 1,810 km^2, they accounted for 2% of the land area of Scotland. The 1994 population density was about a fifth of the average for Scotland. Prospects for agriculture and forestry in the Shetland Islands were highly restricted.[1]

Figure 24.1   Shetland Islands.

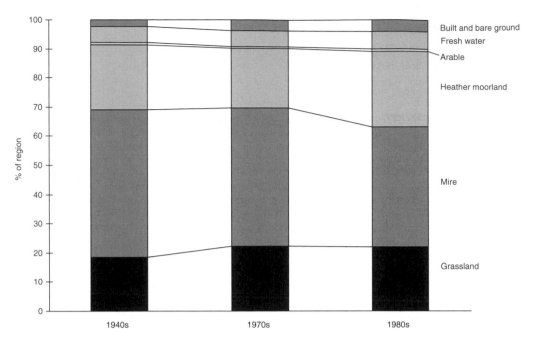

Figure 24.2   Summary of land cover change in Shetland Islands.

Results from the study (Figure 24.2) show a 1940s scene of mire and heather moorland, with grassland. The grassland area expanded from the 1940s to the 1970s. The mire area contracted. Having been reduced from the 1940s to the 1970s, the heather moorland area expanded from the 1970s to the 1980s.

24.1 Increases

More detail is provided in Tables 24.1 and 24.2, from which it can be seen that the area of smooth grassland expanded. The length of ditches increased.

Table 24.1   Land cover stock estimates for Shetland Islands (total area: 1810 km^2).
See Table 4.1 for explanation.

Areal features

Feature group	Feature type	1940s (km^2)	(%)	1970s (km^2)	(%)	1980s (km^2)	(%)
Grassland	Rough grassland	260	14	271	15	246	14
	Intermediate grassland	61	3	112	6	100	6
	Smooth grassland	15	1	18	1	53	3
	Group total	336	19	401	22	400	22

continued

Table 24.1 – *continued*

Feature group	Feature type	1940s (km²)	(%)	1970s (km²)	(%)	1980s (km²)	(%)
Mire	Blanket mire	913	50	859	47	740	41
	Lowland mire	0	0	0	0	0	0
	Group total	913	50	859	47	740	41
Heather moorland	Heather moorland	405	22	370	20	474	26
	Group total	405	22	370	20	474	26
Arable	Arable	17	1	10	1	14	1
	Group total	17	1	10	1	14	1
Woodland	Broadleaved woodland	0	0	0	0	0	0
	Mixed woodland	0	0	0	0	0	0
	Broadleaved plantation	0	0	0	0	0	0
	Parkland	0	0	0	0	0	0
	Coniferous woodland	0	0	0	0	0	0
	Young plantation	0	0	0	0	0	0
	Coniferous plantation	0	0	0	0	0	0
	Felled woodland	0	0	0	0	0	0
	Group total	0	0	0	0	0	0
Fresh water	Lochs	74	4	74	4	75	4
	Reservoirs	3	0	3	0	0	0
	Rivers	1	0	1	0	1	0
	Canals	0	0	0	0	0	0
	Marginal inundation	1	0	2	0	1	0
	Wet ground	21	1	25	1	31	2
	Group total	99	5	104	6	108	6
Built and bare ground	Built	18	1	40	2	47	3
	Recreation	0	0	0	0	1	0
	Transport corridor	15	1	16	1	18	1
	Quarry	1	0	2	0	2	0
	Rock	5	0	5	0	5	0
	Bare ground	1	0	2	0	2	0
	Group total	39	2	65	4	75	4
Bracken and scrub	Bracken	1	0	0	0	0	0
	Low scrub	0	0	0	0	0	0
	Tall scrub	0	0	0	0	0	0
	Group total	1	0	0	0	0	0

Linear features

Feature type	1940s (km)	(km/km²)	1970s (km)	(km/km²)	1980s (km)	(km/km²)
Hedgerows	5	0.0	4	0.0	11	0.0
Treeline	10	0.0	5	0.0	1	0.0
Streams	2872	1.6	2896	1.6	3367	1.9
Ditches	328	0.2	628	0.3	1018	0.6
Tracks	488	0.3	532	0.3	705	0.4

Table 24.2   Shetland Islands land cover change, 1940s–1980s. Features ordered by magnitude of change (with statistically significant change judged at the 5% level). See Table 4.4 for explanation.

Areal features

Feature type	Lower (km²)	Change (km²)	Upper (km²)	(%)
Significant increases				
Smooth grassland	14	38	62	250
Quarry	0	1	2	168
Non-significant increases				
Heather moorland	−23	69	160	17
Intermediate grassland	−10	39	88	64
Built	−9	29	67	163
Wet ground	−1	10	21	49
Transport corridor	0	3	6	18
Bare ground	0	1	3	171
Recreation	−1	1	3	764
Lochs	−6	0	6	1
Rock	−1	0	2	8
Low scrub	*	0	*	433
Rivers	0	0	0	15
Canals	*	0	*	*
Marginal inundation	−2	0	2	3
Broadleaved plantation	*	0	*	*
Broadleaved woodland	*	0	*	*
Young plantation	*	0	*	*
Tall scrub	*	0	*	*
Coniferous plantation	*	0	*	*
Coniferous woodland	*	0	*	*
Felled woodland	*	0	*	*
Lowland mire	*	0	*	*
Mixed woodland	*	0	*	*
Parkland	*	0	*	*
Non-significant decreases				
Bracken	−2	−1	0	−100
Reservoirs	−7	−3	2	−98
Arable	−18	−3	12	−17
Rough grassland	−58	−14	30	−5
Significant decreases				
Blanket mire	−304	−173	−43	−19

Linear features

Feature type	Lower (km)	Change (km)	Upper (km)	(%)
Significant increases				
Ditches	285	690	1094	210
Non-significant increases				
Streams	−38	495	1027	17
Tracks	−17	217	451	45
Hedgerows	−5	5	16	99
Non-significant decreases				
Treeline	−27	−9	9	−91

Shetland Islands summary

1940s baseline

- 50% mire, all of which was blanket mire
- 22% heather moorland
- 19% was grassland, three-quarters of which was rough
- most of the remainder comprised fresh water (5%) and built and bare ground (2%)
- less than 0.05 km/km^2 of hedgerows and treeline
- 0.2 km/km^2 of ditches and 0.3 km/km^2 of tracks

1940s–1980s change

- expansion in smooth grassland (250%)
- contraction in blanket mire (19%)
- ditches extended by 210% and likely increases in streams (17%) and tracks (45%)

Dynamics of change

- substantial drainage of blanket mire
- mire also lost to built
- substantial interchange between rough grassland and heather moorland with net gain by heather moorland
- evidence of grassland improvement

1980s outcome

- 41% mire
- 26% heather moorland
- 22% was grassland, 61% of which was rough
- most of the remainder comprised fresh water (6%) and built and bare ground (4%)
- less than 0.05 km/km^2 of hedgerows and treeline
- 0.6 km/km^2 of ditches and 0.4 km/km^2 of tracks

24.2 Decreases

Blanket mire was reduced in extent.

24.3 Interchange

The interchange of gains and losses (Figure 24.3) shows that blanket mire was evidently drained and thus converted to heather moorland or grassland, as well

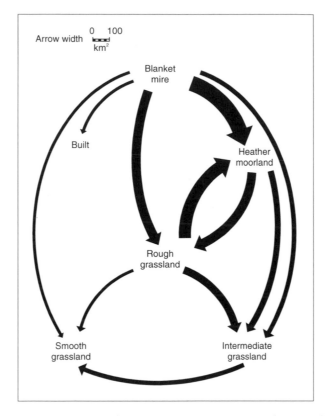

Figure 24.3   Shetland Islands: 1940s–1980s changes >0.5% of total land area.

as built land. Heather moorland was converted to grassland, although the interchange between heather and rough grassland was in favour of heather moorland. There was a marked tendency towards grassland improvement.

References

1   Government Statistical Service (1996). *The Scottish Environment Statistics*. Edinburgh: HMSO.

25 WESTERN ISLES

The Western Isles (Figure 25.1), lying off the northwestern Atlantic coast of mainland Scotland, are approximately 200 km in length, extending from the latitude of Fort William to Cape Wrath. With an estimated area of 2,847 km^2, they represented 4% of the land area of Scotland. The 1994 population density was about a fifth of the average for Scotland. Prospects for agriculture and forestry in the Western Isles were highly restricted.[1]

Figure 25.1   Western Isles.

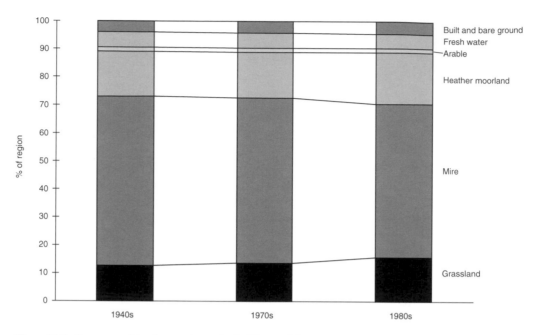

Figure 25.2   Summary of land cover change in the Western Isles.

Results from the study (Figure 25.2) show a 1940s scene of mire, with heather moorland and grassland, and lochs. Heather and grassland expanded, and the mire area contracted.

25.1   Increases

Tables 25.1 and 25.2 show that the area of smooth grassland expanded, as did built and bare ground. Results also suggest that rough grassland and heather moorland expanded, and that mire became more grassy. The length of ditches increased.

Table 25.1   Land cover stock estimates for Western Isles (total area: 2847 km²).
See Table 4.1 for explanation.

Areal features

Feature group	Feature type	1940s (km²)	1940s (%)	1970s (km²)	1970s (%)	1980s (km²)	1980s (%)
Grassland	Rough grassland	244	9	254	9	320	11
	Intermediate grassland	110	4	108	4	72	3
	Smooth grassland	5	0	28	1	54	2
	Group total	359	13	390	14	447	16

continued

Table 25.1 – *continued*

Feature group	Feature type	1940s (km²)	(%)	1970s (km²)	(%)	1980s (km²)	(%)
Mire	Blanket mire – heather-dominated	1083	38	1065	37	908	32
	Blanket mire – grass-dominated	634	22	610	21	645	23
	Lowland mire	0	0	0	0	0	0
	Group total	1717	60	1675	59	1553	55
Heather moorland	Heather moorland	462	16	464	16	525	18
	Group total	462	16	464	16	525	18
Arable	Arable	43	2	43	2	43	2
	Group total	43	2	43	2	43	2
Woodland	Broadleaved woodland	0	0	0	0	0	0
	Mixed woodland	0	0	0	0	0	0
	Broadleaved plantation	0	0	0	0	0	0
	Parkland	0	0	0	0	0	0
	Coniferous woodland	0	0	0	0	0	0
	Young plantation	0	0	0	0	0	0
	Coniferous plantation	0	0	0	0	0	0
	Felled woodland	0	0	0	0	0	0
	Group total	0	0	0	0	0	0
Fresh water	Lochs	136	5	136	5	134	5
	Reservoirs	0	0	0	0	0	0
	Rivers	1	0	1	0	1	0
	Canals	0	0	0	0	0	0
	Marginal inundation	1	0	1	0	5	0
	Wet ground	10	0	15	1	12	0
	Group total	149	5	154	5	153	5
Built and bare ground	Built	5	0	5	0	8	0
	Recreation	0	0	0	0	0	0
	Transport corridor	14	0	16	1	18	1
	Quarry	0	0	1	0	0	0
	Rock	90	3	91	3	84	3
	Bare ground	7	0	9	0	17	1
	Group total	116	4	121	4	127	4
Bracken and scrub	Bracken	0	0	0	0	0	0
	Low scrub	0	0	0	0	0	0
	Tall scrub	0	0	0	0	0	0
	Group total	0	0	0	0	0	0

Linear features

Feature type	1940s (km)	(km/km²)	1970s (km)	(km/km²)	1980s (km)	(km/km²)
Hedgerows	0	0.0	0	0.0	0	0.0
Treeline	0	0.0	0	0.0	3	0.0
Streams	6573	2.3	6526	2.3	6864	2.4
Ditches	610	0.2	736	0.3	1095	0.4
Tracks	803	0.3	817	0.3	705	0.2

Table 25.2   Western Isles land cover change, 1940s–1980s. Features ordered by magnitude of change (with statistically significant change judged at the 5% level). See Table 4.4 for explanation.

Areal features

Feature type	Lower (km²)	Change (km²)	Upper (km²)	(%)
Significant increases				
Smooth grassland	4	49	95	972
Bare ground	2	10	18	135
Built	1	3	5	59
Non-significant increases				
Rough grassland	−32	76	184	31
Heather moorland	−37	63	163	14
Blanket mire – grass-dominated	−159	11	181	2
Transport corridor	−3	4	11	28
Marginal inundation	0	4	7	313
Wet ground	−6	2	10	20
Low scrub	*	0	*	*
Canals	*	0	*	*
Recreation	*	0	*	88
Tall scrub	*	0	*	*
Reservoirs	*	0	*	2
Bracken	*	0	*	*
Broadleaved plantation	*	0	*	*
Broadleaved woodland	*	0	*	*
Coniferous plantation	*	0	*	*
Coniferous woodland	*	0	*	*
Felled woodland	*	0	*	*
Lowland mire	*	0	*	*
Mixed woodland	*	0	*	*
Parkland	*	0	*	*
Young plantation	*	0	*	*
Non-significant decreases				
Rivers	*	0	*	−9
Arable	−6	0	6	0
Quarry	−1	0	0	−100
Lochs	−5	−2	1	−1
Rock	−23	−6	12	−6
Intermediate grassland	−99	−38	22	−35
Blanket mire – heather-dominated	−374	−175	23	−16

Linear features

Feature type	Lower (km)	Change (km)	Upper (km)	(%)
Significant increases				
Ditches	239	485	730	79
Non-significant increases				
Streams	−953	291	1536	4
Treeline	−3	3	9	*
Hedgerows	*	0	*	*
Non-significant decreases				
Tracks	−460	−98	265	−12

Western Isles summary

1940s baseline

- 60% mire, all of which was blanket mire

- 16% heather moorland

- 13% was grassland, two-thirds of which was rough

- 5% fresh water, almost all of which was lochs

- the remainder comprised built and bare ground (4%) and arable (2%)

- less than 0.05 km/km² of hedgerows and treeline

- 0.2 km/km² of ditches and 0.3 km/km² of tracks

1940s–1980s change

- expansion in smooth grassland (972%), bare ground (135%) and built (59%)

- no significant reductions but likely decline in heather-dominated blanket mire (16%)

- ditches extended by 79%

Dynamics of change

- interchange between grass- and heather-dominated blanket mire favouring grass

- evidence of drainage of blanket mire

- exchange between rough grassland and heather moorland

- expansion in smooth grassland largely from intermediate

1980s outcome

- 55% mire

- 18% heather moorland

- 16% was grassland, 72% of which was rough

- 5% water, almost all of which was lochs

- the remainder comprised built and bare ground (4%) and arable (2%)

- less than 0.05 km/km² of hedgerows and treeline

- 0.4 km/km² of ditches and 0.2 km/km² of tracks

25.2 Decreases

There were no significant reductions but results suggest that heather-dominated blanket mire was reduced in area.

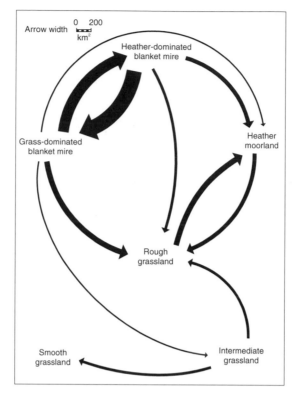

Figure 25.3   Western Isles: 1940s–1980s changes >0.5% of total land area.

25.3 Interchange

The interchange of gains and losses (Figure 25.3) shows that between heather-dominated and grass-dominated blanket mire there was a tendency towards grass at the expense of heather. Mire was evidently drained and thus converted to heather moorland or grassland.

References

1   Government Statistical Service (1996). *The Scottish Environment Statistics*. Edinburgh: HMSO.

PART FIVE

SECTORAL ANALYSIS AND CONCLUDING POINTS

26 DISCUSSION

Factors which influence individual land management choices include land suitability (determined by environmental factors and technical opportunity), investment potential (taking account of economic viability, returns on investment and risk), social acceptance (within planning policy guidelines and society at large) and individual motivation (including personal preferences, knowledge and skills). Land managers on better-quality land have fewer constraints and thus more choice than those on marginal land, where livestock grazing, forestry, sport or recreation may be the main options.

In an ever-changing economic climate, legislation, policy signals, incentives and development control may seek to influence collective behaviour. The Town and Country Planning Act 1947 brought building, engineering and mining under the consideration of planning permission and moved beyond the important regulatory function of development control by setting out local authority land use intentions in the form of development plans. In the Town and Country Planning (Scotland) Act 1969, the single development plan was replaced by a tiered system of Structure and Local Plans.[1]

While the rapid pace of urban development was regulated within the town and country planning system, many aspects of countryside change fell outside that framework.[2] Between the 1940s and the 1980s British law tended not to regard the use of land for agriculture and forestry as 'development'. Although in the 1960s some especially large or tall agricultural buildings were brought under development control, environmental assessment and planning permission were not required for major changes in agricultural practice (such as farm amalgamation, the siting of agricultural buildings, the ploughing up of rough grassland, or large afforestation schemes).[3] As such, post-war policies promoted rapid agricultural and forestry growth and their freedom of operation.[4,5]

The NCMS analysis of land cover change and its geographical variation suggests the involvement of a number of broadly defined land use sectors. Notable are the effects of:

- urban development;

- agricultural intensification in relation to arable and lowland grassland production systems; and

- the utilisation of the uplands, where the expansion of forestry has been particularly distinctive.

Figure 26.1

Net reduction
% reduction in extent, 1940s–1980s

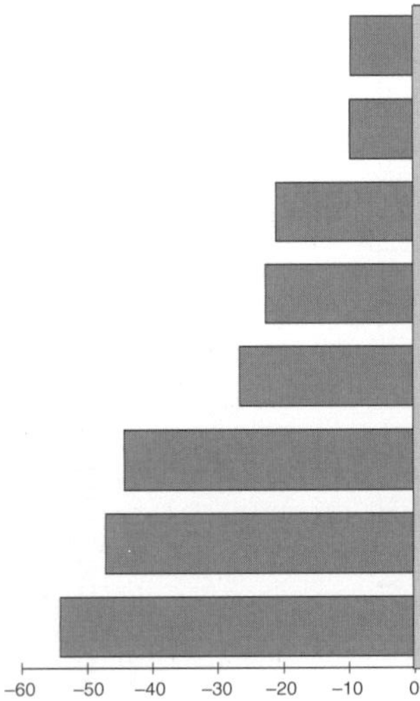

Factors responsible
Net change attributable to factor (km² or km)

% reduction	Feature	1980s estimate	Net change 1940s–1980s	Afforestation	Mire drainage	Grassland expansion	Grassland improvement	Arable expansion	Urban development	Reservoir expansion	Bracken expansion	Other	Explanation of 'other'
-10	Lochs	(km²) 1078	-115							-104		-11	Remainder mainly lost to marginal inundation
-10	Rough grassland	11130	-1201	-2354	1108	1111	-691		-54		-298	-24	Also losses to wet ground and scrub, gains from some woodland types
-21	Blanket mire	17930	-4786	-2434	-2089				-126		-58	-79	Also losses to wet ground and rock
-23	Heather moorland	11294	-3321	-2224	842	-1530		-54	-46	-32	-229	-47	Also losses to wet ground and scrub, gains from rock
-27	Broadleaved and mixed woodland	1505	-547	-288		-98		-11	-30		-25	-95	Remainder mainly lost to heather moorland, other woodland types and scrub
-44	Lowland mire	127	-102	-47	-28				-6		-21		Remainder mainly lost to scrub
-47	Coniferous woodland	108	-97	-90		-13						6	Also some gains from broadleaved and mixed woodland
-54	Hedgerows	(km) 19463	-23093									-23093	Hedgerow removal

Figure 26.1 Causes and consequences of change, 1940s–1980s. The chart shows the percentage change in a number of semi-natural features. Figures to the right show how much of the net change can be attributed to the listed factors, defined as follows:

- afforestation: young and coniferous plantation and felled woodland;
- drainage: grassland and heather moorland where these were originally mire;
- grassland expansion: spread of grassland through heather moorland or woodland clearance;
- grassland improvement: smooth or intermediate grassland which was originally rough grassland;
- arable expansion: arable expanded from 1970s to 1980s;
- urban development: built, transport corridor, recreation and bare ground;
- reservoirs: reservoirs replaced former lochs and flooded surrounding land, especially 1940s to 1970s; and
- bracken expansion: spread of bracken especially from 1970s to 1980s.

A negative figure indicates a net loss due to the factor, a positive figure indicates a net gain.

While recognising that there are interdependencies between sectors as well as interactions between different forms of land use (Figure 26.1), the key sectors are now considered in detail.

26.1 Urban development

Although the population of Scotland remained at around five million from 1951 to 1991,[6] the number of households increased from fewer than 1.4 million[7] to more than 2 million[8] over the same period. Thus, despite a near-static population the pressure on housing rose by 40%.

Since 1945 there has been a rapid growth of car ownership and mobility.[9] Between 1950 and 1990, vehicles on British roads increased from around 4 million to around 25 million. Of these, about 20 million were private cars.[10] Roads therefore formed a major focus of transport policy but, despite a massive road building programme, the unrelenting increase in traffic has made roads evermore crowded.

Key results in the NCMS study quantify the expansion of built land and transport corridor (roads), as well as associated construction works (bare ground) and peri-urban recreational land use (playing fields, golf courses, etc.). The key findings are as follows:

- built land increased by an estimated 46%, mainly on smooth grassland and arable farmland;

- recreational land increased by around 138%, mainly on grassland and arable land;

- bare ground increased four-fold, mainly related to peat extraction on mire or urban and road development;

- the area of transport corridor (roads) increased by about 22%, mainly on mire, arable, smooth grassland and heather moorland; and

- the length of unsurfaced tracks (mainly in the uplands) increased by around 29%.

With population concentrated in large cities and conurbations, and having extensive upland pasture and rough grazing, the proportion of urbanised land in Britain is low relative to neighbouring European countries.[11] In relation to urban growth, the concern is not with the amount of agricultural land lost but rather with the disproportionate loss of better-quality land.[12] The encroachment of urban development on to farmland was compensated for by bringing lower-grade land into production. There is evidence from NCMS to support observations elsewhere that where conditions were favourable, moorland was converted to pasture, grassland was improved, and some of the better-quality grassland was changed to arable use.

26.2 Agricultural intensification

With an economy founded upon industry and commerce, and free trade secured by supremacy on the seas and colonial ties, the UK in the early twentieth century was heavily dependent on food imports. Two-thirds of domestic food needs were imported at the outbreak of the Second World War. The subsequent national food shortage, massive balance of payments deficit and need for dollar savings called for a radical change in the role of agriculture.[13] The Agriculture Act 1947 and subsequent Acts provided a framework for a secure agricultural industry and a dramatic expansion in agricultural production.[14]

Agricultural policy from 1945 to 1950 was marked by wholesale expansion of output, with domestic production contributing towards the ending of Britain's dependence on Marshall Plan aid from the United States.[15] As the sterling crisis eased in the early 1950s, together with a general improvement in world food supplies, fixed prices were replaced by deficiency payments (set according to the shortfall between the commodity sale value and its guaranteed price). Research and advice were directed to increasing efficiency through labour-saving and yield-increasing technologies. Production grants from the early 1950s onwards promoted intensification and specialisation, increased fertiliser use and stocking rates, the ploughing up and reseeding of permanent pasture and long-term productivity improvement through hedgerow removal and land drainage.

The Agriculture Act 1947 has been viewed from such a perspective as 'one of the most successful and long-standing pieces of major legislation in British parliamentary history'.[16] Major gains were secured through agricultural mechanisation, the application of fertilisers and pesticides, selective plant and animal breeding, together with capital investment in buildings, plant and machinery, and the shedding of labour.[17] Agricultural land values, representing capitalised income opportunities, escalated with the introduction of subsidies from the 1950s onwards.[18]

The mechanisms applied to foster continued agricultural growth changed markedly in the early 1970s. In preparation for joining the European Economic Community and embracing the Common Agricultural Policy (CAP), deficiency payments were phased out. Agricultural support price guarantees were secured under CAP through controlled consumer prices, by means of levies on imports from third countries and by intervention buying.

One outcome was that, with little overall change in the agricultural land area from 1947 to 1988, the number of agricultural holdings in Scotland fell from nearly 75,000 to just over 26,000.[19, 20] At the same time, the agricultural labour force fell (albeit with definition changes) from around 88,000 to around 63,000. Having provided only one-third of food needs at the outbreak of the Second World War (population 47 million), by the mid 1980s the UK had become two-thirds self-sufficient (population of 56 million).[21]

26.2.1 Arable farming

Technological developments and mechanisation removed former restraints on the management of arable land. Agro-chemicals permitted simplified cropping rotations. From the late 1940s to the late 1970s the barley area expanded to displace oats as the leading cereal crop, particularly in the drier eastern lowlands, and potatoes as a cash crop.[22] Continuous cereal growing became possible on many soils, leading to a decline in mixed arable and livestock farming. As livestock production requires substantial inputs of arable products, particularly feed grains, there was a built-in tendency for cereals to increase in profitability relative to livestock.[23]

When the UK began operating within the Common Agricultural Policy (CAP) in the mid-1970s, new productivity support measures speeded the adoption of technology and gave further stimulus to arable expansion and grassland improvement. A consequence of this was an increasing concentration of arable farming in the east and of livestock farming in the wetter and hillier areas of the west and north. Further pressure to intensify came from a sharp, speculative increase in land values which followed EEC entry.[24]

Mechanisation, economies of scale and state subsidy drove forward the consolidation of agricultural holdings and field enlargement. Changes in production systems are reflected in three NCMS results:

- in the 1940s arable land covered about 10% of Scotland, and expanded (by 11%) to cover 11% of Scotland in the 1980s;

- the increase in the arable area, especially in the east, was mainly at the expense of smooth grassland (improved pasture); and

- hedgerow length was reduced by half, from over 40,000 km in the 1940s to under 20,000 km in the 1980s.

26.2.2 Grassland systems

Dairy and beef-cattle production systems are reliant on grass, grazed in summer and conserved as hay or silage for use in the winter. Influenced by soil and climate, the distribution of lowland grassland and cattle are strongly correlated. Encouraged by selective subsidies, beef cattle numbers increased rapidly from the 1940s to the mid 1970s, especially in the south-west of Scotland. By then around 90% of the agricultural area in Scotland was either grazing land or utilised for the production of hay or silage. Two-thirds of the acreage of tillage crops was employed in the growing of feedstuffs.[25]

Agricultural improvement on British grasslands was accomplished through land drainage, reseeding and increased use of fertilisers. Despite a reduction in the grassland area due to arable expansion, output of British beef and lamb doubled from the 1940s to the mid-1980s, and that of milk increased more than three-fold. From the 1960s to the 1980s the average use of nitrogen on grassland in the UK trebled, while silage making increased five-fold (replacing hay and turnip feeds).[26]

Changing grassland production systems, noting interactions with grassland utilisation in the uplands, are reflected in two NCMS results:

- grassland, which covered 30% of Scotland in the 1940s, was reduced to 28% in the 1980s; and

- while grassland improvement took place (notably in the uplands, see below), smooth grassland (permanent pasture in the lowlands) decreased by 11%, mainly due to conversion either to arable use or urban development.

26.3　The uplands

In relation to the agricultural productivity of the lowlands, the extensive uplands were more marginal in terms of economic opportunity and returns. They were thus utilised for hill farming and sporting interests (most importantly for red deer (*Cervus elaphus*), red grouse (*Lagopus lagopus*) and salmon (*Salmo salar*)), forestry, water catchment, informal recreation and nature conservation.

In considering NCMS findings in the uplands, it is necessary at the outset to look at the appreciable expansion of coniferous plantation forestry.

26.3.1 Afforestation

Faced with much-depleted timber reserves at the end of the Second World War, the Forestry Act 1945 introduced measures for expanding private and state planting. To avoid competition with agriculture, forest expansion was directed into marginal upland areas. There the sale of large estates also helped to supply land for afforestation. Plough development allowed blanket peat to be drained for afforestation.

Results confirm that afforestation took place mainly on mire (utilising about 2,437 km^2), heather moorland (2,245 km^2) and rough grassland (2,505 km^2). The mire area was further reduced by drainage operations (1,932 km^2). Under-planting also changed the character and extent of established woodlands and native woodlands. Seven NCMS results are particularly indicative of these changes:

- woodland cover expanded from an estimated 5% of Scotland in the 1940s to around 14% in the 1980s;

- broadleaved woodland decreased by 23%, mainly being replaced by coniferous plantations;

- mixed woodland decreased by 37%, mainly being replaced by coniferous plantations;

- coniferous woodland decreased by 47%, mainly being replaced by coniferous plantations;

- young coniferous plantation increased nine-fold, mainly on blanket mire, rough grassland and heather moorland;

- mature coniferous plantation increased more than four-fold, mainly on heather moorland, rough grassland and blanket mire; and

- felled woodland more than doubled in area.

The effects of afforestation on mire were also appreciable. Four such indicators are as follows:

- mire covered an estimated 29% of Scotland in the 1940s and 23% in the 1980s;

- blanket mire decreased by around 21%, mainly due to afforestation and drainage;

- lowland mire decreased by around 44%, mainly due to afforestation and drainage; and

- the length of ditches, which is largely associated with mire drainage, doubled.

26.3.2 Hill farming

Sheep and red deer have suppressed tree regeneration over much of the uplands. Together with muirburn for the management of heather moorland, they have exerted a considerable influence on upland vegetation composition.[27] The second factor to consider in the uplands then is the effect of grazing, particularly in relation to hill farming.

The Hill Farming and Livestock Rearing Act 1946 introduced a 'Livestock Rearing Land Improvement Scheme' to encourage upland stock rearing. As the hill farmer's livelihood is ultimately constrained by the productivity of stock, further measures were taken throughout the 1950s and 1960s in order to improve hill sward quality and thereby to increase stock-carrying capacity and productivity. The Agriculture Act 1957 established a 'Farm Improvement Scheme', targeted on hill and upland farms, with grants for land improvement and reclamation.[28] Measures such as drainage, liming, bracken control and reseeding continued into the 1970s. They were then largely replaced by the introduction of livestock headage payments in the Hill Livestock (Compensatory Allowances) Regulations 1975, which provided an annual compensation allowance in designated Less Favoured Areas.[29]

In terms of land utilisation, the overall policy aim was to improve grazing potential and increase stocking rates in the uplands. At the same time, there was a marked increase in red deer numbers, from an estimated 100,000 in 1950 to 300,000 in 1989.[30] The expected land cover effects of grazing and land improvement would be conversion of heather moorland to grassland (arising from increased grazing pressure, possibly combined with reduced moorland management) and the improvement of rough grassland (arising from land and sward improvement). These are seen in the following NCMS results:

- heather moorland, which covered an estimated 19% of Scotland in the 1940s, was reduced to 15% in the 1980s;

- a 23% decrease in heather moorland area was due mainly to afforestation and conversion to rough grassland;

- rough grassland decreased by around 10%, mainly due to afforestation and grassland improvement;

- intermediate grassland increased by 15%, mainly due to creation from rough grassland, heather moorland and drained mire;

- bracken covered an estimated 1% of Scotland in the 1940s and 2% in the 1980s; and

- an increase of 79% in bracken cover was mainly by its spread onto rough grassland and heather moorland.

A third aspect of land cover change, especially in the uplands, was the utilisation of fresh water.

26.3.3 Water catchment

The relatively favourable conditions for hydro-power generation in Scotland have been exploited over the past hundred years, and especially in the 20 years following the Second World War. The first significant schemes in the late nineteenth and early twentieth centuries were built for the smelting of aluminium, but a high-voltage grid in the early 1930s made possible large-scale transmission of electricity. Between 1945 and 1965, some 28 conventional hydro-schemes were constructed by the North of Scotland Hydro-Electric Board, incorporating 66 dams. A characteristic of Scottish schemes is their extensive networks of reservoirs, with aqueducts and tunnels for diverting water from neighbouring catchments into the main storage reservoirs, augmenting power production and accommodating seasonal variations in rainfall. By the mid-1960s most of the economically attractive catchments had been developed, although some pumped-storage schemes were constructed thereafter to store and release energy surpluses from large thermal and nuclear power stations.[31]

In terms of extent, little definitive change was detected for fresh water, but the conversion of lochs to reservoirs and inundation of moorland was evident:

- fresh water covered 3% of Scotland in both the 1940s and the 1980s; and

- reservoir development resulted in a slight increase in the area of standing fresh water.

26.4 Summing up

The start date of the NCMS study in 1947 coincides with the period of economic reconstruction in the aftermath of the Second World War. The closing date of 1988 falls shortly before the first comprehensive policy document on the UK's environment.[32] Countryside change in the intervening period was fuelled by pol-icies for growth in farming and forestry and associated technological advances. Only towards the end of the study period were environmental considerations coming to be expressed in key policies which would affect Scotland's land cover.

The role of the planning process in the rural environment had been limited essentially to the prevention of encroachment of urbanisation.[33] The framing of the first comprehensive Town and Country Planning Act 1947 in the immediate post-war years assumed that prosperity in agriculture and forestry would virtuously enhance the countryside.[34] In practice the drive to increase national food production pushed forestry expansion into the uplands, offering little opportunity for multiple land use.[35]

Agriculture, forestry, nature conservation, amenity, rural services and regional development policies tended to be drawn up and implemented in isolation from each other, and came into conflict where the concerns of one interest could not be accommodated within the policy instruments of another.[36] Disparate grant programmes of central agencies might promote the destruction of habitats which others sought to protect.[37] By the 1970s it became clearer that human pressures on the land of Britain had caused a rate and scale of attrition of wildlife and habitat greater than that foreseen in the National Parks and Countryside Act 1949.[38]

The structure and appearance of the British countryside since the late 1940s has been markedly altered. Farm amalgamation, intensification of production and enterprise specialisation were reflected in the value of farmland which, in real terms, outstripped inflation.[39] Industrial-scale farming transformed the appearance of the lowland countryside and, through the shedding of farm labour, changed the social and economic character of rural areas. In the uplands the appearance of coniferous plantation forests has perhaps been most visually striking, alongside more subtle changes in Scotland's heaths and moorlands.

Key changes from the 1940s to the 1980s were that urban development expanded, as did features associated with more intensive agriculture. There was evidence of the displacement of livestock production systems by arable farming. Afforestation expanded appreciably in the uplands. Six key statistics emanating from the NCMS are as follows:

- built and associated features: 37% increase;

- arable: 11% increase;

- smooth grassland: 11% decrease;

- intermediate grassland: 15% increase;

- young plantation: 929% increase; and

- coniferous plantation: 462% increase.

Consequently, semi-natural habitats which evolved through a long history of use and management of the land (and which are often regarded as distinctive elements in Scotland's cultural landscapes) contracted. Displacement of cattle in the uplands by sheep, together with reduced management of moorland for sport, may have allowed bracken to expand. Key statistics for these changes are as follows:

- mire: 21% decrease;

- heather moorland: 23% decrease;

- rough grassland: 10% decrease; and

- bracken: 79% increase.

During the study period, increased mobility, income and leisure time brought about a growth of recreation in the countryside. At the same time, reduced hedgerow length may be indicative of reduced access opportunities along footpaths and field margins. A consequence of changing agricultural techniques has been that the countryside has generally become less suitable for recreational use and less visually and ecologically diverse.[40]

Protected areas and fragments of habitats are influenced not only by processes going on within them but by larger-scale processes outside. Isolated fragments of semi-natural habitat are insufficient on their own to achieve the conservation of biodiversity. Habitat size, structure and connectivity are vital to both the visual appearance of the countryside and to the long-term protection of its wildlife. Lying in a matrix of other land, habitat patches are greatly influenced by the characteristics of surrounding land use.[41]

It has proved hard to achieve integrated policies that cut across economic sectors. A strength of the National Countryside Monitoring Scheme is that it has been able to look across the key sectors in order to provide an integrated view of land cover change throughout Scotland from the late 1940s to the late 1980s. It has certainly been a period of incredible dynamism, with huge changes in the land cover. In retrospect the economic driving forces for these changes can be seen, but in the future will similar forces, or others, change the face of Scotland?

References

1   Cullingworth, J.B. (1982). *Town and Country Planning in Britain*. The New Local Government Series, No. 8. London: George Allen and Unwin.

2   Gilg, A.W. (1978). *Countryside Planning – The First Three Decades 1945–76*. Problems in Modern Geography. Newton Abbott: David & Charles.

3   Harte, J.D.C. (1992). Land development: the role of planning law. In Howarth, W. and Rodgers, C.P. (eds). *Agriculture Conservation and Land Use*. Cardiff: University of Wales Press.

4   Lowe, P., Cox, C., MacEwen, M., O'Riordan, T. and Winter, M. (1986). *Countryside Conflicts: The Politics of Farming, Forestry and Conservation*. Aldershot: Temple Smith/Gower.

5   Marsden, T., Murdoch, J., Lowe, P., Munton, R. and Flynn, A. (1993). *Constructing the Countryside*. Restructuring Rural Areas 1. London: UCL Press Limited.

6   Whitaker, J. and Sons Ltd. (1997). *Whitaker's Almanack*. London: J. Whitaker and Sons Ltd.

7   HMSO (1952). *Census of Scotland 1951*. Edinburgh: HMSO.

8   HMSO (1993). *Census of Scotland 1991*. Edinburgh: HMSO.

9   Farrington, J.H. (1983). The development of transport systems. In Clapperton, C.M. (ed.). *Scotland: A New Study*. Newton Abbott: David & Charles.

10   Cullingworth, J.B. and Nadin, V. (1997). *Town and Country Planning in the UK*. London: Routledge.

11   Soper, M.H.R. and Carter, E.S. (1985). *Farming and the Countryside*. Ipswich: Farming Press.

12   Mather, A.S. (1983). Rural land use. In Clapperton, C.M. (ed.). *Scotland: A New Study*. Newton Abbott: David & Charles.

13   Marsden, T., Murdoch, J., Lowe, P., Munton, R. and Flynn, A. (1993). *Constructing the Countryside*. Restructuring Rural Areas 1. London: UCL Press Limited.

14   Carter, E.S. and Stansfield, J.M. (1994). *British Farming – Changing Policies and Production Systems*. Ipswich: Farming Press Books.

15   Winter, M. (1996). *Rural Politics: Policies for Agriculture, Forestry and the Environment*. London: Routledge.

16   Gilg, A.W. (1978). *Countryside Planning – The First Three Decades 1945–76*. Problems in Modern Geography. Newton Abbott: David & Charles.

17   Lowe, P., Cox, C., MacEwen, M., O'Riordan, T. and Winter, M. (1986). *Countryside Conflicts: The Politics of Farming, Forestry and Conservation*. Aldershot: Temple Smith/Gower.

18   Bowers, J.K. and Cheshire, P. (1983). *Agriculture, the Countryside and Land Use*. London: Methuen.

19   Ministry of Agriculture and Fisheries, Department of Agriculture for Scotland and Ministry of Agriculture, Northern Ireland (1947). *Agricultural Statistics 1946–7*. London: HMSO.

20   Ministry of Agriculture, Fisheries and Food, Department of Agriculture and Fisheries for Scotland, Department of Agriculture for Northern Ireland and Welsh Office (1988). *Agricultural Statistics United Kingdom 1988*. London: HMSO.

21   Lowe, P., Cox, C., MacEwen, M., O'Riordan, T. and Winter, M. (1986). *Countryside Conflicts: The Politics of Farming, Forestry and Conservation*. Aldershot: Temple Smith/Gower.

22   Mather, A.S. (1983). Rural land use. In Clapperton, C.M. (ed.). *Scotland: A New Study*. Newton Abbott: David & Charles.

23   Bowers, J.K. and Cheshire, P. (1983). *Agriculture, the Countryside and Land Use*. London: Methuen.

24   Raymond, W.F. (1984). Trends in agricultural land use: the lowlands. In: Jenkins, D. (ed.) *Agriculture and the Environment*. pp 7–13. Cambridge: Institute of Terrestrial Ecology.

25   Mather, A.S. (1983). Rural land use. In Clapperton, C.M. (ed.). *Scotland: A New Study*. Newton Abbott: David & Charles.

26   Hopkins, A. and Hopkins, J.J. (1993). UK grasslands now: agricultural production and nature conservation. In Haggar, R.J. and Peel, S. (eds) *Grassland Management and Nature Conservation*. British Grassland Society Occasional Symposium No. 28. Reading: British Grassland Society.

27   Miles, J. (1987). Effects of man on upland vegetation. In Bell, M. and Bunce, R.G.H. (eds). *Agriculture and Conservation in the Hills and Uplands*. ITE Symposium No. 23. Cumbria: Institute of Terrestrial Ecology.

28   Marsden, T., Murdoch, J., Lowe, P., Munton, R. and Flynn, A. (1993). *Constructing the Countryside*. Restructuring Rural Areas 1. London: UCL Press Limited.

29   Fenton, A. (1991). The farming of the land. In Magnusson, M. and White, G. (eds). *The Nature of Scotland – Landscape, Wildlife and People*. pp 97–106. Edinburgh: Canongate.

30   Scottish Natural Heritage (1994). *Red Deer and the Natural Heritage*. SNH Policy Paper. Perth: Scottish Natural Heritage.

31   Johnson, F.G. (1994). Hydro-electric generation. In Maitland, P.S., Boon, P.J. and McLusky, D.S. (eds). *The Fresh Waters of Scotland – A National Resource of International Significance*. pp 297–316. Chichester: John Wiley & Sons.

32   Cm 1200 (1990). *This Common Inheritance – Britain's Environmental Strategy*. London: HMSO.

33   Booth, A.G. (1984). Ecology and planning. In Roberts, R.D. and Roberts, T.M. (eds). *Planning and Ecology*. London: Chapman & Hall.

34   Ibid.

35   Sinclair, G. (1992). *The Lost Land: Land Use Change in England 1945–1990*. London: The Council for the Protection of Rural England.

36   Mowle, A. and Bell, M. (1988). Rural policy factors in land-use change. In Usher, M.B. and Thompson, D.B.A. (eds). *Ecological Change in the Uplands*. Special Publications Series of the British Ecological Society Number 7, pp 165–182. Edinburgh: Blackwell Scientific Publications.

37   Roberts, R.D. and Roberts, T.M. (eds) (1984). Ecological considerations in rural planning. In *Planning and Ecology*. London: Chapman & Hall.

38   Ratcliffe, D.A. (ed.) (1977). Introduction . In *A Nature Conservation Review. Vol. 1*. Cambridge: Cambridge University Press.

39   Body, R (1982). *Agriculture: The Triumph and the Shame*. London: Temple Smith.

40   Bowers, J.K. and Cheshire, P. (1983). *Agriculture, the Countryside and Land Use*. London: Methuen.

41   Adams, W.M. (1997). *Future Nature*. London: Earthscan Publications Ltd.

EPILOGUE

Biodiversity, the health and variety of the natural world, is a key indicator of success in achieving sustainable development.[1] Yet the development process has altered ecological systems and reduced biological diversity.[2] International evidence points to an escalating rate of species loss across a whole range of life forms and to human activity as the chief cause.[3] The continuing decline of biodiversity is a telling measure of the imbalance between human wants and the functional capacity of the natural world.[4]

Habitat destruction is widely considered to be the most pervasive reason for biodiversity loss.[5] Challenges in the 1990s and into the next century include the development of a better understanding about how ecosystems operate at a landscape scale over long time periods, especially with respect to the cumulative effects of land use practices.[6] In that regard, the broader geographical and policy relevance of results from the National Countryside Monitoring Scheme can be illustrated by considering various sustainable development issues. These might include:

- the structure and function of habitats at a landscape scale;

- cross-sectoral considerations in habitat management; and

- information needs for policy development and evaluation.

Each of these is discussed in more detail below.

The structure and function of habitats at a landscape scale

Studies across the globe have shown that habitat fragmentation and isolation can restrict species dispersion and lead to a reduction in habitat heterogeneity. Competition from invasive species can increase.[7] Small isolated populations become more vulnerable, either through disturbance or through reduced genetic variability. The numbers of individuals of many species decline and extinctions may follow.[8, 9] Landscape boundaries, or 'ecotones', are important for many organisms and, by virtue of 'the edge effect', are often characterised by high levels of biological diversity.[10] Human management of the land often creates new boundaries or sharpens previous ones. Less intensively managed areas in landscapes can become relict habitat patches or corridors, subject to stress by their managed surroundings.[11]

The 1957 Treaty of Rome which established the European Economic Community reflected the dominant concerns of post-war Europe, which were economic reconstruction and growth, modernisation and improved living standards.[12] A discernible theme to the Commission's environmental programme did not become apparent until the end of the 1980s.[13] That is reflected in trends showing the direction and rate of habitat change during that time (Figures 4.2–4.5). While landscape-scale changes continued apace, conservation measures were directed at the protection of rare species and at the designation of key sites, as remnants of once much larger biotic communities.

European wetlands were degraded and reduced in extent, with the loss of associated species.[14] In Sweden, remnants of cultural landscapes and habitats which obstructed cultivation were removed.[15] Among European bird species alone, more than one-third continued to be reduced in numbers and/or range. The widely reported decline of farmland birds in Britain and in other European countries has also been linked to losses of other, less visible, groups of plants and invertebrates.[16,17] In the British countryside, the diversity of plant species declined during the 1980s, especially in the lowlands. Diversity also declined among the linear habitats of hedges, verges and streams, which serve as species-rich refuges for meadow and other plants that are no longer able to grow and reproduce in fields.[18] Intensive agricultural land use and land drainage resulted in the loss of lowland flood-plains, wetlands and woodlands. In the uplands, pre-plantation ploughing associated with coniferous afforestation, as well as overgrazing by sheep and deer, degraded wildlife habitats and resulted in increased siltation and bank erosion in streams and rivers.[19] In Scotland, intensive farming, forestry and urban development expanded whilst semi-natural habitats were reduced (Figure 26.1).

It is now widely accepted that biodiversity management cannot be achieved by simply establishing reserves as islands of protection in a sea of unregulated agriculture, forestry, fisheries and urban development. Rather, it relies upon the incorporation of conservation and sustainable use practices within all components of the landscape, supported by policies, agreements and institutional arrangements that foster co-operation between all forms of water and land use.[20] The conservation importance of site protection can thus be visualised as the apex of a much broader pyramid of sustainable land management measures required to maintain and improve important habitat characteristics in the wider environment.[21]

Cross-sectoral considerations in habitat management

A challenge facing Europe is to halt and reverse the decline in the continent's biological and landscape diversity.[22] Reductions in the number and range of plant and animal species in the UK over the last 50 years have been associated principally with urban and transport development, forestry expansion and the intensification of agricultural production.[23] The causes and consequences of land cover change in Scotland reflect, to varying degrees, changes which have taken place across Europe.[24]

Four key influences affecting land cover both in Scotland and in Europe have been:

- the loss of diversifying landscape features, such as hedges, ponds and woodlands of native species;

- the increase of monocultural systems on farms and in forests;

- fragmentation and disappearance of semi-natural habitats; and

- alteration of landscapes through industrial and urban development, and road building.

Projected growth in European economic activity suggests that the rate of loss of biodiversity is likely to increase within ecosystems (loss of habitats), within habitats (loss of species) and among species (loss of genetic or molecular diversity).[25] To maintain and enhance the ecological functioning of the country-side as a whole there is a need to relate landscape conservation and management to biodiversity and nature conservation objectives, within an over-arching framework for sustainable development.[26]

The fate of the corncrake, *Crex crex*, illustrates the problem and points to a possible solution. As one of 27 bird species in Europe which are at risk of global extinction, it is in steady decline. Its distribution has become discontinuous.[27] It has been listed as a strictly protected species on Appendix II of the 1979 Council of Europe Bern Convention (Conservation of European Wildlife and Natural Habitats) and on Annex I of the 1979 European Communities Birds Directive (for the Conservation of Wild Birds) for the protection of the species and its habitat. In Britain, it has been reduced in numbers and range by 100-or-more years of agricultural advancement. Its retreat across Scotland[28] bears a similarity to the pattern of land cover change (Part 4: Figure 1).

Despite being afforded the highest level of species protection within Schedule 1 of the Wildlife and Countryside Act 1981, the corncrake remains vulnerable to extinction in the UK through loss of traditional grassland mosaics and through grass management that is inappropriate to its life cycle. The corncrake is now confined almost entirely to the northwest of Scotland and the Hebridean islands.[29] There, the degree of land cover change has been relatively low (e.g. Figure 25.2).

Retaining only a tenuous hold as a UK breeding species, the corncrake has nevertheless been shown to respond rapidly to more favourable management of meadows. A Species Action Plan[30] now advocates a cross-sectoral, landscape-scale approach to the safeguard and recovery of this species in the UK. This will be through such measures as agricultural education and advice, grant schemes, management agreements within environmentally sensitive areas and agricultural policy development. Local biodiversity action plans provide a mechanism for translating national priorities into effective action at the local level, promoting also the conservation and wider understanding of habitats and species which are important locally.[31]

At a landscape scale, the NCMS illustrates the inter-dependence between the main land use sectors and their relative influences on habitat change. Consideration of the structure and function of habitats, for instance through ecological networks and environmentally sensitive areas, has become much more widely accepted in the land use policies of the 1990s. Yet in 1996, environmental support constituted only 2% of the Common Agricultural Policy budget,[32] illustrating the continuing need to integrate conservation objectives more fully into land use policy and activity.

Information needs for policy development and evaluation

Many of our essential goods and services, together with the quality of life for Scotland's people and quality of experience for visitors, depend on fertile soils, clean water, attractive countryside and a diversity of plant and animal life. Land is a key resource for a wide range of socio-economic activities (agriculture, wood production, industry, recreation) and infrastructure (settlements, transportation and communication networks), and a critical factor in the establishment of new activities.[33] In providing for a secure future, sustainable development needs to have regard for the structure, functions and diversity of natural systems – the diversity of life together with the ecological processes that sustain life.[34]

Yet in Europe, the diversity and distinctiveness of landscapes have been in decline.[35] Difficulties arise in comparing the results of surveys which have been designed for different purposes, with non-matching classification schemes and mapping resolutions, and with different temporal and geographical scales.[36] As a systematic investigation of land cover change during the latter-half of the twentieth century, the NCMS demonstrates the value of a clear and consistent time series for environmental audit and reporting.

Results from the NCMS have been utilised at a range of scales in Scotland. With the dataset mounted on a geographical information system, land cover change results are amenable to use in, for instance, local authority structure planning and environmental audit, or to strategic planning within European Structural Fund areas. The dataset has been re-analysed for integrated natural heritage assessment across 'natural heritage zones', a landscape-scale approach which is being piloted by Scottish Natural Heritage towards integrated environmental management. At the national scale, time series data can be derived for many of the terrestrial habitats in Scotland which have been identified for monitoring biodiversity in the UK.[37]

The NCMS has demonstrated the use of spatial and temporal statistics, together with the development of GIS and remote sensing, for the quantitative evaluation of habitat dynamics. As the NCMS time series has been extended, so its value has increased. It now provides a sequence for policy evaluation, with pre-European Community baseline data in 1947. A milestone in 1973 coincides with UK entry into the European Economic Community and the specification of the first Environment Action Programme. A further milestone in 1988 corresponds with a watershed in key sectoral policies which had driven the growth of agriculture and forestry from the late 1940s onwards. As a European case study, it makes a major contribution to understanding relationships between land use, the distinctive character of landscapes and biodiversity.

Prompted by 'a global agenda for change',[38] the policy agenda in the 1990s has been influenced to a much greater degree by concerns for the environment and sustainable development. The decade was marked in Britain by the publication of an environmental strategy.[39] In Europe, the fifth Action Programme was seen as a turning point towards reconciling environmental concerns with development.[40] Globally, the 'Earth Summit' introduced international conventions for the protection of species and ecosystems.[41, 42] The NCMS benchmark for the late 1980s can contribute to future assessments of sustainable development, towards an improved understanding of factors controlling variability in natural systems and factors responsible for environmental quality and productivity.

During the 1990s, national scale studies have made distinctive contributions to our knowledge and understanding of spatial and temporal variation in the composition of Scotland's land cover. The next major addition to knowledge of land cover change in Great Britain will be from the Countryside Survey programme,[43] for reporting in the year 2000. An opportunity for extending the NCMS time series might arise if, for instance, the Land Cover of Scotland census[44] were to be updated in the future.

There is a need still to make environmental information more accessible and more usable, both through environmental education as well as through improved institutional links that provide more effective access to data. There is a gap between context information provided by national scale studies and the more detailed, often site-specific, needs of the local planner and practitioner. A challenge for the future is to develop more integrated approaches to data acquisition and use, in order to support policy development and evaluation more effectively at national, regional and local scales. Foresight in the NCMS design has allowed considerable progress to be made, but bringing it to this stage of completion is far from the end of the story.

References

1   Scottish Biodiversity Group (1997). *Biodiversity in Scotland: The Way Forward*. Edinburgh: The Scottish Office.

2   Holdgate, M. (1996). *From Care to Action: Making a Sustainable World*. London: Earthscan Publications Ltd.

3   Ehrlich, P.R. (1997). *A World of Wounds: Ecologists and the Human Dilemma*. Excellence in Ecology, 8. Oldenddorf/Luhe: Ecology Institute.

4   World Resources Institute, The World Conservation Union and United Nations Environment Programme (1992). *Global Biodiversity Strategy: Guidelines for Action to Save, Study and Use Earth's Biotic Wealth Sustainably and Equitably*. WRI, IUCN, UNEP.

5   McNeely, J.A., Gadgil, M., Leveque, C., Padoch, C. and Redford, K. (1995). Human influences on biodiversity. *In* Heywood, V.H. (ed.). *Global Biodiversity Assessment*. Cambridge: Cambridge University Press.

6   Naiman, R.J. and Decamps, H. (1991). Landscape boundaries in the management and restoration of changing environments: a summary. *In* Holland, M.M., Risser, P.G. and Naiman, R.J. (eds). *Ecotones: The Role of Landscape Boundaries in the Management and Restoration of Changing Environments*. London: Chapman & Hall.

7   Saunders, D.A., Arnold, G.W., Burbidge, A.A. and Hopkins, A.J.M. (eds) (1987). *Nature Conservation: The Role of Remnants of Native Vegetation*. Chipping Norton: Surrey Beatty & Sons Pty Ltd.

8   Spellerberg, I.F. (1991). *Monitoring Ecological Change*. Cambridge: Cambridge University Press.

9   Sutherland, W.J. (ed.) (1998). *Conservation Science and Action*. Oxford: Blackwell Science.

10   Holland, M.M. and Risser, P.G. (1991). The role of landscape boundaries in the management and restoration of changing environments: introduction. *In* Holland, M.M., Risser, P.G. and Naiman, R.J. (eds). *Ecotones: The Role of Landscape Boundaries in the Management and Restoration of Changing Environments*. London: Chapman & Hall.

11   Correll, D.L. (1991). Human impact on the functioning of landscape boundaries. *In* Holland, M.M., Risser, P.G. and Naiman, R.J. (eds). *Ecotones: The Role of Landscape Boundaries in the Management and Restoration of Changing Environments*. London: Chapman & Hall.

12   Lowe, P. and Ward, S. (1998). Britain in Europe: themes and issues in national environmental policy. *In* Lowe, P. and Ward, S. (eds). *British Environmental Policy and Europe: Politics and Policy in Transition*. London: Routledge.

13   Sharp, R. (1998). Responding to Europeanisation: a government perspective. *In* Lowe, P. and Ward, S. (eds). *British Environmental Policy and Europe: Politics and Policy in Transition*. London: Routledge.

14   Navid, D. (1994). A threatened habitat: wetlands. *In* Bennet, G. (ed.). *Conserving Europe's Natural Heritage: Towards a European Ecological Network*. London: Graham & Trotman/Martinus Nijhoff.

15   Irse, M. (1988). Air photo interpretation and computer cartography: tools for studying the changes in cultural landscapes. *In* Birks, H.H., Birks, H.J.B., Kaland, P.E. and Moe, D. (eds). *The Cultural Landscape: Past, Present and Future*. Cambridge: Cambridge University Press.

16   Donald, P.F. (1998). Changes in the abundance of invertebrates and plants on British farmland. *British Wildlife*, 9, 279–289.

17   Imboden, C. (1994). Threatened species: birds as indicators of unsustainability. *In* Bennet, G. (ed.). *Conserving Europe's Natural Heritage: Towards a European Ecological Network*. London: Graham & Trotman/Martinus Nijhoff.

18   Barr, C.J., Bunce, R.G.H., Clark, R.T., Fuller, R.M., Furse, M.T., Gillespie, M.K., Groom, C.B., Hallam, C.J., Hornung, M., Howard, D.C. and Ness, M.J. (1993). *Countryside Survey 1990: Main Report (and Summary Report)*. Eastcote: Department of the Environment.

19   Raven, P.J., Holmes, N.T.H., Dawson, F.H., Fox, P.J.A., Everard, M., Fozzard, I.R. and Rouen, K.J. (1998). *River Habitat Quality: The Physical Character of Rivers and Streams in the UK and Isle of Man*. Bristol: Environment Agency.

20   Miller, K., Allergretti, M.H., Johnson, N. and Jonsson, B. (1995). Measures for conservation of biodiversity and sustainable use of its components. *In* Heywood, V.H. (ed.). *Global Biodiversity Assessment*. Cambridge: Cambridge University Press.

21   Tucker, G. (1994). A European ecological network and the conservation of birds. *In* Bennet, G. (ed.). *Conserving Europe's Natural Heritage: Towards a European Ecological Network*. London: Graham & Trotman/Martinus Nijhoff.

22   Bennet, G. (1994). A European approach to nature conservation. *In* Bennet, G. (ed.). *Conserving Europe's Natural Heritage: Towards a European Ecological Network*. London: Graham & Trotman/Martinus Nijhoff.

23   Department of the Environment (1996). *Indicators of Sustainable Development for the United Kingdom*. London: HMSO.

24   Park, J.R. (ed.) (1988). *Environmental Management in Agriculture: European Perspectives*. London: Belhaven Press.

25   Stanners, D. and Bourdeau, P. (1995). *Europe's Environment: The Dobris Assessment*. Copenhagen: European Environment Agency.

26   Bennet, G. (ed.) (1994). *Conserving Europe's Natural Heritage: Towards a European Ecological Network*. London: Graham & Trotman/Martinus Nijhoff.

27   Hagemeijer, W.J.M and Blair, M.J. (eds) (1997). *The EBBC (European Bird Census Council) Atlas of European Breeding Birds: Their Distribution and Abundance*. London: T & AD Poyser.

28   Royal Society for the Protection of Birds (1993). *Agriculture in Scotland: Farming for a Living Countryside*. Edinburgh: RSPB.

29   Wingfield Gibbons D., Reid, J.B. and Chapman, R.A. (eds) (1993). *The New Atlas of Breeding Birds in Britain and Ireland: 1988–1991*. London: T & AD Poyser.

30   Biodiversity Steering Group (1995). *Biodiversity: The UK Steering Group Report. Volume 2: Action Plans*. London: HMSO.

31   Convention of Scottish Local Authorities (1997). *Local Biodiversity Action Plans: A Manual*. Edinburgh: The Scottish Office.

32   Reynolds, F. (1998). Environmental Planning: Land-use and Landscape Policy. In Lowe, P. and Ward, S. (eds). *British Environmental Policy and Europe: Politics and Policy in Transition*. London: Routledge.

33   Brouwer, F.M. and Chadwick, M.J. (1991). Future land use patterns in Europe. *In* Brouwer, F.M., Thomas, A.J. and Chadwick, M.J. (eds) *Land Use Changes in Europe: Processes of Change, Environmental Transformations and Future Patterns*. London: Kluwer Academic Publishers.

34   The World Conservation Union, United Nations Environment Programme and World Wide Fund for Nature (1991). *Caring for the Earth: A Strategy for Sustainable Living*. Gland: IUCN/UNEP/WWF.

35   Meeus, J.H.A., Wijermans, M.P. and Vroom, M.J. (1990). Agricultural landscapes in Europe and their transformation. *Landscape and Urban Planning*, 18, 289–352.

36   Wyatt, B.K, Greatorex-Davies, J.N., Hill, M.O., Parr, T.W., Bunce, R.G.H. and Fuller, R.M. (1994). *Comparison of Land Cover Definitions: Countryside 1990 Series Volume 3*. Eastcote: Department of the Environment.

37   The UK Steering Group. (1995). *Biodiversity: The UK Steering Group Report. Volume 1: Meeting the Rio Challenge*. London: HMSO.

38   The World Commission on Environment and Development (1987). *Our Common Future*. Oxford: Oxford University Press.

39   Department of the Environment (1990). *This Common Inheritance: Britain's Environmental Strategy*. London: HMSO.

40   Commission of the European Communities (1992). *Towards Sustainability: A European Community Programme of Policy and Action in Relation to Environmental and Sustainable Development*. Luxembourg: Office for Official Publications of the European Community.

41   Johnson, S.P. (1993). *The Earth Summit: The United Nations Conference on Environment and Development (UNCED)*. London: Graham & Trotman/Martinus Nijhoff.

42   Grubb, M., Koch, M., Munson, A. Sullivan, F. and Thompson, K. (1993). *The Earth Summit Agreements: A Guide and Assessment*. London: Earthscan Publications Ltd.

43   Department of the Environment, Transport and Regions (1998). *Countryside Survey 2000 News* 1.

44   The Macaulay Land Use Research Institute (1993). *The Land Cover of Scotland: Executive Summary*. Aberdeen: MLURI.

INDEX

Page numbers in *italics* refer to tables, figures and boxes.

cidification xxiii

aerial photography xvi, xviii, 5, 7–11, *16*

afforestation
  blanket mire affected 35, 66, *194, 234*, 238–9
  bracken reduced *144*
  broadleaved woodland reduced *91*
  ditches dug for 117
  expansion 241
  heather moorland affected *194, 234*, 238, 239
  heather moorland reduced *74*, 75, 206, 212
  intermediate grassland reduced *51*
  lowland mire affected *67*
  mire affected *69, 234*
  rough grassland affected *199, 234*, 238
  rough grassland reduced 43, 47, *48*, 193, 206, 212, 240
  scrub reduced *146, 148*
  wet ground reduced *121*
  woodland affected *234*

agriculture
  arable 237
  Borders 159
  CAP 236, 237
  Central 165
  changes in land cover xv, xxi–xxii, 37, 85, 124, 151, 236–42, 246–7
  chemical control 78, 236, 237
  and conservation 80–1
  contraction 236
  Dumfries & Galloway 171
  Fife 177
  financial incentives 236, 237
  food supply xv, 236, 237
  Grampian 183
  Highland 190
  historical background 78–81

intensification xxiii, 37, 78, 80–1, 236–8, 241
  Lothian 195
  mechanisation xv, 78–9, 236, 237
  Orkney Islands 213
  pollution xxi, 112
  regulation 233
  Shetland Islands 219
  specialisation 78, 80, 241
  Strathclyde 201
  Tayside 207
  technological advances xv, 237, 240
  urban development affects 235
  and water supply 111, 112
  Western Isles 225

Agrostis spp. 41, 46, 119

alder 146

Alnus spp. 146

amphibians 60, 151

Anthoxanthum odoratum 46

arable
  into built ground 30, *82, 83*, 129, 170, 181, 199–200
  changes to land cover *234*
  classification *12*, 81
  compositional changes *82, 83*
  contraction 43, *198, 199, 216, 217, 218*
  expansion *234*, 237, 241
  expansion (Dumfries & Galloway) *174, 175*
  expansion (Fife) *180, 181*
  expansion (Grampian) *186, 187*
  expansion (Tayside) *210, 211, 212*
  geographical changes *81*
  from grassland 30, *82, 83, 84*
  into grassland *82, 83*
  from heather moorland *234*
  historical background 78–81
  interchanges *80*, 81

from intermediate grassland *55, 56, 175, 211*
  into intermediate grassland *55, 56*
  leys 41, 52, 81
  mapping *10*, 11, 13, *14*
  projected extent *79*
  into quarries *199*
  into recreational land *131*
  regional trends *80, 84*
  from rough grassland 182
  from smooth grassland 37, 43, *55, 84, 154, 175, 211*, 237
  into smooth grassland *55, 205, 206, 217, 218*
  smooth grassland rotation *164, 170, 199*
  into transport corridor 30, *82, 83, 139, 140, 217*, 235
  trends *80, 84*
  urban development affects *84*
  from woodland *234*

Arctostaphylos uva-ursi 61

ash 85

banks 9

bare ground
  from blanket mire *137, 138*
  classification *12*, 64
  compositional changes *126, 127, 139*
  expansion *36, 128*, 235
  expansion (Central) *168, 170*
  expansion (Fife) *181*
  expansion (Grampian) *186, 187*
  expansion (Lothian) *198, 199*
  expansion (Strathclyde) *204, 205*
  expansion (Tayside) *210, 211*
  expansion (Western Isles) *228, 229*
  interchanges *137, 138*
  mapping *14*
  from mire 235
  regional trends *137, 138*

from transport corridor 235
trends *126, 128, 137, 138*
bearberry 61
bedstraw
common marsh 118–19
heath 46
bell heather 72
bent
common 46
creeping 119
Betula spp. 85, 143, 146
bilberry 46, 60
biodiversity xix–xx, xxiii, xxiv,
242, 245–8
Biodiversity Action Plan xvii, xxiii
birch 85, 143, 146
birds xxiii, 60, 119, 120, 151, 247
bladderwort, intermediate 60
blanket mire
afforestation affects 35, 66,
194, 234, 238–9
into bare ground *137, 138*
into bracken *149*
into built ground *223, 224*
classification 61, 62–4
compositional changes *62,
67–8*
into coniferous plantation 33,
101, *102, 175*, 238
contraction *63*
contraction (Borders) *162, 164*
contraction (Dumfries &
Galloway) *174, 175*
contraction (Highland) *192, 194*
contraction (Orkneys) *216, 217*
contraction (Shetlands) *222,
223*
contraction (Western Isles)
228, 229
defined 58
drained 35, 49, *205, 206, 223,
229, 230*
flora 60–1
geographical changes *64*
grass-dominated *48*, 61, *63*
into grassland *217, 218*, 223,
224, 230
into heather moorland *67–8,
74–6*, 163, *175, 187, 205–6,
217–18*, 224
heather-dominated 61, *63, 228*

interchanges *64, 65, 194, 210,
211, 229, 230*
into intermediate grassland 49,
51
mapping *14*
into plantation *67, 68, 107, 164*
regional trends *63, 65*
into rough grassland 47, *55–6,
67–8*, 163, *175, 205, 206*
into smooth grassland 54
trends *62, 63, 65, 234*
into wet ground *122, 123*
into young plantation 100, *101,
238*
bog cotton 60
bog myrtle 61
bogbean 60
bogs 58–9, 60, 66
Borders 159–64
boundaries, mapping 9, 11, 19
bracken
afforestation reduces *144*
from blanket mire *149*
from broadleaved woodland
105, 149
character 141–2
classification *12, 13, 15*, 142
compositional changes *141, 149*
expansion 37, *142*
expansion (Dumfries &
Galloway) *174, 175*
expansion (Highland) *192, 194,
234*, 240, *241*, 242
geographical changes *144*
from grassland *149*
from heather moorland 30,
75–6, 144, 149, 211–12
into heather moorland *149*, 240
insects 142
interchanges 19, *142, 143*
mapping 9, *13, 14*, 142
expansion *28*
into plantation *149, 170*
regional trends *143, 144*
from rough grassland 30,
*55–6, 144, 149, 164, 170,
175, 205–6*, 240
into rough grassland *149, 170*
toxicity 142
trends *141, 142, 144*
into wet ground *121*
bramble 145

broadleaved plantation
expansion *168, 170*
regional trends *93*
trends *93*
broadleaved woodland
afforestation reduces *91, 234*
into arable *234*
into bracken *105, 149*
into built ground *105*
classification 89–90
clearances *91*
compositional changes *105*
into coniferous plantation *105,
238*
contraction 30
contraction (Fife) *180, 181*
contraction (Grampian) *186,
187*
contraction (Highland) *192, 194*
contraction (Lothian) *198, 199,
238*
defined 90
geographical changes *94*
from heather moorland *105*
into heather moorland *105*
interchanges *90, 91*
mapping *10*
from mixed woodland *105*
into mixed woodland *105*
into plantation *105, 107*
projected extent *89*
regional trends *90, 91*
from rough grassland *105*
into rough grassland *105*
from scrub *105*
into scrub *105, 148*
from smooth grassland *105*
into smooth grassland *105*
into transport corridor *105*
trends *90, 91, 234*
broom 145
built ground
from arable 30, *82, 83, 129,
170, 181, 199–200*
birds 125
from blanket mire *223, 224*
from broadleaved woodland
105
classification *12*, 128–9
compositional changes *126,
128, 139*
expansion 30, *36, 128, 235*, 241

expansion (Central) *168, 170*

expansion (Dumfries & Galloway) *174, 175*

expansion (Fife) *180, 181*

expansion (Grampian) *186, 187*

expansion (Lothian) *198, 199*

expansion (Strathclyde) *204, 205*

expansion (Tayside) *210, 211*

expansion (Western Isles) *228, 229*

flora 124–5

geographical changes *127*

from grassland 129

historical background 124–6

interchanges *129*

from intermediate grassland *199, 200*

mammals 124–5

mapping 13, *14*

projected extent *125*

regional trends *128, 129*

from smooth grassland 30, *55–6, 170, 181, 187, 199–200, 205*, 235

trends *126, 128, 129*

built-up areas *see* built ground

bulrush 118

burns 110

bur-reed, branched 118

buttercup, meadow 46

Calluna vulgaris 9, 46, 60, 61, 71, 72

canals
    interpretation problems 117
    mapping 112

Carex spp. 60

case studies
    arable *82*
    grassland *57*
    heather moorland *77*
    hedgerows *154*
    mire *69*
    urban development *140*
    woodland *108*

cattle farming 41, 42, 241

Central 165–70

Cerastium fontanum 46

cereals 9, 78, 80, 237

Cervus elaphus see red deer

classification
    arable *12*, 81
    bare ground *12*, 64
    blanket mire 61, 62–4
    bracken *12*, 13, 15, 142
    broadleaved woodland 89–90
    built ground *12*, 128–9
    features *12*
    fresh water *12*, 112
    grassland *12*, 42
    heather moorland *12*, 13, 14, 72
    hedgerows *12*, 151
    hierarchical xvii
    intermediate grassland 47
    land types xvi–ix
    land use xix
    linear features xviii
    lowland mire 66
    mire 9, 11, *12*, 13, 14, 62–4, 66
    misclassification 12–15
    mixed woodland 13, 15
    objectivity xviii
    plantation 13, 15
    problems xvi, xviii
    recreational land 129
    regional 6
    rock 13
    rough grassland 13, 15
    scrub *12*, 142–3, 145, 146
    smooth grassland 52–3
    systems xvi–xviii
    transport corridor 130, 132
    treeline 153–4
    wet ground 120
    woodland *12*, 87

clearfelling 102–3

cliff *see* rock

climate 42, 78, 85, 110, 124

climate change xxi, xxii–xxiii, 59

clover, white 46

cock's-foot 46, 52

Common Agricultural Policy (CAP) 236, 237, 248

coniferous plantation
    from blanket mire 33, *67, 68,* 101, *102, 107,* 108, *175,* 238
    from bracken *149*
    from broadleaved woodland *105, 107,* 238

    into broadleaved woodland *105*
    commercial factors 97–8
    compositional changes *107*
    from coniferous woodland 238
    defined 100
    expansion *36*
    expansion (Borders) *162, 164*
    expansion (Central) *168, 170*
    expansion (Dumfries & Galloway) *174, 175*
    expansion (Grampian) *186, 187*
    expansion (Highland) *192, 194*
    expansion (Lothian) *198, 199*
    expansion (Tayside) *210, 211,* 241
    geographical changes *104*
    from heather moorland 33, *75–6, 102, 107, 170, 175, 187, 211,* 238
    interchanges *102*
    mapping 13
    from mixed woodland 238
    projected extent *99*
    regional trends *101, 102*
    from rough grassland 33, *55–6, 102, 107, 170, 175, 181, 187,* 238
    into rough grassland *107*
    from scrub *107, 145, 149*
    trends *101, 102*
    underplanted *102*
    young plantation *107*
    from young plantation *101, 107*

coniferous woodland
    afforestation affects *234*
    character 95
    compositional changes *106*
    into coniferous plantation 238
    and conservation 95
    contraction 30
    geographical changes *98*
    interchanges *97, 98*
    into plantation *106*
    projected extent *96*
    regional trends *97, 98*
    into rough grassland *106, 107*
    trends *97, 98, 234*

conifers
    introduced 86

conservation
    and agriculture 80–1
    and forestry 85–6, 87, 95

fresh water 111
hedgerows 151
and land use xix–xx, xxii–xxiv, 233, 238, 241, 242, 245–9
of peat 58, 60
and sport 58
corncrake 247
Corylus avellana 85, 143, 146
cotton grass 60
Countryside Commission xvii
Countryside Surveys of Great Britain xvii, xxi–xxii, xxiii, 4
cranberry 60
Crataegus monogyna 143, 146, 151
Crex crex 247
crowberry 60, 72
curlew 120
Cytisus scoparius 145

Dactylis glomerata 46, 52
decreases
Borders region 160, *162, 164*
Central region 166, *168–9*
Dumfries & Galloway *174–5,* 176
Fife *180–1,* 182
Grampian region *186–7,* 188
Highland region *192–3,* 193, *194*
Lothian region *198–9,* 200
Orkney Islands *216–17,* 218
Scotland total 27, *28–36*
Shetland Islands *222–3*
Strathclyde region *204–5,* 206
Tayside region 208, *210–11*
Western Isles *228–9*
deer 41–2, 70, 238, 239
deer grass 58, 60, 72
Deschampsia spp. 46, 120
digital mapping 11–12, *16*
distribution maps 20
disturbance 27, 30, 124
ditches
afforestation link 27, 117
increase in *36, 82*
increase in (Borders) *162, 164*
increase in (Dumfries & Galloway) *174, 175*
increase in (Grampian) *186, 187*

increase in (Orkneys) *216, 217*
increase in (Shetlands) *222, 223*
increase in (Tayside) *210, 211*
increase in (Western Isles) *228, 229,* 239
mapping 9, *14,* 112
regional trends *118*
trends *118*
Douglas fir 86, 87
Drosera spp. 58
Dumfries & Galloway 171–6
dunes 47
dykes *see* ditches

ecological succession xx–xxi, xxii
economic factors xxi–xxii, 27, 97–8, 233–42
elder 146
emissions xxi, xxii–xxiii, 59, 112, 126
Empetrum nigrum 60, 72
enclosures 151
environmental considerations *see* conservation; pollution
Epilobium hirsutum 120
Erica spp. 9, 60, 72
Eriophorum spp. 58, 60, 72
erosion 137
eutrophication xxiii

Falco tinnunculus 125
features
classification *12*
geographical analysis 155–7
interpretation 9, 11–15
linear xviii, 9
mapping 11–12
regional trends *157*
results of survey 19–22
sectoral analysis 233–42
felled woodland
defined 102–3
expansion 239
interchanges *103, 104*
regional trends *103*
trends *104*
fens 47, 58, 66
fescue
meadow 46

red 46
sheep's 46
Festuca spp. 46
Fife 177–82
Filipendula ulmaria 118
fish 119
food supply xv, 236, 237
forestry
Borders 159
Central 165
changes to land cover xxi–xxiv, 85–7, 97–8, 235, 238–9, 240–1, 246–7
and conservation xxii, xxiii–xiv, 85–6, 87
Dumfries & Galloway 171
Fife 177
financial incentives 60, 85–6
Grampian 183
Highland 190
Lothian 195
mechanisation xv, 97–8
Orkney Islands 213
pollution 112
regulation 233
Shetland Islands 219
Strathclyde 201
Tayside 207
technological advances xv, 240
timber production xv, 85–6
Western Isles 225
forests see woodland
Fraxinus spp. 85
fresh water
classification *12,* 112
compositional changes *113, 114, 122, 123*
and conservation 111
fauna 119, 120
flora 117–19, 120
geographical changes *114*
historical background 110–12
projected extent *111*
sporting uses 111
trends *113, 114*

Galium spp. 46, 118–19
Gallinago gallinago 120
geographical analysis
arable *81*

blanket mire *64*
bracken *144*
broadleaved woodland *94*
built land *127*
coniferous plantation *104*
coniferous woodland *98*
fresh water *114*
grassland *43*
heather moorland *74*
intermediate grassland *51*
lowland mire *66*
regional 20–1, 155–7
rough grassland *48*
scrub *148*
smooth grassland *55*
geographical information systems
  see GIS
GIS 5, 15–17
gorse 143
Grampian 183–8
grassland
  acid 42, 45
  from blanket mire *217, 218,*
    223, 224, 230
  burning 42
  calcicolous 42, 46–7
  calcifugous 42, 45
  character of 42
  classification *12*, 42
  compositional changes *43, 44,*
    51, 56, 57
  contraction 238
  expansion *234*
  flora 42, 45–7, 52
  geographical changes *43*
  from heather moorland *211,*
    212, 217, 218
  historical background 41–2
  improvement 41, 55, *181, 199,*
    234, 237–8, 240
  improvement (Borders) *164*
  improvement (Orkneys)
    217–18
  improvement (Scotland total)
    33, 37
  improvement (Shetlands) *223*
  improvement (Tayside) *211, 212*
  lime-loving 42, 46–7
  management 41, 42
  mapping *10, 14*
  mesotrophic 42, 46

from mire 30, *69*
neutral 42, 46
into recreational land *131*
trends *43*
see also smooth; intermediate;
  rough
gravel 137
grazing
  changes land cover 41, 239–40,
    242
  as management 58, 70, 242
ground *see* bare ground; built
  ground; wet ground
grouse 70, 238

habitat management 245–9
hair moss, woolly 60
hair-grass
  tufted 120
  wavy 46
hawthorn 143, 146, 151
hazel 85, 143, 146
heath, cross-leaved 11, 60, 72
heather 11, 46, 60, 61, 71, 72
heather moorland
  afforestation affects *194*
  afforestation reduces *74, 75,*
    206, 212, *234,* 238, 239
  into arable *234*
  from blanket mire *67–8, 74–6,*
    163, *175, 187, 205–6,*
    217–18, 224
  from bracken *149,* 240
  into bracken 30, *75–6,* 144,
    149, 211–12
  from broadleaved woodland
    105
  into broadleaved woodland *105*
  burning 239
  character 72
  classification *12, 13, 14,* 72
  compositional changes 75, *76*
  into coniferous plantation 33,
    102, 170, 175, 187, 211, 238
  contraction *36,* 239, 242
  contraction (Borders) *162, 164*
  contraction (Central) *168, 170*
  contraction (Dumfries &
    Galloway) *174, 175*
  contraction (Fife) *180, 181*
  contraction (Grampian) *186, 187*

contraction (Highland) *192, 194*
contraction (Tayside) *210, 211*
flora 72
geographical changes *74*
into grassland *211, 212, 217,*
  218
grouse 70, 71
historical background 70–2
interchanges 19, *73, 74*
into intermediate grassland 49,
  51, 55, 56, 75, 76, 240
management 70, 71, 72
mapping 9, 11, 13, *14*
from mire 30, 35, 66, 193, *199,*
  200
into parkland *95*
into plantation *75–6, 164*
projected extent *71*
red deer 70
regional trends *73, 74*
into reservoirs 30, *234,* 240
from rock *135, 139*
from rough grassland 33, 54,
  55–6, 199–200, 205–6, 223–4
into rough grassland 35, 47,
  48, 55–7, 74–7, 175, 187,
  194, 239
from scrub *149*
into scrub 145, *146, 148*
sheep farming 70
from smooth grassland *224*
into smooth grassland 54
sport 70, 71
into transport corridor 235
trends *73, 74, 234*
into wet ground *121, 122, 123*
into young plantation 34, 100,
  101, 238
heathland
  dry 72
  flora 60
  human influence 72
  mapping 9
  maritime 72
  species 46
  wet 72
  see also heather moorland
hedgerows
  classification *12,* 151
  clearance 30, 151–2, *154*
  and conservation 151
  defined 151

fauna 151

historical background 151

mapping xviii, 9, 13, *14*

reduction in *36, 82, 152*, 237, 242

reduction in (Borders) *162, 164*

reduction in (Central) *169, 170*

reduction in (Dumfries & Galloway) *174, 175*

reduction in (Fife) *180, 181*

reduction in (Grampian) *186, 187*

reduction in (Highland) *193, 194*

reduction in (Lothian) *198, 199*

regional trends *152*

trends *152*, 234

Highland 189–94

hill farming 238, 239–40

Holcus lanatus 46

human influence xvi, xvii, xxi–xxii, xxiii, 59, 60, 72

hydro-power *36*, 110, 240

increases

Borders region 160, *162, 164*

Central region 166, *168–9*

Dumfries & Galloway 172, *174–5*

Fife 178, *180–1*

Grampian region 184, *186–7*

Highland region 190, *192–3, 194*

Lothian region 196, *198–9*

Orkney Islands 214, *216–17*

Scotland total 27, *28–36*

Shetland Islands 220, *222–3*

Strathclyde region 202, *204–5*

Tayside region 208, *210–11*

Western Isles 226, *228–9*

industry

changes to land cover 124

pollution 112

and water supply 111, 112

insects 125, 151

interchanges

arable *80*, 81

bare ground *137, 138*

blanket mire *64, 65*

Borders region *163, 164*

bracken *142, 143*

broadleaved woodland *90, 91*

built ground *129*

Central region *169, 170*

coniferous plantation *102*

coniferous woodland *97, 98*

defined 19–20

Dumfries & Galloway *175, 176*

felled woodland *103, 104*

Fife *181, 182*

Grampian region *187, 188*

heather moorland *73, 74*

Highland region 193, *194*

intermediate grassland *50, 51*

lochs *115, 116*

Lothian region *199–200*

lowland mire *66*

mixed woodland *92*

Orkney Islands *217, 218*

parkland *94, 95*

quarries *134, 135*

recreational land *130, 131*

reservoirs *116, 117*

rock *135, 136*

rough grassland *47, 48*

Scotland total 27, 30, 33–7

scrub *145, 146, 147*, 150

Shetland Islands *223, 224*

smooth grassland *53, 54*

Strathclyde region *205, 206*

Tayside region *211, 212*

transport corridor *132*

Western Isles *229, 230*

wet ground *121*

young plantation *100, 101*

intermediate grassland

afforestation reduces *51*

from arable *55, 56, 82, 83*

into arable *55, 56, 82, 83, 175, 211*

from blanket mire *49, 51*

into bracken *149*

into built ground 129, *199, 200*

classification 47

expansion 240, 241

expansion (Borders) *162, 164*

expansion (Fife) *180, 181*

expansion (Grampian) *186, 187*

expansion (Orkneys) *216, 217*

geographical changes *51*

from heather moorland *49, 51, 55, 56, 75, 76, 164*, 240

improvement 49, *51*

interchanges *50, 51*

from mire 240

projected extent *49*

from rough grassland 35, *51, 55–7, 170, 175, 181*, 240

into rough grassland *55–6, 187*

from scrub *149*

into scrub *149*

from smooth grassland *55–6, 181, 229*

into smooth grassland *54, 55–7, 170, 175*

trends *50, 51*

urban development affects *49, 51*

into wet ground *122, 123*

interpretation

data 19–22

features 9, *11–15*

maps 9, 11

problems 8–9, 11

invertebrates 60, 119, 151

Juncus spp. 120

Juniperus spp. 85, 143, 145

kestrels 125

Lagopus lagopus see red grouse

land cover, defined xvi

Land Cover of Scotland (LCS88) xvii, 4, 15, 20

land use

changes in xv

classification xix

and conservation xix–xx, xxii–xxiv, 233, 238, 241, 242

defined xviii–xix, 3

management 233

mapping 5

sectoral analysis 233–42

sustainable xv, xxii–xxiv, 60, 245–9

Landsat Multi-Spectral Scanner 6

lapwing 120

larch 86, 87

Larix spp. 86, 87

leys 41, 52

lichens 126

linear features xviii, 9
liverworts 126
lochans *see* lochs
lochs
  interchanges *115, 116*
  mapping *14*, 112
  reduction in *36*
  regional trends *115, 116*
  into reservoirs *36, 116, 117, 122, 123, 234*, 240
  size of 110
  trends *115, 116, 234*
Lolium perenne 52
Lothian 195–200
lowland mire
  afforestation affects *67*
  classification 66
  contraction 30, *63, 174, 175*
  geographical changes *66*
  interchanges *66*
  regional trends *65, 67*
  into rough grassland *67*
  trends *67, 234*
lowlands
  cattle farming 42, 78
  farming 237, 238
  fens 58
  grassland 44, 46
  raised bogs 58–9
  sheep farming 41
  woodland species 85

machair 47
mammals xxiii, 60, 151
mapping
  arable *10*, 11, 13, *14*
  bare ground 9, 13, *14*
  blanket mire *14*
  boundaries 9, 11, 19
  bracken 142
  broadleaved woodland *10*
  built ground 13, *14*
  canals 112
  coniferous plantation 13
  density 20
  developments 15–17
  digital 11–12, *16*
  ditches 9, *14*, 112
  fresh water features *12*, 112
  grassland 9, *10, 14*

heathland 9
hedgerows xviii, 9
interpretation 9, *10*, 11
linear features xviii
lochs *14, 112*
method 11–12
mire 11, 13
reservoirs 112
rock *14*
scrub 9, *10*, 13, *14*
tracks 134
transport corridor *14*
treeline 9, *14*
wet ground *14*, 112
woodland 13, *14*
marginal inundation
  defined 117
  fauna 119
  flora 117–19
  mapping 112
  regional trends *119*
mat-grass 46, 72
meadow-grass, smooth 46
meadowsweet 118
Mentha aquatica 118
Menyanthes trifoliata 60
mint, water 118
mire
  afforestation affects *69, 234*
  into bare ground 235
  blanket *see* blanket mire
  classification 9, 11, *12*, 13, 14, 62–4, 66
  compositional changes *62, 67–8*
  conservation 58
  contraction *36, 63*, 242
  defined 58
  drained 30, 64, *194, 199, 200, 234*, 235, 240
  fauna 60
  flora 11, 58, 60–1
  into grassland 30, *69*
  into heather moorland 30, 35, 66, 193, *199, 200*
  historical background 59–60
  human influence 59, 60
  into intermediate grassland 240
  lowland *see* lowland mire
  mapping 11, 13
  projected extent *61*

radiative influence 59
  into rough grassland 35, 66, 193
  into transport corridor 235
  trees 59
  trends *62, 63, 234*
  vegetation 9
  into young plantation 34
misclassification 12–15
mixed woodland
  afforestation affects *234*
  into arable *234*
  from broadleaved woodland *105*
  into broadleaved woodland *105*
  classification 13, 15
  compositional changes *105*
  into coniferous plantation 238
  contraction 30, *192, 194, 210, 211*
  defined 91
  felling *91*
  interchanges *92*
  into plantation *91, 105*
  regional trends *91, 92*
  into rough grassland *105*
  from scrub *105*
  into scrub *105*
  trends *91, 92, 234*
Molinia caerula 61, 72, 120
moor grass, purple 61, 72, 120
moorland *see* heather moorland
mosses 58, 60, 126
mouse-ear, common 46
muirburn 42, 239
Myrica gale 61

Nardus stricta 46, 72
National Vegetation Classification xvi, xviii, 46
Nature Conservancy Council 5
Norway spruce 86, 87
Numenius arquata 120

oak 85
Orkney Islands 213–18

parkland
  background 78

compositional changes *105*
contraction *198, 199*
defined 93
into farmland *95*
from heather moorland *95*
interchanges *94, 95*
regional trends *94, 95*
into smooth grassland *105*
trends *94, 95*
from woodland *95*
peat
  archaeological significance 59
  bare 64
  conservation 58, 60
  cultivation 85–6
  extraction 11, 58, 60, 138, 235
  formation 58
  as a habitat 47, 60–1
Phalaris arundinacea 117–18
Phleum pratense 52
Phragmites australis 117
Picea spp. 86, 87
Pinus spp. 85, 87, 143
Plantago lanceolata 46
plantain, ribwort 46
plantation
  from blanket mire *164*
  into bracken *170*
  classification 13, 15
  compositional changes *105*
  coniferous 86
  expansion xxiii, *204, 205*
  from heather moorland *164*
  mapping 9, *14*
  from mixed woodland *91*
  from rough grassland *164*
  see also broadleaved; young;
    coniferous
Poa pratensis 46
political factors xv, xxi
pollution xxi, xxii–xxiii, 59, 112,
  125
population
  Borders 159
  Central 165
  Dumfries & Galloway 171
  Fife 177
  Grampian 183
  Lothian 195
  Orkney Islands 213
  Scotland total 235

Shetland Islands 219
Strathclyde 201
Tayside 207
Western Isles 225
Potentilla erecta 46
Pseudotsuga menziesii 86, 87
Pteridium aquilinum see bracken

quarries
  from arable *199*
  interchanges *134, 135*
  regional trends *134, 135*
  trends *134, 135*
  vegetation 126
Quercus spp. 85

Racomitrium lanuginosum 60
railways 125–6, 130
rainfall 78, 141
Ranunculus acris 46
recreation 30, 128, 129, 235, 238,
  242 *see also* sport
recreational land
  from arable *131*
  classification 129
  expansion 30, *36, 128*
  expansion (Central) *168, 170*
  expansion (Fife) *180, 181*
  expansion (Grampian) *186, 187*
  expansion (Lothian) *198, 199*
  expansion (Strathclyde) *204,
    205*, 235
  from grassland *131*, 235
  interchanges *130, 131*
  regional trends *130*
  trends *131*
red deer 41, 70, 238, 239
red grouse 70, 238
redshank 120
reed, common 117
reed-grass 118
reptiles 60, 125, 151
reservoirs
  expansion 30, *36, 192, 194*
  from heather moorland 30,
    234, 240
  interchanges *116, 117*
  from lochs *36, 116, 117, 122,
    123, 234*, 240
  mapping 112

regional trends *115, 117*
from rough grassland 30
rhododendron 146
rivers
  interpretation problems 117
  mapping 112
  size of 110
roads 25, 125–6, 128, 130, *140*, 235
rock
  classification 13
  into heather moorland *135, 139*
  interchanges *135, 136*
  mapping *14*
  regional trends *136*
  into rough grassland *135*
  trends *135*
  vegetation 126
rough grassland
  afforestation affects *199, 234,*
    238
  afforestation reduces 43, 47,
    48, 193, 206, 212, 240
  from arable *82, 83*
  into arable *82, 83*, 182
  from blanket mire 47, *55–6,
    67–8, 163, 175, 205, 206*
  from bracken *149, 170*
  into bracken 30, *55–6*, 144, *149,
    164, 170, 175, 205–6*, 240
  from broadleaved woodland
    105
  into broadleaved woodland *105*
  character 45
  classification 13, 15
  into coniferous plantation 33,
    102, 170, 175, 181, 187, 238
  from coniferous woodland
    106, 107
  contraction *48*, 240, 242
  contraction (Borders) *162, 164*
  contraction (Central) *168, 170*
  contraction (Dumfries &
    Galloway) *174, 175*
  contraction (Fife) *180, 181*
  contraction (Lothian) *198, 199*
  expansion *48, 192, 194*
  geographical changes *48*
  from heather moorland 35,
    *47, 48, 55–7, 74–7, 175, 187,
    194*, 239
  into heather moorland 33, 54,
    55–6, 199–200, 205–6, 223–4

improvement 44, 47, 48

interchanges *47, 48*

from intermediate grassland *55–6, 187*

into intermediate grassland 35, *51, 55–7, 170, 175, 181*, 240

from lowland mire *67*

mapping *10*, 13

from mire 35, 66, 193

into mixed woodland *105*

from plantation *107*

into plantation *55, 56, 164*

projected extent *45*

into reservoirs 30

from rock *135*

from scrub *149*

into scrub 145, *146, 148, 149*

from smooth grassland *55–6, 187*

into smooth grassland *54, 55–7, 170*

species *45–7*

into transport corridor *139*

trends *46, 48, 234*

from wet ground *122, 123*, 169

into wet ground *121, 122, 123, 175, 205*

into young plantation 34, 100, *101, 108*, 238

rowan 85, 143

Rubus spp. 145

rushes 120

rye-grass, perennial 52

Salix spp. 143

Salmo salar 238

salmon 238

Sambucus spp. 146

sampling 6–7

satellite imagery xvi, xviii, 6

Scirpus cespitosus see Trichophorum cespitosum

Scots pine 143

Scottish Natural Heritage 5

scree *see* rock

scrub

afforestation reduces *146, 148*

from broadleaved woodland *105, 148*

into broadleaved woodland *105*

classification *12, 142–3, 145,* 146

compositional changes *141, 149*

into coniferous plantation 145

defined 145, 146

expansion *142, 204, 205*

geographical changes *148*

from grassland *149*

into grassland *149*

from heather moorland 145, *146, 148*

into heather moorland *149*

interchanges *145, 146, 147*, 150

low 145, *146*

mapping 9, *10*, 13, *14*

into plantation *149*

regional trends *145, 147*

from rough grassland 145, *146, 148, 149*

into rough grassland 146

species 143, 145, 146

trends *141, 142, 145, 146, 148*

sedges 60

sheep farming 41, 70, 78, 239, 241

Shetland Islands 219–24

Sitka spruce 86, 87

smooth grassland

from arable *55, 82, 83, 205, 206, 217, 218*

into arable 37, 43, *55, 80–4, 154, 175, 211*, 237

arable rotation *164, 170, 199*

from blanket mire 54

from broadleaved woodland *105*

into broadleaved woodland *105*

into built ground 30, *55–6, 129, 170, 181, 187, 199–200, 205*, 235

classification 52–3

contraction 53, 238, 241

contraction (Dumfries & Galloway) *174, 175*

contraction (Fife) *180, 181*

contraction (Grampian) *186, 187*

expansion 53, *216, 217, 222, 223, 228, 229*

geographical changes *55*

from heather moorland 54

into heather moorland *224*

interchanges *53, 54*

from intermediate grassland *54, 55–7, 170, 175*

into intermediate grassland *55–6, 181, 229*

mapping 9, *10*

from parkland *105*

projected extent *52*

from rough grassland *54, 55, 56, 57, 170*

into rough grassland 56, *187*

from scrub *149*

into scrub *149*

into transport corridor 30, *55, 56, 139*, 235

trends *53, 54*

into urban development 238

snipe 120

social factors xxi–xxii, 27, 233

soil 41, 78, 85, 124, 137, 142

Sorbus spp. 85, 143

Sparganium erectum 118

Species Action Plan 247

Sphagnum mosses 60

sport

and conservation 58

on grassland 41

heather moorland 70, 71

reduction in 241

in upland areas 238

water activities 111

stock estimates

Borders region *160–1*

Central region *166–7*

Dumfries & Galloway *172–3*

Fife *178–9*

Grampian region *184–5*

Highland region *190–1*

Lothian region *196–7*

Orkney Islands *214–15*

Scotland total *25–7, 157*

Shetland Islands *220–1*

Strathclyde region *202–3*

Tayside region *210–11*

Western Isles *226–7*

Strathclyde 201–6

stratification 5–6, *6, 7, 10*

streams

increase in *222, 223*

interpretation problems 117

mapping *14*, 112

sundew 58

survey
  checking 13–14, 19
  mapping 11–17
  method 5–17
  results 19–22, 248

sustainability xv, xxii–xxiv, 60,
  245, 248, 249

sweet vernal-grass 46

Tayside 207–12

technology xv, 237, 240

timber production xv, 85–6

timothy 52

tormentil 46

town planning 233, 241

tracks
  increase in *36, 128*
  increase in (Borders) *162, 164*
  increase in (Central) *168, 170,
    186, 187*
  increase in (Lothian) *198, 199*
  increase in (Shetlands) *222,
    223,* 235
  mapping *14,* 134
  reduction in *216, 217*
  regional trends *133*
  trends *133*

transport corridor
  from arable 30, *82, 83, 139,
    140, 217,* 235
  into bare ground 235
  birds 125
  from broadleaved woodland
    105
  classification 130, 132
  contraction *132*
  expansion 30, *36, 128, 132,* 235
  expansion (Dumfries &
    Galloway) *174, 175*
  expansion (Grampian) *186, 187*
  expansion (Lothian) *198, 199*
  expansion (Orkneys) *216, 217*
  expansion (Tayside) *210, 211*
  from farmland *132,* 235
  from grassland 30, *139, 140*
  from heather moorland 235
  interchanges *132*
  mapping *14*
  from mire 235
  regional trends *131, 132*

from smooth grassland *55,* 235
trends *131, 132*

treeline
  classification 153–4
  defined 153–4
  increase in *153, 216, 217*
  mapping 9, *14*
  reduction in *153, 169, 170, 180,
    181, 192, 194*
  regional trends *153*
  trends *153*
  unaltered 30

trees *see* treeline; woodland

trends
  arable *80, 84*
  bare ground *126, 128, 137, 138*
  blanket mire *65,* 234
  Borders region *160–1, 164*
  bracken *141, 142, 144*
  broadleaved woodland *234*
  built ground *126, 128, 129*
  Central region *166–7, 170*
  coniferous plantation *101, 102*
  coniferous woodland *97, 98,
    234*
  ditches *118*
  Dumfries & Galloway *172–3,
    175*
  felled woodland *104*
  Fife *178–9, 181*
  Grampian region *184–5, 187*
  in grassland *43*
  heather moorland *73, 74, 234*
  hedgerows *152, 234*
  Highland region *190–1, 194*
  intermediate grassland *51*
  lochs *115, 116, 234*
  Lothian region *196–7, 199*
  lowland mire *65, 67, 234*
  mire *62, 63*
  mixed woodland *91, 92, 234*
  Orkney Islands *214–15, 217*
  parkland *94, 95*
  plantation *93*
  quarries *134, 135*
  recreational land *131*
  rock *135*
  rough grassland *46, 48, 234*
  Scotland total *25, 28–36*
  scrub *141, 142, 145, 146, 148*
  Shetland Islands *220–1, 223*

smooth grassland *54*
Strathclyde region *202–3, 205*
Tayside region *208–9, 211*
tracks *133*
transport corridor *131, 132*
treeline *153*
Western Isles *226–7, 229*
woodland 87, 88

Trichophorum cespitosum 60, 72
Trifolium repens 46
Tringa totanus 120
Typha spp. 118

Ulex europaeus 143

uplands
  bare ground 137
  farming 237–40
  fens 58
  grassland 42, 44
  red deer 41–2
  sheep farming 41–2, 78
  sporting activities 41, 238
  transport corridor *132*
  woodland species 85

urban development
  agriculture affected 235
  arable reduced *84*
  changes to land cover 37, 124,
    233, 235, 241, 246
  expansion 30, *234,* 235
  expansion (Fife) *180, 181*
  expansion (Grampian) *186, 187*
  expansion (Strathclyde) *204,
    205*
  expansion (Tayside) *210–11*
  historical background 124–6
  intermediate grassland reduced
    49, 51
  regulation 233, 241
  from smooth grassland 238
  transport corridor reduced *132*
  and water supply 110

Utricularia intermedia 60

Vaccinium spp. 46, 60
Vanellus vanellus 120
vegetation xvi
verges 44, 125–6, 132

water
  power 110, 240

supply *36*, 110–11, 238, 240
see also fresh water
water snails 119
Western Isles 225–30
wet ground
  afforestation affects *121*
  from blanket mire *122, 123*
  from bracken *121*
  classification 120
  contraction *168, 170*
  expansion *174, 175*
  fauna 120
  flora 120
  from grassland *121, 122, 123*
  into grassland *122, 123*
  from heather moorland *121, 122, 123*
  interchanges *121*
  mapping *14*, 112
  occurrence 120
  regional trends *120, 121*
  from rough grassland *175, 205*
  into rough grassland 169
wetland *see* mire

willow 143
willowherb, great 120
woodland
  afforestation affects *234*
  classification *12*, 87
  compositional changes *87, 88*, 104, 106
  contraction *36*
  expansion 238
  historical background 85–7
  improvement 78
  management 85–7
  mapping 13, *14*
  into parkland *95*
  'policies' 78, 91
  species 85, 86, 87
  timber production xv, 85–6
  trends *87, 88*
  underplanting *102*, 238
  see also broadleaved; coniferous; felled; mixed; parkland; plantation

Yorkshire fog 46
young plantation

background 99–100
from blanket mire *67, 68*, 100, *101, 107*, 238
from bracken *149*
from broadleaved woodland *105*
into broadleaved woodland *105*
from coniferous plantation *107*
into coniferous plantation *101*
defined 99
expansion 241
expansion (Borders) *162, 164*
expansion (Central) *168, 170*
expansion (Dumfries & Galloway) *174, 175*
expansion (Grampian) *186, 187*
expansion (Highland) *192, 194*
expansion (Strathclyde) *204, 205*
from heather moorland 34, *75, 76*, 100, *101, 107*, 238
interchanges *100, 101*
from mire 34
regional trends *100, 101*
from rough grassland 34, *55–6*, 100, *101, 107, 108*, 238
from scrub *149*